POPULAR MECHANICS
SHOP NOTES

FOR 1917 VOL. 13

Algrove Publishing ~ Classic Reprint Series

Algrove Publishing Limited
1090 Morrison Drive
Ottawa, Ontario
Canada K2H 1C2

Canadian Cataloguing in Publication Data

Main entry under title:

   Popular mechanics shop notes for ...

(Classic reprint series)
Includes indexes.
Originally published: Chicago : Popular Mechanics Co., 1905-
"Compiled from the "Shop notes" department of Popular mechanics
      magazine, and "Written so you can understand it;" tells easy
      ways to do hard things" --Added t.p., v. 1.
Contents: v. 1. 1905 - v. 2. 1906 - v. 3. 1907 - v. 4. 1908 - v. 5. 1909 - v. 6. 1910 - v. 7. 1911 -
      v. 8. 1912 - v. 9. 1913 - v. 10. 1914 - v. 11. 1915 - v. 12. 1916 - v. 13. 1917 - v. 14. 1918 -
      v. 15. 1919 - v. 16. 1920 - v. 17. 1921 - v. 18. 1922 - v. 19. 1923.
ISBN 0-921335-87-3 (v. 11) - ISBN 0-921335-91-1 (v. 12) - ISBN 0-921335-94-6 (v. 13) -
ISBN 0-921335-96-2 (v. 14) - ISBN 0-921335-98-9 (v. 15) - ISBN 0-921335-93-8 (v. 16) -
ISBN 0-921335-95-4 (v. 17) - ISBN 0-921335-97-0 (v. 18) - ISBN 0-921335-99-7 (v. 19) -

      1. Do-it-yourself work. 2. Industrial arts. I. Title: Shop notes for ... II. Series: Classic
reprint series (Ottawa, Ont.)

TJ1160.P66 2000   600   C99-900763-7

Printed in Canada
#10800

Publisher's Note

Virtually every woodworking magazine in the English-speaking world has a shop notes section and has published an accumulation of them in book form. This was all started in 1905 with the first annual issue of *Popular Mechanics Shop Notes*, a compilation of advice on jigs, fixtures, methods of work, processes and projects. The earlier issues focussed primarily on metalworking, but with tips for a variety of other trades liberally sprinkled throughout. As years went by, the contents shifted more and more to woodworking and handyman projects. Each book is profusely illustrated. The line drawings of the earlier issues were supplanted by superb engravings until photographs started to creep in during the 1920s. Each year has its charm but all issues share the attribute of being clear, concise and widely informative.

Leonard G. Lee, Publisher
Ottawa
September, 1999

WARNING

This is a reprint of a book compiled in the early 1900s. The book describes what was recommended to be done in accordance with the knowledge of the day.

It would be advisable to treat all corrosive, explosive and toxic materials with much greater caution than is indicated here, particularly any materials that come in contact with the body.

Similarly, some of the recommended projects were dangerous then and remain so now. All of this material should be regarded with a judicious eye and necessary precautions taken.

POPULAR MECHANICS

SHOP NOTES

FOR

1917

EASY WAYS TO DO HARD THINGS

OF DAILY USE
TO EVERY MECHANIC

Vol. XIII—Table of Contents, Pages 2679-2686

POPULAR MECHANICS, CHICAGO

This Volume is Reprinted from the

Shop Notes Department

of

Popular Mechanics

Edited by H. H. WINDSOR

Shop Notes

A Homemade Automobile Turntable

By FRANK G. SWARTZ

THE location of a home garage made it necessary to back the automobile about 200 ft. either in entering or going out, and for this reason it was desirable to construct some kind of an inexpensive turntable in the garage floor. The floor being made of boards, a circle was drawn upon them having a diameter equal to the length of the automobile, and a little more for convenience. The boards were numbered, cut, and laid aside, and the earth was removed from the center; then an old mowing-machine wheel with an un-broken rim was bedded in concrete so that the center of the hub was in the center of the circle cut out of the floor. The concrete was built up halfway on the spokes and rim.

A piece of wood-pump log was procured, and eight holes bored in it in the manner of constructing a hub for a wheel, and eight spokes were cut from discarded broom handles and inserted in the holes. The lengths of the spokes should be such that the periphery of the ends extend over the rim of the mowing-machine wheel 1 in., or more.

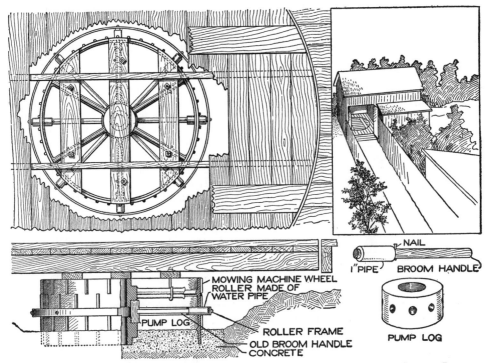

MOWING MACHINE WHEEL
ROLLER MADE OF WATER PIPE
PUMP LOG
ROLLER FRAME
OLD BROOM HANDLE
CONCRETE

NAIL
1" PIPE
BROOM HANDLE
PUMP LOG

Two Old Mowing-Machine Wheels with a Center Wheel Carrying Rollers Make the Turning Part of the Table, on Which a Floor is Laid Level with the Garage Floor

These ends were evened up to fit in a band made of an old buggy tire. A roller was made for the end of each spoke by cutting a piece of 1-in. pipe 4 in. long, all rollers being held in position with pins run through holes in the spokes at their inner ends and in the rim at the outer ends of the spokes.

This wheellike arrangement was placed on the mowing-machine wheel set in the concrete so that the rollers rested on the rim. Another mowing-machine wheel was set on top of the built-up wheel, and the three were kept in line by a shaft run through the hubs.

On the upper surface of the top wheel, two timbers, about 7 ft. long, 4 in. wide, and 2 in. thick, were secured with bolts having a hook on the head end to engage the spokes near the rim. A center timber of the same size, and as long as the diameter of the circle cut in the floor, was secured to the center of the upper wheel in the same manner. On these timbers joists were placed, and the floor boards securely nailed to them. About ¾ in. of the boards were sawed off all the way around, to make a clearance. Two boards, 12 in. wide, were laid crossways on top of the flooring to take the tread of the automobile. A support was placed under the edge of the turntable where the automobile is driven on, but low enough so that when the machine is standing on the platform the weight will rest entirely on the rollers.

Wire Cutter Made of Old Files

A simple and powerful wire cutter can be made of two old flat files. The  ends should be annealed and drilled for a bolt. In one piece, near the bolt hole, to produce a large leverage, must be drilled a hole to fit the wire to be cut. If several sizes of wire are to be cut, holes of corresponding diameters must be provided, the largest one nearest the bolt hole, in order to obtain the best leverage in cutting them. The narrow edges of the cutting file should be ground sharp, and when one becomes dull, the file can be turned over and the other side used.— Contributed by D. C. Goff, Knoxville, Tennessee.

Replacing Parts Properly in Assembling an Engine

When reassembling the engine of an automobile after an overhauling, extreme care should be taken to replace the various valves, valve springs, spring washers, tappets, etc., with their respective cylinders. A good plan is to number each set by means of steel figure punches, and in this manner the engine can be reassembled properly.

Cement-Floor Covering to Prevent Dust

If it is desired to make a concrete floor in a factory or mill that will not sand off or make dust, a coating for the purpose can be prepared when making the floor. This coating consists of one part cement to two parts crushed rock or hard gravel, which will pass through a ½-in. sieve, and from which the fine dust has been removed. This is thoroughly mixed in a mixing box, or by a machine mixer, with a sufficient amount of water to produce a plastic but not sloppy consistence, and spread on the under concrete before either the finish or the under concrete has had time to set. It is floated with a wood float to a true level, and then slightly troweled with a steel trowel, to bring it to a proper level and to smooth the top slightly. This will give a finish which is pebbly, and not dead smooth or slick like a sand finish. After the finish has been troweled and has set sufficiently so that the covering will not mar the surface, it should be covered with sawdust, sand, cloths, or any other material which will hold water continuously. The finish should be kept soaking wet for at least a week, or, better, for 10 days.

Range Finder to Locate Points of Interest

Tourists stopping at points of interest seldom have the chance, or take the time, to travel the surrounding country to see some spot that would take hours to reach. For this reason the general viewpoint, in some places, is provided with a device to point out, or locate, the most interesting bits of scenery so that the traveler can use his field glasses to a good advantage.

The device consists of a standard, solidly set in the earth and provided with a round top, about 1 ft. in diameter, on which is mounted a revolving finder. The standard is made of a 1¼-in. pipe, and the top, which is of hard wood, is fastened to a flange screwed to the pipe end. A hole is bored through the center of the wood disk in which a ¾-in. pipe is fitted, projecting down into the standard so that it will revolve freely without changing its position vertically. The weight of the pipe, if it freely slips into the standard, will be sufficient to keep it in one position, and a pin run through a hole drilled in the pipe at the proper place will prevent it from dropping too low.

A yoke, shaped from a piece of metal, is fastened into the upper end of the smaller pipe, which provides the support for the "telescope," or range finder. This range

To Locate a Place of Interest Turn the Pipe "Telescope" and Set It in the Proper Notch, Then Look through the Opening finder consists of a piece of 1-in. pipe, about 18 in. long, and is hung in the yoke on pins centrally located and fastened in the walls of the pipe.

Around the circumference of the disk, and properly located, are pieces of sheet metal with their upper ends cut out to receive the circular form of the pipe. If a certain point of interest is higher than the view point, the piece of sheet metal for that point must be of such height that the range-finder pipe will point to it when placed in the notch. The pieces of metal must, therefore, be made separately for each point of interest, and if a point is at a lower altitude, a portion of the board top can be cut out to receive the pipe end in place of the metal standard.

When the pipe "telescope" is turned on its swivel and set into a notch labeled "Bears Head," etc., the observer looks through the opening, and the field of view is narrowed down so that the point of interest, which may be a good many miles away, can be easily located. The field glasses are then brought into use and the object viewed without having to make a long trip to see it.

The same device would be of interest on a country estate, located where most of the surrounding country can be seen. In this instance the device can be so constructed that a moderate-priced telescope can be placed in the yoke and standards around the wood-disk edge, permitting the things to be seen enlarged without the use of a field glass. The yoke is made in the same manner, but, instead of pins for fastenings, the inside of the metal is lined with rubber, or felt, and a thumbscrew fitted in the upper end of one arm, to use as a clamp to fasten the telescope in place. In this manner the telescope can be removed to prevent loss by theft.

Motorcycle Trailer for Ice-Cream Kegs

To make quick delivery of bulk ice cream one druggist made a trailer for his motorcycle as shown in the illustration. Two ordinary bicycle wheels were fitted on a straight axle, and on top of it a platform of boards was fastened. The surface of this platform was made large enough to carry one extra-large ice-cream keg, or four small ones. To the front end of the cart a curved rod was attached, so that it could be fastened to the brace on the rear mud guard of the motorcycle. The connection was made flexible so that turns could be accomplished without trouble or tipping of the trailer.

Hat Hook Used as a Switch in a Bell Circuit

Where a set of electric bells were installed in a high-school building to be rung from the school clock, it was necessary to place a cut-out switch in the line, to prevent the bells from ringing at night and when the school was

A Trailer Serving the Purpose of Delivering Ice-Cream Kegs, but Which could be Used for Many Other Kinds of Light Delivery If Provided with a Covering

closed, thus avoiding unnecessary use of the batteries. Knowing that an ordinary switch would be frequently forgotten, the scheme illustrated, which is positive and as good as automatic, was adopted.

On the face of a block, about ½ in. thick, 3 in. long, and 2 in. wide, is fastened an ordinary coat or hat hook. On the back at the upper end is fastened a brass hinge, and in electric contact with this is a brass strip that runs down the center. The hinge is then secured to the wall and connected to one terminal. A second contact strip, connected to the other terminal, is fastened to the wall directly behind the brass strip on the back of the block. Near each lower corner of the block an oblong hole is made, and through these brass screws are driven into the wall, around each of which a short piece of coiled spring is placed to keep the contacts apart.

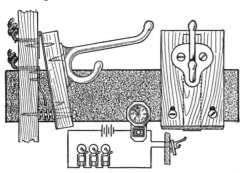

The Weight of a Hat Closes the Contact Points and Makes the System Operative

When the head master hangs his hat on the hook the springs are compressed, the break in the circuit is closed, and the controller in the clock is connected to the system and becomes operative. The removal of the hat opens the circuit, and there is no chance of the bells operating out of school hours unless the head master goes home bareheaded.—Contributed by J. A. Bannister, Chesley, Ont.

❡It is well to know that rapid cooling of a liquid produces fine crystals; the slower it changes form, the larger the crystals.

Display Board for Moving-Picture Show Posters

An enterprising owner of a moving-picture theater uses a bill or poster board as shown. As the program is

The Outer Surface of the Board Has a Hinged Skeleton Door to Hold the Poster

changed nightly, the posters must be removed and new ones put in daily. The skeleton door frame on the board holds the poster in place without the use of paste. The panel shape of the upper part of the door automatically frames the headline. The door is fastened with a small hook and eye. This method is far handier and much less mussy than where paste is used.

A Doorstop

A simple and effective doorstop can be made in a short time by nailing together two pieces of pine board, cut as shown in the sketch. In use, the long wedge-shaped piece is shoved under the bottom of the door, which, when released, holds the doorstop firmly in place, making

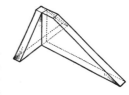

it impossible for the door to close. If desired, a strip of rubber, or felt, can be glued to the bottom of the doorstop. —Contributed by A. J. Stover, Corvallis, Ore.

Repairing a Reamer

A reamer is easily broken on the points of the cutters at the end. As the cost of these reamers is rather high, it

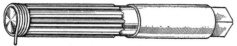

The Cutters are Ground Down and Then Wrapped with Fine Wire and Soldered

is desirable to repair them whenever possible. A very good repair can be made by grinding the end of each cutter down to a level a trifle lower than the break and winding this part with copper or soft-iron wire, then soldering it in place. The solder is then smoothed up with a file.

To Prevent Automobile Crank Handle from Sticking

Sand and dust collecting in the sleeve of an automobile starting-crank handle

will cause it to stick. To remedy this trouble, remove the handle and turn the pin down in the center about ⅛ in. deep for a length of 2¼ in. This groove is then filled with ordinary packing. In this manner the sleeve will be kept well lubricated, and the sleeve will always slide loosely on the shaft pin. If two small grooves are cut lengthwise of the raised end portions, the grease, or oil, can easily reach these bearings.

An Adjustable Lap

In the ordinary lap, a piece of brass rod of suitable size is slotted in the

A Headless Screw Controls the Adjustment Accurately, and Holds the Parts Rigidly

center for some distance, and a wedge-shaped piece of metal is inserted in the slot. This will not give a fine, or solid, adjustment. An improvement, which

will give a better adjustment, consists of a tapped hole in the portion A, and a headless screw, C, used in it. The screw, when turned in, will force the portion B away to any desired position.

A Thread-Cleaning Tool

The tool illustrated will be of great help for anyone handling rusted bolts. It is made of a piece of steel of suitable size with a number of holes

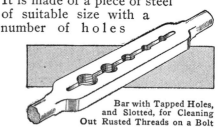

Bar with Tapped Holes, and Slotted, for Cleaning Out Rusted Threads on a Bolt

drilled of sizes necessary to tap with standard taps. After cutting the threads with the taps, the steel bar is slotted as shown. This tool, run over the threads of an old bolt, will clean off the rust and dirt that may have collected, making it an easy matter to start the nut, which otherwise would be a troublesome task.

To Make Gear-Shift Lever Move Easily

Quite frequently a chauffeur will tug frantically at the shifting lever, in

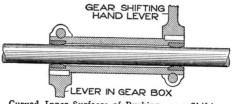

Curved Inner Surfaces of Bushings on a Shifting Lever, to Make It Move Easily

an effort to engage the transmission gears, without success. Trouble of this sort is in many cases caused by the holding of the shaft connected to the shifting lever. To eliminate this trouble insert two bushings, one at each end, having curved surfaces. The clearance between the shaft and bushing should be not less than .005 or more than .01 inch.

A Homemade Metal Fence

By T. T. STURGEON

THE metal fence shown was constructed by myself, who am only an amateur mechanic, and can be duplicated by any mechanic of average ability who has an accurate eye and a good stock of patience. The tools used to build and erect the fence were a hand drill press, a pipe-fitting outfit, and the ordinary set of bench tools; the jigs, and other appliances, illustrated were made of junk, picked up about the home shop.

The length of the fence is 100 ft.; the height above the wall, 30 in.; space between pickets, 2 in.; distance between rails, 12 in.,

The Fence is Built Up of Pipe and Fittings, with Pickets of Heavy Wire and Attached to Short Pieces of Pipe Anchored in the Concrete Base, Either with Brimstone or Lead

and the posts were set about 5 ft. apart. The material used consisted of 320 ft. of ¾-in. pipe for the rails and gate; 54 ft. of 1-in. pipe, to make 18 posts, 3 ft. long; four pieces of 2-in. pipe, 5 ft. long, and 1,500 ft. of No. 2 annealed fence wire to form the pickets. If soft-steel rods of the proper diameter, such as concrete-reinforcing rods, were used instead of the wire, it would eliminate the construction of the wire straightener and the work of straight-

ening the large number of pickets. The smaller things required are four 2-in. ball ornaments; eighteen 1-in. pipe caps; eighteen 1-in. couplings; twelve ¾-in. ells; six ¾-in. tees; one double-swing floor hinge; a box of ¼ by 3-in. stove bolts, and 30 lb. of brimstone, or crude sulphur.

This completes the list with the exception of the gate ornament, which once adorned a gasoline stove in a different form and was bent to suit its present use. The total cost of the material, including that of the 14-in. wall, was 51 cents per lineal foot.

The first operation in constructing the fence is to build the drill bench, and on it and the drill jig depends the accuracy of the large number of holes to be drilled. The table of the press is swung out of the way and a perfectly straight plank—one without a twist in it is absolutely necessary—12 in. wide, 2 in. thick, and 12 ft. long, is placed at the proper height with the drill about 2 ft. from its right end. The plank is adjusted so that its surface is level and at perfect right angles to the drill spindle, thus taking the place of the drill table.

The construction of the drill jig is clearly shown in Fig. 1. The grooved blocks at each end are hollowed out slightly larger than the diameter of the pipe, thus permitting a slight side play for centering by the screws, as shown at A. The spring clamp is pulled out when placing the pipe in the jig and snaps back to hold it securely against the centering screws, which are ordinary setscrews secured with locknuts. The holes in the top, or guide plate, are 2 in. from center to center, and are used to make the pattern rail only. The guide for the drill is half of a motor-car chain and is fastened loosely to the plate so that the jig may be set at an angle with the drill, if necessary, and still guide the drill true to the center without binding.

In drilling the pattern rail the outer end is supported at the proper height, the pipe is entered in the jig from left to right, and the first hole is drilled 1 in. from the end; then the pipe is shifted until the pin will slip through the guide hole in the top plate, through the hole in the pipe and into the base plate, which locks the pipe for the drilling of the next hole, and so on until the length of pipe is drilled, which will be about 125 holes. Extreme care must be used when drilling the pattern rail,

to take up the lost motion around the pin in the following manner: After the pin is in place, twist the pipe from the operator and also shove it to the left. For the next hole the opposite course is pursued, alternating for each hole. If this is not done, the variation of a small fraction of an inch on the same side of all holes will bring the last hole out of true ½ in. or more.

After the pattern rail is drilled, it is clamped on top of the next pipe, and a center punch of a size to snugly fit the drilled holes, in this case $\frac{9}{32}$ in. in diameter, is used to mark the next pipe. The operation of drilling the second pipe is the same as for drilling the pattern, except that the sliding jig is used to keep the pipe from turning under the drill, and the punch marks are used for a guide to start the drill. All the pipes are drilled in the same manner, except those intended for the bottom rails, which are drilled through the top only, except where necessary to put the sliding-jig pin through. The drilling operation is shown in Fig. 2.

The wire-straightening apparatus is shown in Fig. 3. There are many different forms of straighteners on the market, and one can be easily worked out that will answer the purpose. The one illustrated consists of three rolls, set in a frame of metal so that one roll may be adjusted against the other two. Gears are used on the rolls to make a positive movement.

The picket former is shown in Fig. 4. A circular piece of cast iron, 5½ in. in diameter, forms a mandrel around which the pickets are bent. The bending lever consists of a piece of strap iron, 1½ in. wide and ½ in. thick, with a sash-weight pulley wheel bolted to it, so that it will clear the mandrel just enough to permit the picket wire to pass in between them. The guide and clamp to hold the wire is made of a piece of angle iron, B, and a short piece of strap iron, C, 1 in. wide and ½ in. thick, with a notch filed in the lower end in such a manner that, when the wire end is against the stop D and the clamp is pulled to the left, it locks itself, and the wire is held tightly to the angle iron. The wire is placed in the bender with the bending lever in the downward position. To form the picket, swing the lever to the vertical.

the jig shown in Fig. 5 was used to simplify the operation. The jig is placed on the wall with the clamp directly over the post hole, and the brace

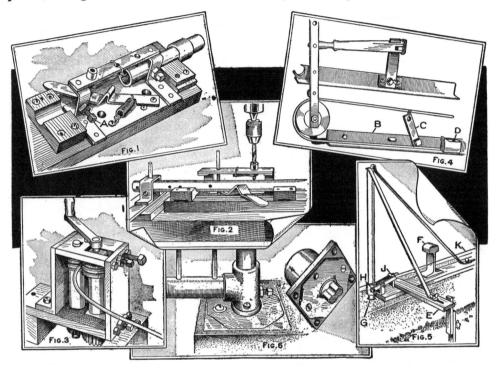

The Jig That Takes the Place of the Drill-Press Table for Drilling the Holes Accurately in the Rails, the Wire-Straightening Machine, the Picket Former, the Post Setter, and the Gate Hinge

As the fence is to be set over a concrete wall, the posts must be prepared in such a manner that the fence can be dismantled at any time by making the posts in two pieces, one 25 in. long and the other 11 in. The short lengths of pipe are set in the concrete base so that the upper end extends above the surface just enough to fit on a coupling. The upper part of the post is screwed into the coupling. The bottom rail is bolted to the coupling, which just clears the surface of the wall; the other holes for the rails are 12 in. apart, thus leaving just enough end to screw a cap on top when the upper rail is in place.

In erecting this fence, the same procedure is followed out as in building a wood fence. When the wall is built, holes about ½ in. larger than the posts are left at the exact location where the posts are to be set. In setting the posts

E, at the end of the side arm, is adjusted with the ground to hold the arm solid. A weight, F, is placed on the jig to hold it steady. The post G is then dropped into the hole and adjusted in the clamp H, by placing a pin through a hole in the coupling. The post is then raised or lowered by means of the wing nut J in the clamp, until some certain point marked on the coupling is in line with the guide line K. The top braces are then adjusted, and the post plumbed by sliding the lower end of the braces, the bolts holding them sliding in slots, until plumb, then clamped with the thumbscrews. The brimstone is melted and poured in the hole around the post and allowed to cool.

After the posts are all set, the rails are coupled together on the straight run with couplings, and on the corners with ells. They are then clamped to the posts in their respective positions and drilled for stove bolts by means of a breast drill. The pickets are then driven in and the fence is complete, all but the gate.

The gate is the most difficult part to construct, and the illustration shows better than words can tell its form of construction. The threading of the pipes should be all right threads and has to be done with the utmost accuracy. The two middle rails are run in on one side, and then back into the other side and calked. The pickets are then set, and the top rail put on by means of a run-back of each of the

short nipples on each side. The top bearing is simply a pipe plug screwed into the top tee, the square part being filed round to fit the hole in the supporting bracket.

The hinge used to hang the gate is shown in Fig. 6. This hinge is the type used for double-swing doors, and is countersunk in the cement walk and filled with a very heavy oil. As it is ball-bearing, the gate is absolutely silent in its action. There is no need of a latch on the gate, as the powerful springs of the hinge prevents any of the smaller animals from opening the gate.

Switch Arm for Use on Basement-Light Circuit

Although it is the usual custom to put a basement-light switch at the head of the steps for convenience, there

Long Arm Placed on an Electric Switch to Strike the Person Leaving the Basement Steps

is a serious drawback to this position. In a certain basement storeroom it became an annoyingly frequent occurrence to find the light burning hours after the person using it had left, for it was an easy matter to go out into the daylight and forget to turn the switch.

In order to avoid this waste of light, the device shown in the illustration

was adopted. First, the switch was removed and mounted horizontally on a small wood bracket, with the wires leading up through a hole in the center. A light wood arm, 15 in. long, was attached to the switch, as shown, so that the light would be turned off as long as the arm rested against the wall. When the switch is turned to the "on" position, the projecting arm forms a positive means of turning out the light, since it is right in the path of the person leaving the stairs. The card disk at the end makes it easily seen.—Contributed by Morris G. Miller, New Rochelle, New York.

A Protection for the Acid Bottle

The bottle used as a container for nitric acid, that is kept in a shop for etching steel, is often struck with some piece of metal and broken. As this is a dangerous acid when not confined, it is well to be careful and use all caution possible in handling the liquid. A good safeguard is to glue a cardboard disk to the bottom of the bottle, then coat the outside surface with glue, and when it becomes tacky, roll it in small particles of cork. The cork may be obtained from a fruit dealer selling imported grapes. When the glue hardens to hold the cork, it makes a very satisfactory guard against breakage. Owing to its touch, the bottle can also be used as a poison bottle for the home.

Mucilage Used to Stop Leak in Gasoline Connection

A leak started in the ground-joint connection between the gasoline-supply pipe and the carburetor on my automobile. It was in a place where it could not be reground easily, although I tried to stop it in this manner. Soap and other lubricants were used to no avail. The thought came to me that some liquid which gasoline would not cut might do, and I used a small portion of old mucilage which had become thick, applying it to the connection and letting it stand to harden, then screwing the joint together. This stopped the leak.—Contributed by Bert H. Stanley, Portage, Wash.

Holding Work in Lathe to Cut Taper Threads

In cutting an inside taper thread on a lathe, I have found the device illustrated an excellent substitute for a yoke that rocks on the lathe dog.

The device, which is only intended for light work, consists of a bolt, threaded for a nut on one end, and formed to a hook on the other, to engage the setscrew of a lathe dog. The bolt is amply long to receive a rubber washer, between two metal washers, on the threaded end. The rubber washer is made by cutting a 1-in.

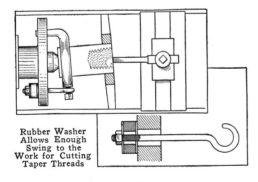

Rubber Washer Allows Enough Swing to the Work for Cutting Taper Threads

length from a discarded clothes-wringer roll. The application is clearly shown in the sketch.—Contributed by L. Nash, Chesley, Ont.

Housing for a Large Flag

Many business firms have a flagpole on their buildings so that the national flag can be raised on special occasions. Sometimes it may be necessary to use the flag for several days, or weeks, and in such cases,

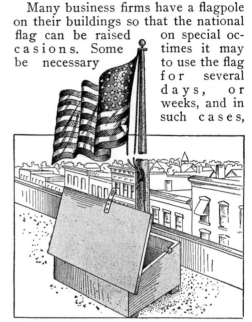

The Box Protects the Flag at Night, without the Need of Taking It from Its Halyards

the flag will be exposed to the weather at night unless it is taken from its halyards and put up again in the morning. One merchant, desiring to protect his flag and keep it as clean as possible, made a box on the roof, as shown in the illustration, to house it when not in use.

The box was made about 18 in. deep, 2 ft. wide, and 3 ft. long, which was large enough to hold two flags of the size used for such purposes. The box was placed on two timbers on the roof at the base of the flagpole. The cover was made slanting, with its edges projecting over on all edges. A notch was cut in the upper edge of one end to admit the halyards when the flag was placed in the box. This made it very easy to haul down the flag and store it for the night. A hasp is provided to lock the flag in with a padlock, and in this case the box was protected from view of the street by a balustrade on top of the building front.—Contributed by John Kohlbecher, San Francisco, California.

Street-Lamp Glare Shield

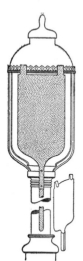

Any fixed form of light deflector for a street lamp was strictly forbidden in our city, and the one in front of our house caused considerable annoyance by its glare when we were sitting on the porch in the evening. The light on the porch, during the time it was burning, made an excellent burglar protection.

To overcome all difficulties I designed the deflector shown in the sketch, which can be easily placed on and taken off a lamp, and has given perfect satisfaction. It is in the shape of a shovel, the blade being made of galvanized iron and the handle constructed from an old broom handle. The position of the hooks by which it is hung, the manner of shaping the sheet metal, and the way in which it is placed on a lamp, are all plainly shown.—Contributed by Irving M. Hayward, Brooklyn, N. Y.

Hinged Molding for Window Screen

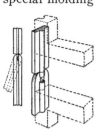

Window screens held in place by special molding strips can be easily removed for cleaning or other purposes, if arranged as shown in the illustration. In order to do this, the molding on both sides of the window should be sawed in two, so the lower piece will be a little longer than the height of the screen. If the molding is already fastened in place, the lower pieces should be removed so their upper edges may be rounded off to permit the molding to swing either out or in, as desired, when pinned near its upper edge, as shown. Holes should be drilled and countersunk for loosely fitting wood screws, which are used as hinge pins, and are fastened in place by being screwed into the window jambs. To lock the hinged strips in their regular upright position, a hole should be drilled near the bottom edge, and continued into the window jamb, to fit a wire nail, or bolt.

In using this arrangement both hinged strips, after being secured at their upper ends, are swung out, and the screen is slipped in place; it can then be swung to its regular upright position. To fasten it in place, the nails, or bolts, are inserted in the lower holes. In order to take out the screen, the molding must first be unlocked by the removal of the nails. The screen can then be swung away from the window and removed.—Contributed by M. Baudier, New Orleans, La.

Doweling Loose Bearings

In order to stop the turning of loose bearings in connecting rods, a simple

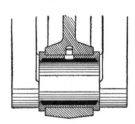

method would be to provide the rod with a tightly fitting dowel pin, projecting sufficiently far to enter a corresponding hole drilled in the bearing. Care should be taken that the top of the dowel is always below the surface of the bearing metal.

Cover for an Automobile Starting-Crank Handle

An extremely handy addition to the starting crank of an automobile in winter is a piece of rubber hose placed over the handle. The usual type of crank is fitted with a metal sleeve of either brass, copper, or steel, and in winter the sleeve becomes more or less slippery, due to the ice and snow, resulting in making it very difficult to crank. The addition of the rubber sleeve over the metal one readily eliminates the trouble.

Removing Tar and Asphalt Spots

Do not use soap on tar or asphalt spots in cloth first, as this will set it in a way to make the cleaning almost impossible. Rub the spots with soft grease, and set aside until the grease penetrates the tar. Remove the tar and grease with gasoline, or by washing in hot suds. Asphalt should be well wetted with kerosene and left to stand, then washed out in turpentine or alcohol.

Easily Made Steam Trap

An inexpensive steam trap can be constructed from a piece of 8-in. pipe, 6 or 8 in. long, two flanged heads, and a float. The pipe is threaded for the flanges, which are to hold the heads after they are prepared. One side of the pipe is drilled near one edge, to receive a pipe from the lowest part of the steam system. The other side is fitted with a ball float and lever, hinged near its center. The float lever is fitted with an arm shaped properly to carry a tapered valve on that end which enters the outlet pipe.

The action of the trap is as follows: The water from the condensation in the steam system falls to the lowest part and enters the trap. When the level has risen sufficiently to lift the ball float, the valve is opened and the

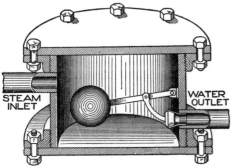

Steam Trap Made of a Large Pipe with a Float to Operate the Outlet Valve

steam pressure forces the water out. The lowering of the water in the trap allows the ball float to close the opening.

Micrometer Holder

A holder for a micrometer, which fully answers the purpose of an expensive one, is made as follows: A ¼-in.

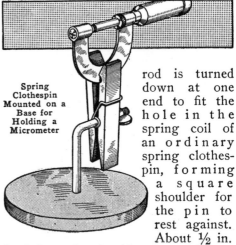

Spring Clothespin Mounted on a Base for Holding a Micrometer

rod is turned down at one end to fit the hole in the spring coil of an ordinary spring clothespin, forming a square shoulder for the pin to rest against. About ½ in. back from the shoulder the rod is bent at right angles, and the end is fastened in a metal base of sufficient weight to hold the micrometer rigidly. The length of the rod is optional. The end of the portion turned down is threaded and fitted with a wing nut. The manner of using the holder, with the clothespin as a vise, is clearly shown.

Tanks for Supplying Air at Low Pressures

In soldering metals, or melting them in small amounts, compressed air at low pressures can be used to great advantage in connection with gas burners. Power blowers are ordinarily used to obtain the necessary pressure, but a good, cheap substitute for small work can be made of two heavy cans, as shown in the illustration. Two sizes of cans should be obtained, so one may freely pass within the other. They should be open at one end, but otherwise air and water-tight. The larger, or stationary, tank should be provided with four strips of metal placed in sets of two on directly opposite sides and fastened with rivets, or solder. The strips of metal are formed to fit two wooden strips used as uprights for a frame which is connected at the top by a

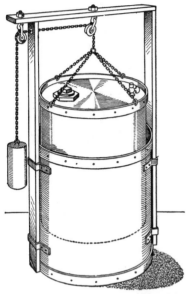

A Low-Pressure Air Tank to Supply Air in Burners for Working Metals Having a Low Melting Temperature

crosspiece provided with two pulleys, one midway between the uprights, and the other suspended from an extension on one side. The upright on this side is drilled for a cable hole in line with the tops of the pulley wheels.

Two openings are made through the closed end of the smaller or movable tank, one to serve as air outlet and the other as an inlet. The outlet is made sufficiently large to fit an ordinary gas cock, which should be soldered in place, and connected to the gas burner with a suitable rubber hose. The inlet opening is cut to fit a suitable pipe flange, which is soldered or riveted in place and fitted with a plug to open or close it. Four chains or cords are evenly spaced and connected to the rim of the movable tank, to hold it in an inverted position. They are fastened at their loose ends to the weight cord, which passes over the pulleys to a regulating weight, used to govern the descent of the movable tank. To get higher pressures than produced by the unbalanced weight of the tank, additional weight may be added on the tank.

To operate the device, the lower tank is filled three-quarters full of water. The movable tank with its outlet open is placed in its upper position, and then closed up with the plug, and connected to the gas burner by a rubber hose. When the gas cock is opened, the excess weight of the tank will cause it to descend, forcing the air through the rubber hose to the burner. When no more air can be forced out of the upper tank, the outlet must again be opened and the tank raised to its upper position. With the outlet again plugged, the operation will proceed as before.— Contributed by J. Koestner, Brooklyn, New York.

Repairing a Broken Magneto Drive

The combination sprocket and shaft, driving the magneto of an automobile gasoline engine, was fractured at a point marked A. The break may have been caused by defective material, or perhaps the heat treatment was not of the proper kind. The shaft was of such design that the drive sprocket was forged integral with the shaft; then, too, the entire piece was heat-treated and ground. This made it an extremely expensive part if a new one had to be purchased.

To make a repair, a new shaft was turned up, without a sprocket, having the same dimensions as the broken shaft, which was removed from each side of the sprocket and the faces of the latter were ground flat on a grinder. A hole was then bored and reamed

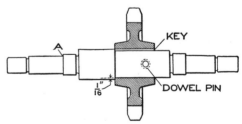

New Shaft Replacing a Broken One Consisting of Shaft and Sprocket in One Piece

centrally in the sprocket, to fit on the new shaft. A keyway was cut in the sprocket and one to match it in the shaft, and a hole was bored for a dowel. The shaft was then casehardened and ground to a press fit in the sprocket bore, with a shoulder $\frac{1}{16}$ in. high to provide a stop. When the sprocket was in place a pin was driven into the hole and riveted on both ends.

Drawing-Board Cover

Having trouble with dust settling on my drawings over night I made a cover, as shown in the illustration, that

can be easily drawn in place and does not interfere with the work on the board. Two pieces of steel, each $\frac{1}{8}$ in. thick, $\frac{3}{4}$ in. wide, and about 2 in. long, are secured at the right end of the board, one on the top and the other on the bottom edge. An ordinary window shade with a spring roller of the proper length is fitted between the two pieces of steel. When not in use, the roller with shade hangs under the board as shown by the dotted lines.—Contributed by Lawrence L. Lane, Jackson, Tenn.

Temporary Repair for a Burned-Out Fuse Plug

When a house fuse plug "blows" out and there is no other at hand, take a bit

of tin foil—the covering from a pack of tobacco or chewing gum will do—and fold it once, making the strip about $\frac{1}{2}$ in. wide, then lay it over the contact points of the plug, as shown, and screw the plug into the receptacle. This will make a connection, and will not produce any more body than if the ordinary fuse wire were used.

¶A streaked top lining on an automobile can be made uniform in color by applying a dye of the proper shade while the top is upside down.

Making Index Cards

Anyone making his own filing systems will find the method illustrated one of the quickest and easiest for con-

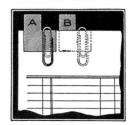

structing index cards. To one of the regular cards in the cabinet attach a piece of cardboard, or any suitable material, cut to the shape shown at A, with a paper clip to keep it in place. The target can be slipped along on the card or it can be placed behind it, as shown at B. Owing to the manner of fastening, any number of cards can be made with targets.

A Twine Holder

A serviceable twine holder can be made from a wire guard of an electric

lamp. The guard is fastened to the wall, or other support, with a single staple over the wire ring at the top. Lift the guard and insert the twine from the back side. The weight of the ball will hold the guard in place. The twine is taken from the small-end opening in the guard.—Contributed by W. H. Sargent, St. Johnsbury, Vt.

An Acid Test for Metals

File, or grind, the pieces to be tested and polish them smooth, then place them in a dilute nitric or sulphuric-acid solution for a day. Wash and dry the pieces, and if they are of the best steel, the surface will have a frosty appearance. Ordinary steel will have a honeycomb surface, and iron will present a fibrous structure running parallel with the direction in which the metal was worked.

Repair for a Small Broken Bracket

A simple and cheap repair for a broken automobile-fan bracket, or a similar casting, can be easily made as

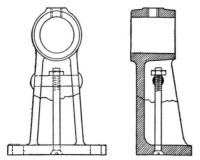

The Parts of the Casting are Held Together with a Screw, or Bolt and Nut

illustrated. A hole is drilled through the sides of the upper, or bearing, portion, and a rivet, or suitable rod, inserted and securely riveted in place. The two parts should then be assembled, and held together with clamps, while a hole is drilled and countersunk through the base and rivet body, to fit a suitable flat-headed machine screw. When assembled, the parts are securely held in place with the screw and nut connecting the base with the rivet.

Removing a Plain Key with a Monkey Wrench

Considerable skill is frequently required to remove plain keys fitted in places where it is impossible to get at them with a drift. One of the simplest

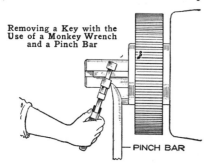

Removing a Key with the Use of a Monkey Wrench and a Pinch Bar

PINCH BAR

successful methods of obtaining the desired result is the use of a monkey wrench and pinch bar, as shown in the illustration. For this purpose a wrench should be used that has sharp edges on its jaws, so these can get a good grip on the key. To further improve the method, grooves may be cut on opposite sides of the key, so the jaws will fit better when straddling the key at a slight angle with the face of the keyed machine part. By using a pinch bar against the movable jaw, sufficient force can be applied to remove the key, unless it is so tightly driven, or rusted in place, that it will have to be drilled out before it can be released.—Contributed by J. V. Romig, Allentown, Pa.

Emergency Repair on Automobile-Engine Manifold

The water-outlet manifold on the gasoline engine of an automobile was very old and corroded, and the pressure of the circulating water fractured the center portion of the pipe and made two pieces of it while out on the road. The repair illustrated was done in a short time and enabled the driver to

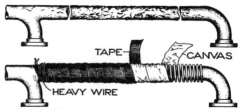

TAPE   CANVAS

HEAVY WIRE

Substitute Manifold Made of Canvas and Electricians' Tape over a Spiral Wire to Form a Hose

reach home, after which it served the purpose until a new manifold could be obtained.

A close-wound spiral spring of ordinary iron wire was wound around the circumference of the hand pump. The spiral ends were fastened to the broken ends of the manifold. Strips 3 in. in width were then cut from an old piece of canvas found in the tool box and wound tightly around the spring for the full length, after which electricians' tape was wound tightly over the canvas. White lead was inserted at both ends to prevent leakage, and the ends were then clamped to the metal with wire.

Shop Notes

An Electric Sign of Unique Construction

The illustration shows a very attractive electric sign that is entirely out of the ordinary, and which can be used for a great number of advertising purposes. It consists of a glass plate on which strips of tin foil are pasted, using shellac as an adhesive; two brass supporting standards; an induction coil, and a battery. The tinfoil strips are placed ¼ in. apart in such a manner as to form letters or figures, which are connected by fine copper wires, also pasted to the plate as shown.

The secondary current of the induction coil flows through the wire A, the brass standard and the wire B to the first letter of the sign around which it passes, leaping in blue flames from one tin-foil segment to the next until it reaches the wire C to the next letter; around the next letter, and so on, until it reaches the induction coil, as indicated by the arrow marks. To ob-

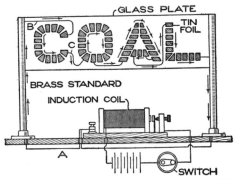

The Flashes of Light Caused by the Jumping of the Current between Strips Illuminate the Letters

tain the best effect the back of the glass plate should be painted black.— Contributed by F. B. Hays, Houston, Texas.

Watering Second-Floor Window-Box Flowers from the Outside

The management of a hotel placed a number of flower boxes on the sills of the second-story windows, and as

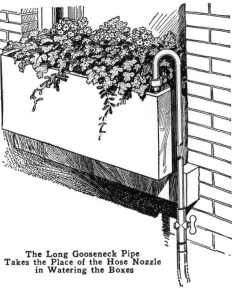

The Long Gooseneck Pipe Takes the Place of the Hose Nozzle in Watering the Boxes

the boxes required watering each day, men had to enter the rooms for doing the work, to which the guests objected. The boxes were changed to a self-watering kind, having a false bottom in which some sponges were fastened so that they pressed against holes in the box that holds the dirt. A 1-in. feed pipe was run down the side of the box to the pan holding the sponges, the surplus water overflowing through a small hole in the side of the box when the pan was full. These boxes required water once a week. The guests still objected to the annoyance of having the boxes watered from the inside, so the chief gardener devised a plan as follows: A 2-in. to ½-in. reducer was slipped into the top of each feed pipe to form a sort of funnel into which the water was run with a long gooseneck-shaped pipe attached to the hose.

When the boxes need watering the gardener takes the hose with the gas-pipe connection and inserts the gooseneck end into the reducer and turns on the water, filling each box without annoying the guests.—Contributed by W. F. Held, Chicago.

Grocery-Order Box for Suburbanites

An enterprising groceryman whose store was located on a street traveled by many suburbanites on their way to

DROP ORDERS HERE

LEAVE YOUR ORDERS HERE
NOW
CALL FOR IT
ON YOUR
WAY
HOME

the railroad station, devised a plan to further his business by the use of an order box. This box is hung conspicuously in front of his store so that a person coming to work in the morning may deposit his orders without stopping to enter the store, and during the day the groceryman fills them and makes a neat bundle, ready for the customer when he passes in the evening from the station. It is only necessary for the customer to step in and call his name to get his bundle quickly and without having to wait for it. The box is about 28 in. long and 8 in. square. A sliding door is fitted near the bottom on one side for taking out the orders.

¶As a safeguard against fire in paint or machine shops prepare bags of sand, marked "Sand for Fire," in several sizes, and have them placed within easy reach.

Restoring Tan Color to Leather

After considerable experimenting, a leather company found that oil of citronella would restore various shades of tan and brown leathers to their original colors. Any shoe shop can adopt the method, as the process is simple. The odor from the oil is strong, which is objectionable to many, but by drying the leather in a current of air much of the perfume evaporates. It is only necessary to rub the leather over with the oil and later polish with a good leather dressing.

Air and Gas Mixer for Gas Engines

By means of the illustrated device, the fuel charge of a gasoline engine can be considerably improved, resulting in additional power. To make the device, an ordinary $\frac{1}{2}$-in. grease cup must be provided. The inner end of the cup is drilled about $\frac{1}{4}$ in. deep, to tightly fit a $\frac{1}{2}$-in. piece of thin tubing, 1 in. long. This should be drilled for a row of $\frac{1}{64}$-in. holes, and securely plugged at one end. The other end is fitted in the grease cup and soldered in place. A circular disk must be made to easily fit inside the large end of the cup. With disk and cap carefully centered, three $\frac{1}{8}$-in. holes are drilled to serve as air inlets of the device; another hole should be drilled through the center for a disk pin. This pin is provided with a shoulder to fit against the outside of the cap, so that it cannot slip in. The cap hole serves as bearing for the pin which fits through the disk and is riv-

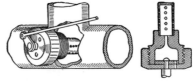

Device Made of an Oil Cup, to Admit Air to the Manifold Inlet of a Gasoline Engine

eted in place to form a close fit against the cap, at the same time permitting a slight movement sufficient to bring the disk holes in or out of alinement with the corresponding cap holes. To the outside end of the pin is attached a crank arm which connects with a controlling wire, conveniently attached near the throttle control. When attaching the device to an engine, it should be screwed into a threaded hole, provided for it in the engine manifold, between the carburetor and engine cylinder. In using the device, the disk should first be set with its openings closed until the engine is running well, then, by adjusting the disk, additional air may be sprayed in through the small tube holes, thereby finishing up the work of the carburetor and producing a more thorough and better mixture.—Contributed by O. H. Waychoff, Koenig, Colo.

Repairing a Broken Water-Pump Vane

The cost of replacing a broken rotor in the water pump on an automobile engine led the owner to make a repair as shown in the sketch. The rotor was 1 in. in width. A piece of flat steel stock of suitable length, ⅞ in. wide and ⅛ in. thick, was procured and bent to the same shape as the other blades. The bottom was bent over in the shape of the letter "L" to fit into a groove cut in the hub of the rotor. The new blade was held firmly in place with two blind studs riveted over on the outside.

Easily Constructed Concrete Culvert

Our borough construction force builds a very good concrete culvert in the manner shown in the sketch. The sides A are first built, and the forms removed before the concrete is completely set. Benchlike wood forms are then placed at intervals between the sides A, and boards laid on them, then

paper spread over the surface of the boards. The concrete is then put on top of the paper. Short pieces of railroad

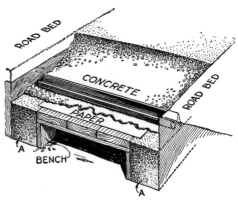

Simple Method of Making a Concrete Culvert by Using Ordinary Construction of the Forms

iron are laid in the concrete to reinforce it.

After the top has properly set, the supports are driven out, or broken down with a long iron rod. The boards are then easily withdrawn. This culvert is strong enough to stand the travel of heavy teams as well as automobile trucks.—Contributed by James M. Kane, Doylestown, Pa.

Support for End of Gear Teeth on a Transmission

One of the gears in the transmission case of an automobile was so designed that its web was placed on one side, as shown in the illustration. The teeth, being supported on one side only, had a tendency to give away on the other, and it was necessary to strengthen the unsupported end. The old gear was damaged and distorted beyond repair, but a new one was purchased, and the flat plate A was riveted to it, as shown, with four rivets. Both the plate and gear were turned down on a lathe.

❡A lathe tool will make a smoother and brighter finish with water than when run dry.

Procuring Fresh Water from the Ocean

By the process of distillation fresh water suitable for drinking purposes can be obtained from sea water, but

An Unglazed-Clay, or Earthen, Pot Used to Secure Fresh Water from the Sea

this method requires special apparatus and a person trained in laboratory work, conditions which are not easily or cheaply fulfilled. This method, then, is almost out of the question with ordinary seamen. The one illustrated, however, is very simple and inexpensive, and brings good results. The materials necessary are a newly baked earthen pot, a piece of waterproofing material suitable for a covering—a piece of leather or oilcloth will do—and a piece of string or cord with a sinker to hold the pot deeply in the sea. Cover the pot with the waterproofing material, tie on the string, or cord, and sinker, and drop it into the sea. Allow sufficient time for the pressure to force the water through

the porous pot and then haul it in, and clear water will be the result with the salt and dirt on the outside surface.— Contributed by V. M. Apostol, Sorsogon, P. I.

Protector Cutter with a Double-Notched Edge

In many places where money is paid for any legal paper, or permit, a receipt, or voucher, is issued, with the correct amount that was paid registered, or marked, by tearing off proper parts from a series of figures indicating dollars and cents on the left side of the receipt, as shown in the illustration. A sharp-edge rule, or a piece of brass with an offset, is used, and this has to be moved a few times before the receipt is properly marked.

The cutter illustrated eliminates many movements by cutting the receipt at one setting. The cutter is made of a flat piece of brass, A, about $\frac{1}{8}$ in. thick, 1 in. wide, and 9 in. long, which has an offset at one end as wide as the left-hand column on the receipt and about 3 in. long. The piece A is beveled at about a 45° angle for the cutting edge B, and it also has a slot, about $\frac{3}{16}$ in. wide, cut in it as shown at C, the edges of which are beveled off to about a 60° angle to form a slide

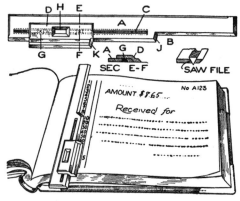

The Piece Forming the Second Offset can be Adjusted for Any Amount of Cents

for the piece D. The slot C is made by drilling a number of holes along the center line of the slot, as close together as possible, and then filing the slot straight. A piece of triangular saw file is used to file the angle in the slot, as shown.

The piece D is made about 2½ in. long, of the same material as the piece A, and is bent to the shape shown by the section EF, and beveled off on the cutting edge. Two small pieces, G, are made and riveted to the under side of the piece D for sliders in the slot C. A small square hole, H, may be made in the piece D for the finger.

The cutter is set with the offset J to any number of dollars, and the offset K is moved to the number of cents required by sliding the piece D along the slot C, whereupon the receipt is cut off to the registered amount. The forefinger holds the piece A in place, while the thumb moves piece D.—Contributed by Edward Sieja, Chicago.

Goggles to Eliminate Glare of Headlights

To overcome the blinding glare of headlights while driving a car at night, prepare the goggles as follows: Coat the upper portion of each eyepiece down to a line drawn ¼ in. above the center with a transparent color, green preferred. In driving, when another car appears ahead with a bright headlight, lower the head a trifle and look through the colored portion of the glasses. This will reduce the glare sufficiently so that a driver will not be confused.

To Prevent Steady-Rest Jaws from Marring Work

To prevent the jaws of a steady rest from scoring the work, wrap a piece of emery cloth around the material to be turned, with the abrasive side out, draw the ends tightly and insert them between the upper and lower part of the steady rest, where they are clamped together with a bolt. The jaws can then be adjusted with safety.—Contributed by F. G. Marbach, Cleveland, Ohio.

A Safe Way to Carry a Watch

Instead of carrying my watch in the lower vest pocket I place it in the upper, and attach the chain as follows: A buttonhole is cut, as shown in the sketch, and the chain run through it and snapped into the watch-stem ring. The other end is fastened to a key ring and slipped into the lower pocket. Any person at a glance would imagine that the watch is in the lower pocket. In addition to the

safety for the watch, I have a very convenient way of carrying my keys.—Contributed by L. E. Turner, New York City.

An Eye Magnet

The tool shown in the illustration is a very valuable asset for any mechanic's tool chest. It is designed especially for removing steel or iron chips from the eye. Both ends are turned to form perfect spheres and are tem-

Tool Made of Steel, Highly Tempered and Polished, Then Magnetized for Taking Particles of Steel from the Eye

pered very hard and then given a high polish. It is magnetized as strongly as possible.—Contributed by S. Victor Brook, Hartford, Conn.

¶A discarded curtain roller makes a good towel hanger. The ends of the roller can be secured in blocks, or the old roller brackets may be used.

How to Build a Camp House

By E. ARRINGTON

IF it is desired to have a good camping outfit, one that has a tent beat in a good many ways, build it as shown in the illustration, and the parts forming the floor can be folded into the shape of a box that will inclose all the side walls and the roof, and provide a space for camping utensils and bedding. The house is 9 by 12 ft., and 6 ft. high at the eaves. When ready for shipment, the box will be 3 ft. square and 9 ft. long.

The entire house is made up in sections. The floor is made up in four parts, each 3 ft. wide and 9 ft. long, of flooring boards, well battened on the under side and fastened together with strong hinges at the joints, the hinges being attached on the upper side. The same number of hasps are attached to the edges of the outer sections as the hinges used on each joint. The hasps are fastened to the under side

When Set Up, the Building Gives the Appearance of a Well-Made House, and Has the Comforts of One

of the floor. When the sections are folded up with the battens on the outside, the hasps will join the outside sections together in forming the box for shipment. There should be a batten at each end and five spaced between, and two hinges to the section.

The wall and roof sections are made up of furring strips, or pieces of wood, 2 in. wide and 7/8 in. thick. In construction the sections are all alike, but there is some difference in the size. Each is built somewhat similar to a screen-door frame, the joints being mortised, or halved; whereupon a crosspiece is nailed in the center, and each rectangle thus formed cross-braced. The wall

sections for the sides are 2 ft. 5 in. wide and 6 ft. long; the end sections are 3 ft. wide and 6 ft. long, and the roof parts are 2 ft. 5½ in. wide and 6 ft. long. The dimensions of the gables, of which there are three, one for the center, are made for a little more than what is called a square pitch. The difference of ½ in. in size of the side-wall and roof sections is provided in order to make a little extension of the roof at the ends for an eave.

A ¾-in. strip is nailed on the edge of one side-wall section for each side of the house. This is to make the sides extend over the edge of the end sections at the corners.

The gable parts are hinged together at the joint, and a notch is made in the top to admit the ridge. The ridge is made in halves, each 6½ ft. long, and joined together with a fished scarf joint, the slope being about 4 in. long, and side plates of metal.

The sections are covered with 8-oz. canvas, stretched tightly, and tacked on like a screen on a door, using half-round molding on the edges of the cloth. This construction is carried out on all parts except for the end gables, and on these the canvas is allowed to extend over the edge of the frame, so that it will lap over the end sections when in place. The canvas on all sections is covered with boiled linseed oil.

All sections are held together with hooks and eyes. In setting the house up, a level place is selected, and the floor is laid on some stones or blocks of wood so that it will rest on the battens.

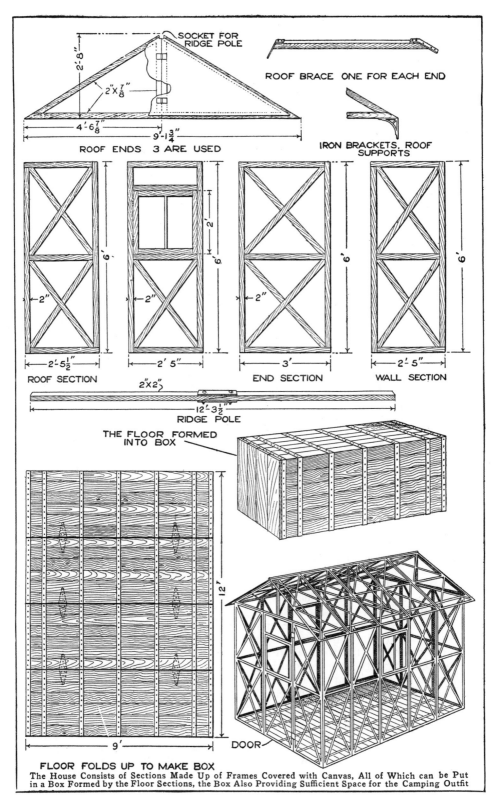

SOCKET FOR RIDGE POLE

ROOF BRACE ONE FOR EACH END

2'-8"

2"X⅞"

4'-6⅞"

9'-1¾"

ROOF ENDS 3 ARE USED

IRON BRACKETS, ROOF SUPPORTS

6'

2'

6'

6'

6'

2"

2"

2"

2'-5½"

2'5"

3'

2'5"

ROOF SECTION

END SECTION

WALL SECTION

2"x2"

12'-3½"

RIDGE POLE

THE FLOOR FORMED INTO BOX

12'

9'

DOOR

FLOOR FOLDS UP TO MAKE BOX

The House Consists of Sections Made Up of Frames Covered with Canvas, All of Which can be Put in a Box Formed by the Floor Sections, the Box Also Providing Sufficient Space for the Camping Outfit

2493

The wall parts are set up around the outside edge of the floor. To hold these parts firmly in place, two or three long wood screws should be driven through the lower frame piece and into the floor edge. If the sections are numbered, the holes for the screws will always match when set up. The joints of the sections are held with hooks and eyes.

After putting up the walls, set the gables in place and lay the ridge in the notches, then it is ready for the roof sections. The ridge is braced at each end. One of the end sections is hinged for a door, and two side-wall parts are fitted with a hinged window sash.

In forming a box of the floor, make ends for it to fit the opening snugly. These ends can be fastened temporarily with screws for shipment. The sides and ends of the building being only 6 ft. long, a space of 3 ft. will be left in one end of the box for bedding and camp utensils.

Broaching Staggered Holes in Assembling Machine Parts

It frequently is found in assembling machinery that the bolt holes will not line up properly, and must be gouged 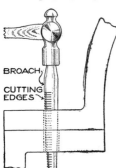 out with a chisel, filed, or reamed, before the bolts will enter. Considerable difficulty is experienced if the bottom hole can be gotten at only from above, but by using a broach, a neat fit can be made in shorter time and with far less labor than would otherwise be required.

To make a broaching tool for cutting out staggered holes, it is necessary to obtain a round piece of chisel or tool steel, having a diameter equal to that of the holes and a length depending on the combined thickness of the two drilled parts—8 in. would be suitable for 2 in. of metal. One end is turned or ground tapering up to about the middle of the tool. Cutting edges or teeth may then be cut, or filed, as shown, about $\frac{3}{16}$ in. apart, but only halfway around the circumference. When finished, the broach should be hardened, and its temper drawn to a bluish straw color.

In using the tool, it is driven through the holes, the same as a drift pin. The cutting edges, each projecting a little farther than the preceding one, will remove the metal in the same way as though a gouge chisel were used. The broaching tool not only acts as a large number of chisels, each taking a small cut, but it also guides itself, and only requires to be driven or forced through the metal.—Contributed by J. V. Romig, Allentown, Pa.

Repairing a Broken Valve-Guide Retainer

One arm of the valve-guide retainer of a gasoline engine broke as shown in the illustration. No doubt the break was caused by overstrain from the stud nut holding the retainer into the engine crank case. It was repaired by filing 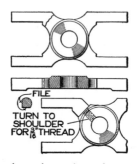 a flat surface at the point of the break, then drilling a hole and tapping it to receive a $\frac{5}{16}$-in. drill rod. The filing was done at an angle of 45 deg. A piece of drill rod was cut to the proper length and a thread cut on one end. It was then screwed in place and hammered to the proper shape. The end was filed to the shape of the other arms.

❡It is a good plan to flush out the crank-case oil reservoir of a gasoline engine with kerosene occasionally, then run it idle for a few minutes to clean it out well.

Safety Coupler for Switching Locomotives

The recent movement of railway companies toward a definite and systematic study of safety appliances for the protection of employes, has afforded many wonderful and gratifying results. Comparison, before and after installing the appliances, of statistics of killed and injured necessarily kept by the companies, has proven the time and expense involved in this movement a good investment.

The work of the switchman and the routine of switching service comprise practically the most hazardous duties in railway employment. A study of the occupation by one of the western roads, besides leading to some other vital safety suggestions, resulted in the coupling device for switch engines shown in the illustration. A continuous lifter bar had been in use; that is, one running the entire length of the pilot and footboard beam. This was, of course, to lift the knuckle locker in the coupler head, and when pulled up at one end of the beam, the other end was also raised. This was dangerous when two men were on the footboard, as in raising the lifter by a switchman at one end without informing the other, one of them is apt to be thrown or pushed from the footboard. The new arrangement, as can be seen, provides two separate lifting levers, each of which can be operated independently of the other.

The locker block is raised up from the bottom to free the knuckle, instead of being pulled up from the top as with previous arrangements. The weight of the lifting links and the manner in which the leverage parts are assembled make it impossible for the locker block to jump out, a thing that has caused many accidents. The peculiar shape of the locker block also throws the coupling knuckle out when the hands, or lifting levers, are jerked up, making it necessary for the switchman to go between the car and locomotive to open knuckles in any ordinary switching duty.

The mere disabling, let alone the killing, of an efficient employe, is a loss to the railroad company that

The Locker Block is Raised from the Bottom Instead of being Pulled Up from the Top

many do not realize, and from the standpoint alone of financial loss through claims, setting aside the loss of efficient labor, the companies are realizing the immediate returns from eliminating as much danger as possible.

Hammer for Thin Sheet-Metal Work

An extremely useful tool to have around a garage is a soft-faced hammer. One made up as shown in the illustration is especially adapted for use in straightening bent mudguards, hoods and bodies on automobiles, and for all metal work having enameled surfaces that must not be marred. The hammer is similar to a wood mallet, but the head is provided with a pad

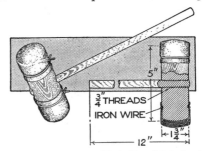

Soft Face on a Hammer Made Up of Felt for Use in Straightening Thin Sheet Metal

of felt, made up of a series of small circular pieces and covered with a larger piece held in place by means of a soft-iron wire wound around in a small groove, as shown.

Electro-Pneumatic Signal and Call Whistle

By F. W. BENTLEY, Jr.

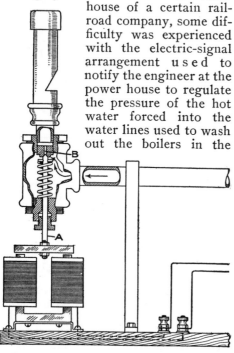

Signal Whistle in Which the Valve Controlling the Air Pressure is Operated by Magnets

IN connection with the boiler-washing system at the terminal roundhouse of a certain railroad company, some difficulty was experienced with the electric-signal arrangement used to notify the engineer at the power house to regulate the pressure of the hot water forced into the water lines used to wash out the boilers in the roundhouse. At times, when the boiler washers were not using the pump for intervals of 20 to 30 minutes, it could be shut off temporarily to the advantage of the other machinery in the engine room, and also much to the preservation of the pipe lines. The roundhouse was some distance away from the power plant in which the pumps were installed, and an electric call bell was used to notify the engineer when the hot-water force pump was needed. It was impossible to locate the bell in the power plant in such a place that it could be heard distinctly by the engineer wherever he happened to be at various times, and it was also impractical to install a number of large expensive call bells.

The illustration shows an electro-pneumatic whistle which was substituted for the bell and tried out with a great deal of success. The body of the device consists of a 1-in. tee with a side outlet of ⅜ in. The air is admitted to the inner portion of the tee through the ⅜-in. pipe, where it is controlled by a ¼-in. brass pin valve, A. To the lower end of the stem is fitted a moderate-sized armature bar, which is subject to the control of the magnet poles. When the push button is pressed the bar is attracted by the magnets, pulling the valve away from its seat on the cap that is screwed in an inverted position in the reducing plug at the top of the tee. This allows the air to flow up and cause a blast of the whistle. Release of the pressure allows the spring around the valve spindle to force it up to its seat. On the lower end, to prevent the escape or waste of air that might pass by the valve spindle, a packing-nut arrangement was made for the spindle from a ¼-in. pipe plug. The strength of the magnets is fully utilized, because of the fact that it is necessary to move the spindle only a slight distance from its seat to cause a shrill blast of the whistle, and the armature can be placed very near the core ends of the magnets. In shops of this kind an air compressor with storage tanks is installed, so that a supply of air can always be had for the whistle.

In the case mentioned, a number of whistles were supplied by a ⅛-in. pipe from the head of the tee to various places around the power house, making the requests from the distant roundhouse comprehended by the engineer, no matter where the calls around the plant may have taken him. The whole whistle device is made of pipe fittings. The whistles are inexpensively made, from ½-in. or ⅜-in. pipe, and they can be put at almost any place within a reasonable distance by using ⅛-in. pipe to connect them to the top of the tee head, the number of whistles depending on the size of the air opening B.

NO.	SIZE OF PIPE	A	B	C	D	E	F	G	H	J	K
1	$\frac{1}{8}$ IN.	$1\frac{1}{2}$ IN.	27	$\frac{5}{32}$ IN.	$2\frac{5}{8}$ IN.	$\frac{3}{4}$ IN.	$\frac{1}{4}$ IN.	SEE NOTE	$2\frac{5}{8}$ IN.	$\frac{3}{32}$ IN.	2 IN.
2	$\frac{1}{4}$ IN. TO $\frac{3}{8}$ IN.	$2\frac{1}{2}$ IN.	18	$\frac{3}{4}$ IN.	$4\frac{1}{2}$ IN.	$1\frac{1}{4}$ IN.	$\frac{1}{2}$ IN.	$\frac{3}{4}$ IN.	$4\frac{1}{2}$ IN.	$\frac{1}{4}$ IN.	2 IN.
3	$\frac{1}{2}$ IN TO $\frac{3}{4}$ IN.	$3\frac{7}{8}$ IN.	14	$1\frac{5}{16}$ IN.	$5\frac{1}{4}$ IN.	$1\frac{7}{8}$ IN.	$1\frac{5}{16}$ IN.	1 IN.	$5\frac{1}{2}$ IN.	$\frac{1}{2}$ IN.	$3\frac{1}{2}$ IN.
4	1 IN. TO 2 IN.	4 IN.	$11\frac{1}{2}$	$2\frac{1}{4}$ IN.	6 IN.	2 IN.	$1\frac{3}{8}$ IN.	2 IN.	6 IN.	$\frac{15}{16}$ IN.	$3\frac{1}{2}$ IN.
5	$2\frac{1}{2}$ IN. TO 4 IN.	6 IN.	8	$4\frac{1}{4}$ IN.	6 IN.	3 IN.	$2\frac{3}{8}$ IN.	4 IN.	6 IN.	$2\frac{1}{4}$ IN.	4 IN.

NOTE: THIS RADIUS IS OMITTED ON NO. 1 MACHINES, AS THIS NO. IS FOR ONE SIZE PIPE ONLY

Table of Dimensions for the Construction of Five Sets of Bushings and Five Sets of Jaws, Providing a Sufficient Number of Lead Threads to Form All Sizes Used on Pipes Up to Four Inches

A Thread-Forming Tool for Thin Tubing

Tubing, such as rain leaders, stovepipes, brass and copper pipes having thin walls, cannot be threaded in the usual manner, and therefore the machine illustrated was designed for rolling the threads into the metal. This tool will quickly form a thread sufficiently full to give a good, tight joint. As the thread is formed in the entire thickness of the metal, it serves for either an inside or outside thread.

In Fig. 1 the tool is shown without the chuck jaws, of which five sizes, required to roll threads in the five standard pitches for pipe from ⅛ in. to 4 in., are given in the table. For example, if it is desired to form a thread on a ¾-in. tube, the table shows that such a pipe is given 14 threads to the inch. The two bushings, L and M, having 14 threads to the inch, are taken from the set, and the tube to be

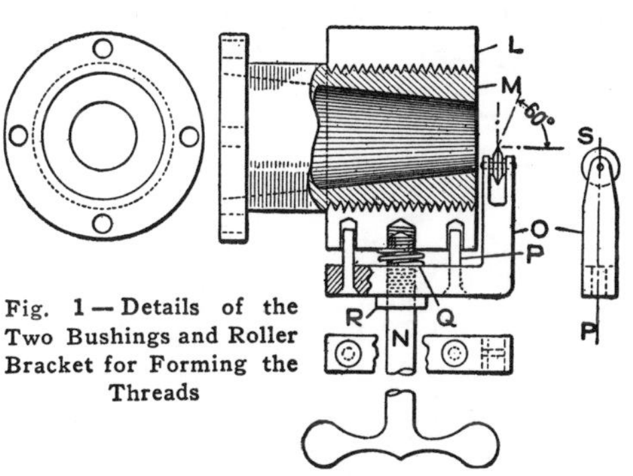

Fig. 1—Details of the Two Bushings and Roller Bracket for Forming the Threads

threaded is filled with lead for a distance of about 5 in. This can be accomplished by filling the other part of the tube with clay, or by pushing in a cork, and pouring the melted metal on top of it. The tube end is placed through the bore in the bushing M, and the four chuck jaws belonging to

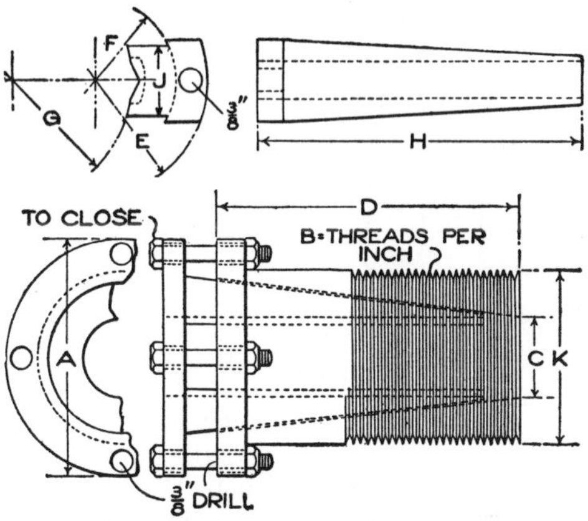

Fig. 2—Four Jaws are Used to Clamp the Pipe in the Inner Bushing of the Machine

this set are placed in the lead-filled pipe. The end of the pipe must project through the bushing M far enough for the thread. Each jaw is located at a point 90 deg. from the other, or where the holes in the flange of the bushing M will meet those in the flange of the jaw, as shown in Fig. 2; then, ⅜-in. bolts are placed through the holes and drawn up to cause the jaws to grip the lead-filled pipe. The traveling feed bushing L is then turned on to M for about five threads, and the handle N, having been passed through the clearance hole in the wheel bracket O, is turned a few threads into the tapped hole in the bushing L. The guide pins P are a push fit in the holes drilled in L, and prevent the lateral play in O. The helical spring Q takes up all the backlash.

The handle N is turned down into the hole in L, causing the fixed collar R to force the bracket O so that the desired pressure is obtained on the threading wheel S. The bushing L is revolved for the length of the thread desired, then another run is taken, with the wheel S set a little deeper, until the thread is made. The tube is then removed and the lead taken out. In removing the lead, care must be taken, if the pipe is plated or finished in any manner. Heat will spoil the finish; therefore the lead must be drilled out as much as possible, and the remaining portion dug out with a sharp-pointed tool.

The tapers in the bushing M and on the jaws should be standard. The torsional strain on the tubing is small, for the reason that the thread is formed with a roller instead of being cut.

Repairing a Broken Steering Lever

Automobiles are as apt to have breakdowns in the country as in the city, but with a few simple tools and a little skill, repairs can be made on the spot or at a neighboring farmhouse, which will avoid the necessity of abandoning the machine until it can be towed in or a new part secured. A simple roadside repair of this nature is shown in the illustration.

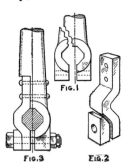

FIG. 1

FIG. 3   FIG. 2

The steering-gear lever broke, as shown in Fig. 1, preventing further continuation of the journey. The repair was made with the aid of a small vise, clamped on the running board, a breast drill, a piece of steel, several rivets, a nut, and such tools as hammer, chisels, punches, and files, which are found in every well-equipped tool box.

In making the repair, the main piece of the lever was chipped and filed to form a flat surface and square shoulder. A suitable piece of steel was heated in a bonfire, and bent to approximately fit the lever pin, so that but little filing was required to make a close fit. The parts were then assembled, clamped in the vise, and drilled for ¼-in. rivets, which were inserted and riveted in place. In order to use the same clamping bolt and nut, an extra washer was provided. For this purpose a nut was found which slipped over the body of the bolt, and one corner was chipped off to fit the lever. The completed repair was very rigid, and caused no trouble during the rest of the trip.

Keeping Flies Out of an Ice-Cream Parlor

One owner of a confectionery and ice-cream parlor kept the flies out and away from the entrance in the following manner: The ventilating fan placed in the transom over the door was housed and the draft from it directed so that it passed down in front of the door. This keeps the door free from flies and does not interfere with the ventilation of the room.—Contributed by C. J. Waters, Jackson, Mich.

Tool to Replace Rubber Tires on Velocipedes

The main part of the tool consists of a yoke, A, made of a piece of metal, 8 in. long and 1 in. square, with a notch cut in each end, ½ in. wide and 1 in. deep, into which side pieces, B, 16 in. long and ½ in. thick, are hinged. A toggle joint, C, is made of pieces, ½ in. thick, which is operated with a screw run through the yoke A. The pieces are drilled and

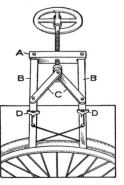

A   B   B   C   D   D

tapped to receive bolts with wing nuts, D.

The wire ends in the tire are fastened under the wing nuts, and the edges of the pieces B are placed against the rubber ends. The screw is turned down to force the pieces B out, thus baring the wire so that it can be tied securely.

Front Sight for a Rifle

File a V-shaped notch in the cross bar of the front sight, about $\frac{3}{32}$ in. deep, with the sides at an angle of 60° for a fine target sight, and about 45° for game. Taper the sides so as to make a smooth, clean edge on the front of the cross bar.

Make a pin, about $\frac{3}{8}$ in. long, from steel, $\frac{5}{32}$ in. in diameter. Cut a thread on one end and drill a $\frac{5}{64}$-in. hole in the other. Fit in this hole an ivory pin accurately pointed to an angle of 70°. Drill a hole in the bottom plate, and tap it to receive the threads of the pin. Turn the pin in position so that the point of the ivory bead will show exactly in the center at the bottom of the notch in the cross bar. A very little of the white pin showing will give the best results.

This sight combines the two best and oldest known sights in use into one, and eliminates guesswork from aiming. —Contributed by Chas. Carroll, State Soldiers' Home, Ohio.

Locating Empty Theater Seats Electrically

There are but few people who have not experienced the difficulty of going into a movie show, or other place of amusement, and finding a seat in the dark. Having this in mind, a practical electrician has devised a switchboard and electric-light system, similar to a telephone exchange, and when a person sits down on a seat a contact is made which completes the circuit and a lamp designating the seat row and number lights up. The unoccupied seats remain dark. The contacts are supplied with a spring arranged so

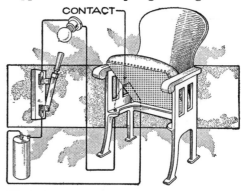

The Switch on Each Seat is Closed When Occupied Which Lights a Globe on the Lamp Board

that they will not meet unless a pressure of 35 lb. is applied. If a chair is vacant or occupied by a child within the free-admission age, the lamp corresponding to that particular seat will remain dark.

It has been found advisable to use a switch in the transmitter circuit so that no current is wasted by keeping the whole number of lamps lit all the time. The lights are small incandescent lamps and are arranged on the switchboard in the relative positions of the seats they represent. With the aid of this device the ushers can seat patrons satisfactorily.—Contributed by M. Ancker, Philadelphia, Pa.

Enlarging Holes in Brass

Several thousand drawn-brass shells, or cups, A, having a hole in them made too small, had to be drilled to enlarge the hole $\frac{1}{64}$ in. As they were made of soft brass, it was more difficult to enlarge the hole by drilling than if there had been

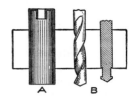

no hole. A drill in good condition passing through metal of this sort will make a hole just a trifle larger than the size of the drill. To take off $\frac{1}{64}$

in. in the diameter would only require the drill to scrape a little from the edges. Various drills were used, also lubricants, but to no avail. The holes were enlarged, however, by the method shown in the illustration. Twist drills have a raised portion, or land, $\frac{1}{32}$ to $\frac{1}{16}$ in. wide, that is the full size of the drill. This forms its cutting edge at its greatest diameter. A part of this raised portion was ground off leaving only a short piece, about $\frac{1}{16}$ in. long, at the point. This cut the hole out to size and the following part did not rub. The removed portion of the raised part is shown at B.

How to Keep a Carving Knife Sharp

It is quite an art to sharpen a carving knife, and there are very few people that know how to do it properly. The secret in caring for the edge of a knife is to sharpen it often, by a few strokes on a good steel. Watching a marketman cut meat, one will notice that he sharpens the knife very

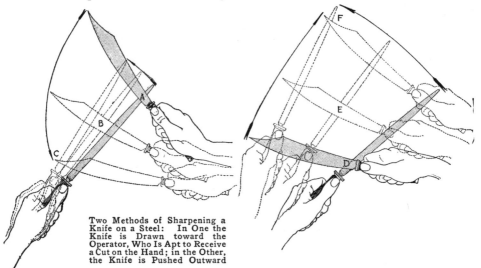

Two Methods of Sharpening a Knife on a Steel: In One the Knife is Drawn toward the Operator, Who Is Apt to Receive a Cut on the Hand; in the Other, the Knife is Pushed Outward

often, only a few rubs on the steel, but every few minutes. A carving knife in the majority of cases has to do much harder work when in use than the knife of the marketman or butcher. Its edge is blunted by contact with the bones in the meat and especially with the bottom of the

platter, yet the majority of people expect the knife to cut easily without sharpening. In most cases the continued use of the knife without any attempt to sharpen it is due to the individual using the knife not knowing how to sharpen it on the steel. The following suggestions may be a help to those not knowing how to properly use the steel.

Hold the steel in the left hand and apply the knife as shown at A. The blade is drawn across the steel downward and inward, holding the blade at an angle of 15° and starting at the back of the blade and finishing at the point. At B and C are shown two stages in the operation. Repeat, first on one side and then on the other, for at least a dozen strokes, being careful to hold the blade at an angle of 15° to the steel at all times.

Another method of sharpening a knife on a steel, which a great many prefer, as a person is less liable to cut the hand, is illustrated at D, E and F. In this case the steel and knife are held at the same angle to each other, but the stroke begins at the base of the steel and ends at the point, and should be repeated a number of times, first on one side and then on the other. This method is not considered as scientific as the first, but is very effective and much safer.

To Locate and Correct Troubles in Direct-Current Dynamos

By A. E. ANDREWS

PART I—Sparking at the Brushes

IT is the purpose of this article to present the methods of locating and correcting the troubles that may occur in generators and motors at any time while they are in service. While the description may not be complete in every detail, it will cover a large percentage of all the cases of trouble that may arise, and will thus serve as a useful guide to those in charge of machinery. In the majority of cases the trouble is very easily remedied after its cause is once found, but the greatest difficulty is to recognize the cause, and for this reason a greater stress will be laid upon a method to determine the cause. It is always best to try to locate the cause with as little interference to the service of the machine as possible. Proper care should be exercised at all times not to expose oneself unduly to electric shock, or contact with bare conductors. With the exception of one or two cases, the following description deals with what are termed low-voltage machines, and nothing above 250 volts. Extra care should be taken in working around machines of higher voltage, as the danger is much greater. In making the simple tests that are suggested, it is assumed that the operator has the use of a voltmeter and an ammeter.

Fault of the Brushes

The one main cause for sparking at the brushes is that they are not set diametrically opposite. The setting of the brushes should be done while the dynamo is at rest, by counting the bars, by measurement, or by the use of reference marks on the commutator. The center of adjacent brushes should be 180° apart. This can be done, if necessary, while the machine is running by moving the rocker arm so that the brushes on one side will show the least spark, then adjust the brushes on the other side to the least-sparking point, and clamp them in place.

Another cause for sparking is that the brushes are not set at a neutral point. This may be remedied by moving the rocker arm back and forth until the sparking stops.

If the brushes are not properly trimmed and set, they will spark. If sparking begins from this cause and

Fig. 1—Smoothing a Commutator with a Piece of Sandpaper Backed with a Piece of Heavy Cloth

the machine cannot be stopped, bend back the brushes and cut off the loose and ragged wires, if metal brushes are used, and retrim them as soon as possible after the run is over. If there are two or more brushes in each set, they may be removed one at a time, and properly trimmed ones put in the place during the run, on any low-voltage machine. To trim the brushes, first clean them from oil and dirt with benzine, soda, or potash, then file, or grind, them carefully by the aid of a standard jig, and reset carefully.

The brushes of a set should be adjusted separately until they are all in line and square with the same commutator bar, bearing evenly for their entire width, unless purposely set staggered. Adjust the pressure by the tension screws and springs until a light, firm, yet even, contact is made. The pressure should be about 1.25 lb. per square inch.

Fault of Commutator or Magnetic Field

The commutator may cause the brushes to spark by its being rough, worn in grooves, not round, or by one or more bars being too high or too low. To grind down a commutator, use fine sandpaper laid in a block, concaved to fit the circumference. Never use emery cloth or paper, nor emery in any form. Polish with a soft, clean cloth. A method that may be employed in clean-

Fig. 2—The Heavy Cloth Extending over the End of the Sandpaper Prevents Any Copper Dust Passing under the Brushes

ing a commutator when the surface is not worn too badly is shown in Fig. 1. A piece of heavy cloth should be placed over the sandpaper, as shown in Fig. 2, which prevents the fine copper dust from being carried under the brushes. If the surface of the commutator is rough, the sandpaper should be held against the surface by means of a curved piece of pine instead of the fingers. The sandpaper should be given a slight endwise movement along the commutator, to prevent the formation of grooves.

If the surface is too badly worn to be ground down, turn it off with a special tool and rest while the armature is turning slowly in the bearings, or remove the armature and turn off the commutator with light cuts in a lathe. The armature, when set in its bearings, should have from $\frac{1}{16}$ to $\frac{1}{8}$-in. play, so as to distribute the wear evenly and prevent wearing ruts and ridges. The brushes may be shifted sideways occasionally to assist in the distribution of the wear.

If one or more commutator bars are high, set each down with a block of wood, or a mallet, being careful not to bend, bruise, or injure the bar, and then tighten the clamping rings. If this does not remedy the fault, file, grind, or turn the high bar or bars down to the level of the other bars. The high bar may make the brushes

jump or vibrate, and cause them to "sing." If one or more bars are low in a commutator, turn down the others to true the surface and remove the low spots. The insulation between the bars will not wear as fast as the metal, and should be ground or turned down when necessary to remedy this fault.

A weak magnetic field will sometimes cause trouble, and this may be due to a broken circuit in the field. It can be remedied by repairing the broken line, and rewinding if the break is inside of the winding. A short circuit of the coils will cause the same trouble. If the short circuit is external, repair it, but if internal, the coil will need to be rewound. The same trouble will result if the dynamo is not properly wound, or does not have the proper amount of iron. In the latter case, the only remedy is to rebuild it entirely.

Excessive Current in Armatures

Sparking at the brushes is also the result of an excessive current in the armature, which is caused, in a generator, by too many lamps on the circuit (constant-potential system); by a ground or leak from a short circuit on the line, or by a dead short circuit on the line. In motors, it is caused by excessive voltage on a constant-potential circuit; by excessive amperage on a constant-current circuit; by friction, or by too great a load on the pulley.

To overcome the difficulties of the dynamo, reduce the number of lights and thus diminish the current called for on the plate. Test out, locate, and repair the ground. A dead short circuit will blow the safety fuse. Shut down the dynamo, locate the trouble, and repair it. Put in a new fuse before starting again. The fuse should not be inserted until the fault is corrected, as it will blow out again upon starting the machine. If the trouble is not located, the voltage of the machine should be brought up gradually from a low value, and the current output observed. An excessive current will indicate the trouble still exists, and the machine should not be operated until the trouble has been corrected.

In motors, the proper value of voltage should be used and no other. Make sure that the motor has the proper current capacity. Remedy any cause from undue friction, and reduce the load to the proper amount for the rating of the motor.

Fault of the Armature

A short-circuited coil in the armature will cause sparking at the brushes. A method of testing out, to find a short-circuited coil, is shown in Fig. 3. When a coil between the segments to which the voltmeter is connected is shorted, the reading will be very low. Examine the commutator and remove any copper dust, solder, or any metallic substance, that might be making a contact between the commutator bars. See that the clamping rings are properly insulated from the commutator bars, as well as from carbonized oil and copper dust or dirt which may form a short circuit. Test out for an internal short circuit or cross connection. To remedy such a trouble, reinsulate the conductor, change the connection, or rewind the armature. Examine the insulation of the brush holders. Dirt, oil, or copper dust may form a short circuit from the brush holder to the

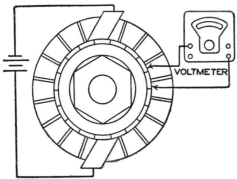

Fig. 3 — Connecting a Voltmeter and Current to a Commutator to Test Out for a Short-Circuited Coil

rocker arm, and thus short-circuit the machine.

A broken circuit in the armature will cause the same trouble. A run may be finished by bridging the break tem-

porarily, which is done by staggering the brushes till the run is finished. This is only a temporary makeshift to stop the sparking of the bar during

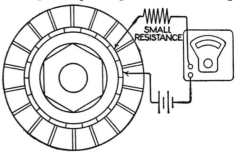

Fig. 4—Connections for an Ammeter to a Commutator to Test Out for an Open Armature Circuit

a run when the dynamo cannot be shut down and must be followed by testing out and repair. A method of testing for an open armature circuit is shown in Fig. 4. When the ammeter reads low, it indicates that there is an open coil between segments. If the dynamo can be shut down, look for a loose or broken connection to the bar, and if one is found, repair it. If the coil is broken inside, the only remedy is to rewind it. The break may be bridged temporarily by hammering the disconnected bar until it makes contact across the mica insulation to the next bar of the commutator. This remedy may be of use to complete a run, but the bars must be repaired and the insulation replaced when the fault is corrected. Another way to make the bridge across, is to solder two lugs of the commutator together or use a piece of heavy wire to cut out the broken coil. In doing so be careful not to short-circuit a good coil and thus make sparking from a short-circuited coil.

A cross connection in the armature will also cause the same trouble. The cross connections may have the same effect as a short circuit, and they are to be treated as such. Each coil should show a complete circuit with no connection to any other coil.

❡In repairing a fair-sized hole in an inner tube, it is better to place a patch on both sides, and then vulcanize.

Adjustable Boring Bar

Quite frequently a tool in a boring bar is to be adjusted for a deeper cut when the cutter is at the inner end of

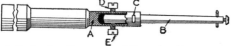

A Boring Bar That can be Adjusted to Make Small Changes without Resetting the Tool

the work. In an ordinary bar, this adjustment can usually be made only after the tool is withdrawn from the work. The illustrated bar overcomes this difficulty. The main bar A is drilled slightly larger than the diameter of the tool holder B, which is held in place in A by means of a taper pin, C. The tool holder B can then be swung back and forth slightly, but is held in any set position by the adjusting screws D and E. When starting an in-cut, the bar B should be held by the screw E only. If it is desired to take a deeper cut when returning, the screw E should be loosened slightly and D turned up tight, again holding B in a rigid position, but at a new setting.—Contributed by Jos. J. Kolar, Maywood, Ill.

Holding Protection Strips on Chuck Jaws

The rechucking of finished work usually necessitates the insertion of

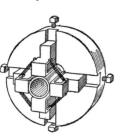

copper or other soft protection strips between the work and the jaws. These strips are not only hard to get in place, but they drop out easily and unexpectedly when the jaws are loosened in centering the job. A simple means of preventing this annoyance is shown in the sketch. Make strips to conform to the shape of the jaws, as shown, but allow for an extra width of about ⅛ in. on each side for drilling holes of a diameter to loosely fit the connecting spring

wires as shown. In adjusting the jaws, the protection strips will move with them, being held in place by a spring of the same strength on each side. This scheme will work on any number of jaws, and is particularly valuable when a large number of pieces must be rechucked.

Changing a New Valve Stem to Fit an Old Valve

In filling an order for a new gate-valve stem of the nonrising type, one

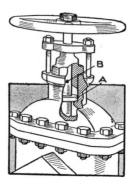

was sent which lacked about 1½ in. at the inner end, as shown in the sketch, to permit closing the valve. There was sufficient extra length on the outer end of the stem to allow it to occupy a lowered position without causing any interference between the hand-wheel and packing-box gland. A hole was drilled, 1½ in. above the shoulder A, and a pin, B, corresponding in length and thickness to the diameter and thickness of the shoulder, driven into it. The shoulder was then chipped off, thereby allowing the stem to drop down to the closed position of the valve, and the pin to fit in the place previously occupied by the shoulder. The parts were then reassembled, the only difference being in the location of the stem, and the substitution of the pin for the chipped-off shoulder. All upward and downward movement of the stem was prevented by the pin, just as it would have been by the shoulder, but an increased length of stem was provided, enabling the valve to close tightly.—Contributed by F. S. Johnson, Corona, Cal.

❡Washing soda, gum arabic, and water make a good writing fluid for fine lines on blueprints.

To Locate and Correct Troubles in Direct-Current Dynamos

By A. E. ANDREWS

PART II—Heating and Noise

Heating of the Armature

THE heating of an armature may be caused by an overload, or by its not being centrally located between the poles; by a short circuit, a broken circuit, or a cross connection, the remedies of which were given in the preceding chapter. Another cause is moisture in the armature coils. The remedy for the latter is to dry out the coils with a slow heat. This may be done by sending through the armature a current regulated not to exceed the proper value. If it is not so bad as to cause a short circuit, cross connection, or too much heat, the moisture may be dried out by the heat of the armature current itself while running.

Eddy currents in the armature core will cause heating. This results from a faulty armature core, which becomes hotter than the coils after a short run. The core should be finely laminated and the laminæ insulated. There is no other remedy than to rebuild the armature. Hot commutator bars and hot journals may affect the armature temperature. These troubles may be eliminated as described.

Heating of the Field Coils

An excessive current in the field circuit will cause the heating of the field coils. If it is a shunt machine, decrease the voltage at the terminals by reducing the speed or by increasing the resistance of the field coils. The latter may be accomplished by winding more wire on the coils, by rewinding with finer wire, or by putting a resistance in series with the field.

In series-wound machines shunt a portion of the current, or take off one or more layers of wire, or rewind the fields with coarser wire. An excessive current may be due to a short circuit or to moisture in the coils acting as a short circuit.

Eddy currents in the pole pieces will cause the heating of the field coils. The pole pieces may be hotter than the field coils after a short run, due to a faulty construction, or to a fluctuating current in the latter. Regulate and steady the current.

The coils may show a resistance lower than normal, which may be caused by a short circuit, or contact

Knife-Edge Leveling Bars Used for Locating the Heavy Side of an Armature

with the iron of the dynamo, or by a short circuit resulting from moisture in the coils. Use the same remedy as in drying out the armature coils.

Heating of Bearings

Among the main things to do is to supply plenty of good, clean oil and see that it feeds into the bearings properly. The best quality of mineral oil, free from grit, should be used. Be careful not to flood the bearings so as to force oil on the commutator, or into the insulation of the brush holders, as the oil will gradually char, gather copper dust and form a short circuit. Vaseline, cylinder oil, or other heavy lubricant, may be used if ordinary oil fails to remedy the hot box. Use it until the run is over, then clean up and adjust the bearings.

If the bearings have collected dirt, grit, or other foreign matter, wash it out by flooding with clean oil until the run is over. Be very careful not to flood the commutator or brush holders. After the run is over, remove the cap and clean the journals and bearings, and when again assembled, lubricate them well. If it is necessary to remove the bearings completely, allow them to cool naturally, then polish and free them from grit, and reassemble. If a journal is rough, smooth and polish it in a lathe, to remove all burrs, cuts, scratches, and tool marks, then make new bearings of babbitt, or other metal, to properly fit the shaft.

If the journals are too tight in the bearings, slacken the bolts in the cap and put in packing pieces until the run is over; then fit them to smooth bearings and easy rotation by hand if the machine is small. Turn down the journal smooth, and repolish, or scrape, the bearings until they fit properly.

A bent, or sprung, shaft, if small, should be straightened by springing it while set between the centers of a lathe.

When bearings are out of line, loosen the base of the bearings, and shift them until the armature turns freely by hand with the belt off, while at the same time it is in the center of the polar space. Remount and, when fastened in place, fit new dowels, to allow the new position to be kept when the bolts are drawn up tightly. If the shaft needs to be raised or lowered, shim up or trim down the foot of the bearing to allow the proper setting.

The end pressure of the pulley hub or shaft collars against the bearings will cause heat. See that the foundation is level, and that the armature moves freely with a small amount of end motion. If there is no end motion, turn off the shoulders on the shaft, or remove a portion of the bearing ends with a file, until the necessary end motion is obtained. Line up the shaft so that the pulley and belt will cause no end thrust on the shaft, allowing the armature to have free end play while in motion.

Too great a load, or strain, on the belt will cause the bearings to heat.

Slacken the belt to reduce the strain. If possible, do not drive a dynamo with a vertical belt. The vibration or flapping of a belt will cause the lamps to flicker. If a belt slips when running slightly slack, use a larger pulley with a wider and longer belt. The slack side of a belt should be run on top so as to increase the adhesion and pull without excessive tightening.

If the armature is not centrally located between the poles, it will cause the bearings to heat, also the wear to come on one side. Center the armature in the polar space, and adjust the bearings to the new position. If the bearings have become worn from this cause, replace them with new ones. The polar space may not be exactly true, and in that case, file it out so that there will be an equal clearance all around the armature. Sometimes it is possible to spring the pole away from the armature enough to right the trouble, and then fasten it in the new position. This, however, is very difficult to do in large and rigid machines.

Noise

When an armature, or pulley, is not properly balanced, it will cause considerable noise. The only way to remedy this is to remove the armature and place it on balancing edges, to determine the heavy side. Weight is added to the light side to make the armature properly balanced. If the armature strikes, or rubs against, the pole pieces, file out the pole where the armature strikes; and should a coil strike, press it down and secure any projecting wires with proper tie bands of strong wire.

The collars, or shoulders, of a shaft, hub, or web of a pulley may strike or rattle against the bearing. The bearing may be loose or worn out and cause a noise. New bearings may be required, or portions may be cut off to prevent their striking moving parts. Tighten up all screws, bolts and connections to make a bearing firm, and keep them so by daily attention. The jar and moving of dynamos tend to work screwed connections loose.

If the brushes sing or hiss, apply a little mineral oil, or, better still, vaseline, or hold a piece of stearic acid to the commutator and then wipe off, just leaving a faint trace of the oil, or grease. Lengthen or shorten the brushes in the holder until a firm, yet gentle, pressure is maintained, free from any hum or vibration.

A laced belt will cause the flapping, or pounding, noise. If possible, use an endless belt. Where a laced belt must be used, have the square joints properly laced. The slipping of a belt, caused by an overload, may be overcome by making the changes described previously.

Humming caused by the armature lugs, or teeth, passing the pole pieces may be overcome by sloping the ends of the pole pieces so that the armature teeth will not pass the edges all at once. This humming also can be greatly reduced by decreasing the magnetism of the fields, or by increasing the magnetic capacity of the teeth.

Forcing Oil into a Bearing

Sometimes when a bearing becomes heated and requires oil it will be found that the oil will not flow down in the oil hole. Either the hole is clogged with dirt or the heat may cause the air to rise and prevent the oil from entering. Where a wire cannot be used effectively, the following remedy, although it is not infallible, is almost sure to make the oil reach the bearing. Fill the hole with oil and quickly place the thumb over it to prevent the air from escaping, and if the oil cup does not leak, the heated air inside will rise above the oil, and in two or three minutes it will be forced into the bearing, even if it has to pass considerable dirt. When a bearing cannot be reached in this way, and when light oils, such as kerosene, are ineffective, try placing a little mercury in the oil hole and allow it to remain a few minutes, then use oil.—Contributed by J. B. Murphy, Plainfield, N. J.

Show-Case Match Box to Prevent Waste of Matches

To reduce the waste of matches placed on a cigar case, one dealer used the following device: The cover on a shallow cigar box was removed and nails were driven into the bottom from the under side so that they projected into the box and about 1 in. apart. Only the thumb and forefinger can be introduced between the nails, and two or three matches at most can be taken.

Drilling the Inside of a Ring

A ring of cast iron, 42 in. in diameter and having a flange on one edge, was designed to have a row of holes on the inside, spaced to given dimensions,

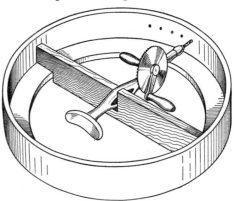

Drilling Holes Accurately and Quickly on the Inside Surface of a Large Ring

drilled in the same horizontal plane of the ring, and accurately radial. The holes were spaced out correctly with dividers and marked with a prick punch. To drill them did not appear so easy, as the holes were on the inside only and small in size. To drill them in a machine meant a lot of rigging up for a small amount of work.

The drilling was accomplished quickly as shown. The block of wood was so cut that it would hold the breast drill perfectly radial when the drill was set in the punch mark. A man stood inside of the ring and drilled the holes in a short time.—Contributed by Donald A. Hampson.

To Locate and Correct Troubles in Direct-Current Dynamos

By A. E. ANDREWS

PART III—Speed and General Suggestions

Speed Too High

IF the governor on the engine fails to respond quickly under a varying load, adjust it to the proper regulation if possible. It should be governed closely from "no load" to "full load" with the proper steam supply. Where a series motor takes too much current for a given load and the motor runs away, put in a shunt, and regulate until the proper current is obtained. If a series motor is run on a constant-current circuit, use the proper regulator for controlling the magnetism of the field for a varying load.

To remedy a motor running at a too high speed on a constant-potential circuit, put in a resistance to cut down the current; use the proper regulator or controlling switch, or change to an automatic speed-regulating motor.

If the regulator, or field rheostat, is not properly set, or the voltage is too high for a shunt motor, the speed will run high. To make the proper change, adjust the regulator, or field rheostat, to control the speed, in the first instance; and use the proper voltage and rheostat, in the latter.

Speed Too Low

A low speed may result from the same cause as a high speed in respect to the engine governor, and its remedy is the same. An overload of too many lamps on the circuit; a short circuit in the armature; striking or rubbing of the armature on the pole pieces, friction or a weak magnetic field, may also cause low speed, and remedies for these troubles have been described in a previous chapter.

Motor Stops

If a motor stops, it may be due to excessive voltage on a constant-potential circuit; to excessive amperage on a constant-current circuit; to friction, or too great a load on the pulley. Open the switch, locate the trouble, and remove the cause. Keep

the switch open and the arm of the rheostat on the position "off" while locating and repairing the trouble, then close the switch and move the arm gradually to the position "on," to see if everything is correct. With a

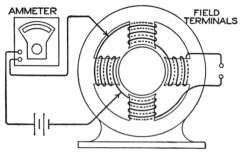

The Manner of Attaching an Ammeter to Test Out the Field Coils for an Open Circuit

series motor no great harm will result from the motor stopping or failing to start. If it is a shunt motor on a constant-potential circuit, the armature may, and probably will, burn out, or the fuse blow.

A motor will stop on an open circuit caused by the melting of the safety fuse; by a broken wire or connection; by brushes in contact; by an open switch, or if the current fails, or is shut off from the station. Open the switch, locate and repair the trouble. If a fuse is out, put in a new one, and in case of a broken line, find it and make the repair. See that the brushes are in close contact. If a switch is open, close it, but before doing so, see that the starting resistance is in the circuit. In case of current failure, open the switch, return the starting lever to the position "off" and wait for the current, testing from time to time by closing the switch and moving the starting lever to the first closed-circuit position.

A complete short circuit of the field will cause a motor to stop. Test out for the fault, and make the repairs if possible. A method for making the test is shown in the sketch. The ammeter should read the same for all coils if there is no trouble. It will read zero if the coil is open, and a maximum if the coil is completely shorted. Inspect the insulation of the binding posts and the holders. Poor insulation, oil, dirt, or copper dust may cause a short circuit.

The same trouble will result from a short circuit in the armature, or complete short circuit of the switch. The same remedy is applied as in making the repairs for the field.

Motor Runs Backward against the Brushes

This trouble will result in making the connections the wrong way. Connect up properly by referring to the diagram sent with the motor. If a proper diagram is not at hand, try reversing the connections to the brush holders. Other changes may be made until the proper connections are found to rotate the armature in the right direction, then connect up permanently.

Dynamo Fails to Generate

This will occur from a reversed residual magnetism, caused by reversed current in the field coils. To correct, send a current from another machine, or from a battery, through the field coils in the proper direction. The polarity may be tested with an ordinary compass. If the connections of the windings are not known, try one and test; if not correct, reverse conditions, try again, and test.

Should reversed connections be the trouble, connect up properly for the rotation desired, using the proper diagram of the connections. See that the connections for the series coils, in a compound dynamo, are properly made, as well as those for the shunt coils. In case of the earth's magnetism interfering, use the same method as for reversed residual magnetism, which method also is applicable where another dynamo is in close proximity. If the brushes are not in the proper position, shift them until evidence of improvement is given. The position of the brushes for the best generating power should be clearly understood, and is generally at, or near, the neutral point. A too weak residual magnetism must be treated in the same manner as reversed residual magnetism. A short circuit will produce the same results, and must be repaired as described in previous paragraphs.

Should a lamp socket, or other part of the line, be short-circuited, or grounded, it may prevent the building up of the shunt, or compound machines. Locate and remedy the fault before closing the switch.

If the field coils should be opposed to each other, reverse the connections of one of the field coils, and make a test. A compass should show the pole pieces of opposite polarity. If, after such a trial, the dynamo does not build up, try sending a current from another machine through the field coils in the proper direction. If the polarity then does not come up in the proper direction, cross the field connections, or remagnetize them in the opposite direction.

The cause of the trouble may also be an open circuit caused by a broken wire; by a faulty connection; by brushes not being in contact; by a fuse having melted or broken; by an open switch, or by an open external circuit. Repairs are made as described, and in the last-mentioned case make a test with the dynamo switch open and kept open until the repairs are completed.

Where there is too great a load on the dynamo and it fails to generate, reduce the load to the pilot lamps alone, for a shunt, or compound machine. After the dynamo comes up to a full voltage, as shown by the pilot lamps or voltmeter, close the other circuits in succession and regulate the voltage at the same time. Where there is too much resistance in the field regulator, or field rheostat, gradually turn the regulating switch to cut out the resistance, and watch the pilot lamps or voltmeter when the dynamo comes up to the voltage, then regulate, etc.

General Suggestions and Precautions

Never use ice water to cool off the bearings, as it may get into the armature and ruin it, unless it has been made waterproof as in the case of street-car motors. Do not shut down because of a hot box resulting from poor oil, dirt or grit in the bearings, tight journals, or too great a load or strain on the belt, until their remedies have been proven useless. If absolutely necessary to shut down, take the belt off the pulley as soon as possible. Do not allow the shaft to "stick" in stopping. Take the boxes, or bearings, out and cool them off naturally as soon as possible, and not in water, as this may ruin them. When cool, scrape, fit, polish, and clean the shaft, and test for free turning by hand, before belting up and starting again.

Cleanliness about a dynamo, or motor, is imperative. Dirt, oil. or copper dust may prove a source of great annoyance or damage. Small tools, bolts, or pieces of iron must be kept away from a dynamo, as they may be drawn into, or fall upon, the armature and ruin it. Never allow loose articles of any kind to be placed upon any portion of a dynamo.

Brass, or copper, oilcans are the best to use, as they are nonmagnetic. All the connections must be large, clean, and firm. Look over and tighten the loose connections, screws, and bolts daily.

Always keep copper brushes raised from the commutator when the dynamo is at rest. Poor, cheap oil is not economical. Use none but the best of mineral oils, and filter new oils before using them.

Keep cotton waste away from the commutator; use canvas or cloth, and a pine stick makes a good burnisher to keep the bars clean and smooth.

A Detachable Shaft Coupling

The simple shaft coupling illustrated was made for a combination water motor and electric-generating outfit. The coupling is inexpensive and has the advantage of being quickly disconnected. The shaft of the dynamo had a ⅜-in. tongue, and that of the water motor an ordinary shoulder. A piece of steel tubing was then cut to the proper length, with the necessary slots on one end to engage the tongue on the dynamo shaft. A standard taper pin held

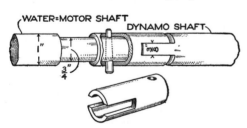

Sleeve Made of Steel Tubing Connecting a Dynamo Shaft with a Water-Motor Shaft

the tubing in position. To disengage, the taper pin is withdrawn, and the bushing is pushed to one side.

Simple Wire Straightener

The few parts necessary to make the illustrated wire straightener are as follows: Two pieces of ¼ by 1-in. iron; two flathead machine screws; one bolt and nut, with a washer to fit, having a thickness approximately equal to the diameter of 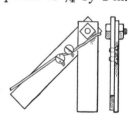 the wire. The ¼-in. pieces should be drilled near one end to fit the bolt. In one piece two holes should be drilled and tapped for the machine screws, these being set in so their heads project an amount approximately equal to the diameter of the wire.

To use the straightener, open out the ends, insert the wire, and close up the parts; then draw the wire back and forth, holding the straightener at an angle with the wire so one screw bears against the top and the other against the bottom of the wire.—Contributed by D. C. Goff, Knoxville, Tenn.

Shop Notes

Water-Heater Controller

The device shown in the sketch is for automatically controlling the temperature of the water in a water heater. It consists of an iron casting, A, screwed into the water tank at B; a steel float, C; an adjusting nut, D, and a gas valve, E, with an arm, F, which is held against the nut D by the spring G. When the arm is in a horizontal position the valve is closed. The casting A is filled with mercury, H.

The operation of the device is very simple. When the water in the tank cools, the mercury contracts, the float C descends, and the gas valve is opened, thus starting the fire in the burner of the tank. When the water reaches the required temperature the mercury expands and closes the gas valve, putting out the fire.

The control mechanism is shown

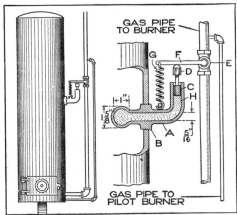

The Expansion and Contraction of the Mercury Caused by the Change in Temperature Operates the Valve

large in proportion to the tank so that its construction may be clearly understood. Dimensions are given for its size.—Contributed by F. B. Hays, Houston, Tex.

Recording Telephone Calls

Having occasion to leave my studio much of the time and my telephone calls being so few, I decided to make

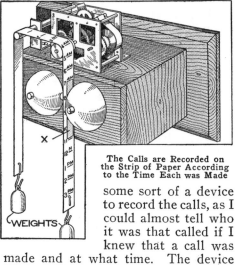

The Calls are Recorded on the Strip of Paper According to the Time Each was Made

some sort of a device to record the calls, as I could almost tell who it was that called if I knew that a call was made and at what time. The device illustrated was the outcome of my efforts. An old clockwork is attached to the top of the telephone-bell case so that a roller, attached to the hour-hand spindle, projects over the side and its edge is in line with the space between one of the bells and the clapper. A strip of carbon paper is placed on one side or the other of the strip of recording paper so it will be struck with the clapper or bell edge. The recording paper is graduated so that the time the call was made is also recorded. When I go out, a strip of the recording paper is placed in the device, and if anyone calls, the information recorded is not only convenient but sometimes valuable.—Contributed by R. F. Pohle, Lynn, Mass.

⟪Use fine emery for grinding a plug valve in its seat.

Watch Holder for Automobile

A cheap and serviceable watch holder for automobiles can be made out of a watch - protector case and the clips from a dis-

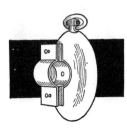

carded bicycle bell. F o r this purpose one of the clips should be fastened to the back of the case with a small flat-head rivet, fitted in a hole drilled through the clip and case. The two ends of the clip may then be clamped in a suitable place on the rim, or spokes, of the steering wheel, and the holder is ready for the watch. In order that this should not be scratched, or suffer from constant jarring, the protector case should be lined with soft material, such as velvet.—Contributed by E. R. Hastings, Corinth, Vt.

The Expansion of Rails

Anyone who is observing will notice, if walking along a railroad track in winter, that the ends of the rails do not

meet. There will be a space between the rails of from ¼ to ½ in. according to the length of the rails, character of the track and climatic conditions. On sidetracks the rails will often be found butting together or spaced 1 in. apart, all within a few hundred feet. This is simply because the tracks are unimportant and are laid with as little expense as possible.

The rails on the main line of a trunk road will be found equally spaced with unending regularity. This is done on account of the expansion of the rails in the hot summer, for if the gap was not provided when the steel was laid, the heat would cause such a tremendous end pressure that the tracks would assume a grapevine appearance.

Should the extreme temperatures be 10° below and 90° above zero, there would be a range of 100°, and as steel expands in length per inch .000006 in. for every degree rise in temperature, a 33-ft. rail would differ .000006 × 100 × 33 × 12 = .2376 in. or almost ¼ in. in length between winter and summer. In laying the rails, a gauge is used to secure the proper spacing.

Combined Belt Pole and Shaft Cleaner

Instead of having one pole for placing belts on pulleys and another for

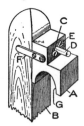

cleaning the shafting, the two can be combined in one, as illustrated. A block of wood, A, which is of a width equal to that of the pole B, is cut to the shape shown. A hole is bored in the part C to fit over the rod D in the belt pole, and a cotter, E, keeps it in place. Two metal strips, F, one on each side, are fastened to the piece A to keep it from turning sideways.

When the belt pole is to be used for cleaning the shafting the block A is slipped on the rod D, the cotter E is inserted, and all is ready to clean the shafting. It is obvious that a piece of emery cloth, or felt, should be fastened in the curve G, which fits the curve of the shafting and does the cleaning.

Emergency Clamps

The holding together of several pieces of wood for fastening with screws or nails, or to hold them while the glue is drying, presents but small difficulty when suitable clamps are available, and when these are not at hand, then clamps of some sort must be improvised. These are almost always of the bar-and-wedge type, and being of a temporary nature, may be made of scrap material around the shop, and if they are fastened together with screws, they are easily taken apart without injury to the stock used.

For gluing table tops, or similar pieces made up of a number of narrow strips, the type of clamp shown in Fig. 1 is best; in fact, it is the best form of wedge clamp for any purpose, all others being modifications of this one or employing the same principle. Its

verse the middle one, as this helps to overcome the buckling tendency.

In Fig. 2 is shown a modification of Fig. 1, which is used for light work. This clamp is made of a single piece of ⅞-in. stock. Two thin wedges driven from opposite sides are used

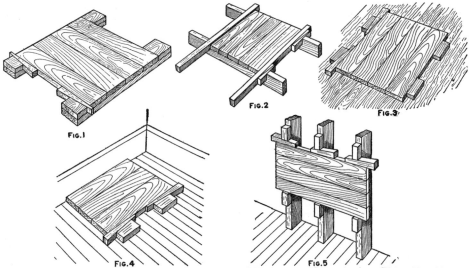

FIG.2

FIG.3

FIG.1

FIG.4

FIG.5

Various Forms of Clamping Devices Using Blocks and Wedges on a Plane Surface, Either Movable or Stationary, to Hold a Number of Pieces Together While Gluing or Fastening Them with Screws or Nails

construction is very simple: a bar of suitable length, with two crosspieces, one fastened at right angles to the edge of the bar and the other set at an angle to match the taper of the wedge. This taper should be about 1 in. to the foot, and it is well to cut the wedge before setting the crosspiece. Screws will do very nicely for fastening these crosspieces, if the clamps are to be used only once or twice; but if they are to be used a number of times, it will be best to use glue, in some cases further strengthened with dowels, to fasten them to the bar.

To counteract the tendency of springing up in the center when the wedges are driven home, it is customary to lay other pieces across the ends and clamp them with hand screws to the bars, but if the joints have been well made and the wedges are not driven too tightly, this is not necessary. Where three clamps are used, however, it is a good plan to re-

instead of one, as both ends of the clamp are cut square with the face.

These devices would appear to be the acme of simplicity both in construction and use, but simple as they are, the lack of material for making them may at times force one to resort to other means for accomplishing the work in hand. In this case a floor, or other plane surface, is necessary, using blocks and wedges as the clamping means. If a baseboard, or something equally firm, is at hand, but one set of blocks will be required.

Some examples of this form of clamp are illustrated. In Fig. 3 is shown the blocks used on a floor or bench top, and in Fig. 4 the clamping is done against a baseboard. The blocks can also be fastened to studs, as shown in Fig. 5. In nailing the blocks, in each instance allow about ¼ in. to project so that they may be easily removed with a claw hammer.
—Contributed by J. A. Shelly, Brooklyn, N. Y.

Brake for Bed of Vertical Boring Mill

A great many types of vertical boring mills are not equipped with a brake arrangement for stopping the rotation

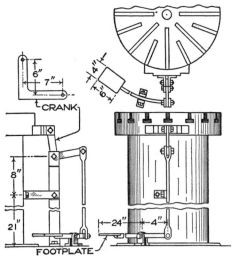

Brake Attachment for Use on Old-Style Boring Mills to Stop the Rotating Table Quickly

of the heavy bed at any point necessary. With many of these machines much time is lost while accurately centering work because of the care which must be taken in attempting to stop the bed at the greatest off-center portion of the work on the table. Of course, the latest machines of this type are supplied with a device for quickly stopping the rotation of the table, yet many of the older, but none the less efficient, machines are not so equipped.

The sketch illustrates the application of a very suitable braking device for the mill tables, which is inexpensive in erection, and in addition to this, is of much help to the operator of the machine. The brake shoe is of wood and acts directly on the side surface of the table, with sufficient leverage and friction to stop almost instantly the heavy rotating part. The foot lever can be curved somewhat around the lower portion, or base, of the machine, to enable the operator to get closer to the work being centered by the needle to the layout lines.

The body of the table can be readily tapped for an angle iron to steady the

top of the lever post holding the bell crank. The device is well worth its construction and application to the types of vertical mills not equipped with a special brake apparatus.

Improving an Oiling System on an Automobile

A certain manufacturer brought out a line of automobiles that proved to have an unreliable oiling system. The system consisted of a geared pump drawing oil from the crank-case sump and delivering it through individual pipes to the lower end of the bore of each cylinder in a ring-shaped reservoir into which the piston dipped on the downward stroke, carrying back with it a film of oil on the cylinder walls.

The theory of this was fine, but in practical use it was not so good, and the automobiles all went bad in respect of the oiling. At the manufacturer's expense, necessary repairs, alterations, and substitutions were made for owners, as a better oiling system was devised. In one locality there were several of these automobiles, and one owner undertook to locate and remedy the trouble. He succeeded and passed the word along to the others, and all of this lot were fixed up for a nominal sum without recourse to the factory.

As shown in the sketch, the delivery was through four outlets arranged around the circle of the pump gears. Originally the outlet A served the

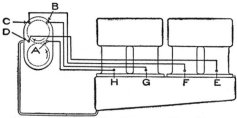

Connections of the Pipe System so That Oil was Forced Equally to All Cylinders

cylinder E; B, the cylinder F, and so on. It was the cylinder E that gave the most trouble; cylinder F, a little less, and the others, no trouble at all. It was discovered, by disconnecting the pipes at the cylinder end, that the cylinder E received little or no oil, and increasing amounts farther back, the cylinder H being well oiled.

The inside construction of the pump is not shown, which is not essential. The outlet D was nearest the source of supply and its pipe was the shortest, which seemed to the investigator to be wrong. The whole piping was changed by reversing it, so that the outlet nearest the supply forced oil through the longest pipe, and the outlet farthest from the supply fed the cylinder closest to the pump. The arrangement was a complete success.

Strainer for a Water Line

To prevent any dirt from entering a pump, I constructed a simple strainer,

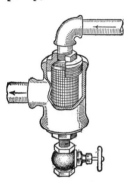

as shown in the sketch. The body of the strainer is made of a large reducing tee, the ends of the main throughway being reduced with bushings.

A brass-wire screen is shaped to fit snugly in the bushings, so that all water passing out through the side outlet will pass through the mesh. A drain valve is attached with a nipple to the lower end. The drain will allow the cleaning of the screen for a considerable length of time. The strainer is suitable for steam, water, or air lines.—Contributed by Geo. J. Little, Passaic, New Jersey.

Homemade Steam Gauge

In running a small steam engine in my shop on the first floor I found it took a great deal of time to run down into the basement every few minutes and look at the gauge on the boiler. With the aid of two chains attached to the damper and running up through the floor, I was able to keep the pres-

sure uniform by means of the gauge shown.

A U-shaped tube was filled with mercury to within about 4 in. of the

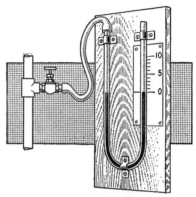

A Mercury-Filled Tube with a Calibrated Card as a Substitute for a Steam Gauge on Low Pressures

top, and one end was connected to the steam pipe with a piece of rubber tubing with a petcock in the line. After fastening this to the wall with leather straps I tacked a card underneath the free arm and drew a line upon it at the level of the mercury. I then raised the pressure in the boiler, and for every pound on the gauge I made a mark on the card at the new level of the mercury. As the pressure never exceeded 10 lb., the improvised gauge served the purpose fully as well as an expensive one.—Contributed by H. H. Raymond, Newburyport, Mass.

Making Use of Broken Gouges

In almost every pattern shop one or more broken gouges can be found. Instead of throwing them away they can be made into very useful tools. Take a full sweep of any width and grind 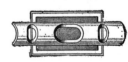 out as many holes as desired, as shown in the sketch, and a corner rounder will be had that is better than the double ender, as it can be worked into small places and used similar to a knife. A large, long opening makes a fine spokeshave.—Contributed by S. H. Bossart, Birmingham, Ala.

Traveling Hooks for Smokestack Painters

Painting high stacks is quite a serious problem and should be done with appliances of absolute safety. The usual method of placing h o o k s over the top of the stack to hold t h e s c a f f o l d makes it difficult to change t h e p o s i t i o n. To make the changing more easy, one stack painter made hooks having rollers, one for the top edge of the stack and the other to prevent the friction on the side, as shown. Each hook consists of a piece of soft steel, having dimensions as given. The rollers are made of pipe, the smaller one ¾ in. and the larger 1½ in. in diameter. They are fitted with hardwood centers to turn on ½-in. pins.

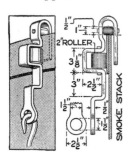

Oil Gauge for an Automobile Crank Case

Quite a few of the older types of automobiles have their engines unequipped with a suitable form of oil g a u g e. A gauge of this kind is extremely handy, as the o w n e r c a n readily tell at a glance the exact amount of oil in the crank case. The float should be made first, and consists of a cylindrical piece of cork, about 2 in. in diameter and 1½ in. long. A piece of brass, or copper, tubing, a trifle more than ½ in. in inside diameter and 1½ in. long, is inserted in the center of the cork. The float is then given two or three coats of shellac. A steel rod, ½ in. in diameter, is fastened in the

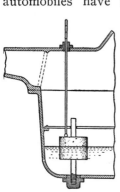

bottom of the crank case by means of a plug. The float will easily slip on the rod.

The gauge staff is made of a piece of ¼-in. drill rod, the length depending on the design of the engine. A hard-fiber ball is attached to the lower end of the rod, to prevent wear on the cork and its shellac coating. The rod is guided at the upper end by means of another plug through which a hole is drilled for it.

The rod is graduated as follows: Drain the crank case and assemble the gauge. Pour in a quart of oil and mark the rod. This process is repeated until the required amount of oil is poured into the crank case. The marks will then show in quarts the amount within at any time.

Window Latch Made of Door Hinge

A latch, making an absolutely safe lock for a window, can be made of an old door hinge. The pin is first removed f r o m the hinge and, if it fits tightly, filed down to allow e a s y removal. One half of the hinge is screwed to the upper window sash and the other half to the lower sash in the center, so that when the window is closed the two parts of the hinge will come together; then the pin is replaced. It is easy to put in place and take out.—Contributed by L. E. Turner, New York City.

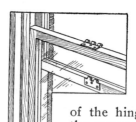

Substitute for Kindling Wood

A very good kindling for fires can be made of waste paper. To make it more effective, wet the papers thoroughly and wring them out as in wringing clothes by hand, and stack up the twisted forms to dry. When dry they are used the same as kindling wood.

Substitute for a Cornet Mute

A new, or discarded, electric globe makes an excellent cornet mute in case of an emergency. Procure a globe of

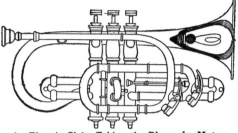

An Electric Globe Taking the Place of a Mute in the Cornet Bell

a size to fit the cornet bell, and paste three felt, or cork, strips on the side of the globe evenly spaced. If possible, use a discarded globe, and remove the metal screw part and grind the glass end smooth. Take out the glass tube and filament. This will produce a better sound, but the entire globe can also be used with good results.—Contributed by George E. Badger, Grays River, Wash.

Extension for a Drawing Board

All draftsmen are familiar with the trouble of removing a drawing from the board in order to draw arcs whose centers are beyond the edge of the paper. This can be avoided by the use of the easily made extension shown in

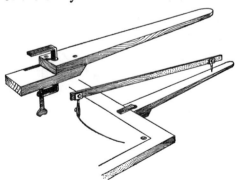

Extension Arm Attached to a Drawing Board for Drawing Arcs with a Long Trammel

the illustration. Two pieces of wood and a small clamp costing a few cents are all that is required. A suitable

width for both pieces is 2 in. The upper piece, which can be made 12 in. long, should be a trifle less in thickness than the drawing board at the base so as to allow the clamp a leverage. From the end of the clamping piece to the tip both edges and under side are tapered to make it lighter and have a better appearance. A hole is bored through both pieces, after they are fastened together, for the clamp to slide in easily. It will be seen that nothing projects above the drawing surface except the upper part of the clamp, and that no difficulty will be experienced in drawing radius lines with a straightedge bearing on a pin stuck in the extension piece at the center of the circle.—Contributed by Morris G. Miller, New Rochelle, N. Y.

Steering-Gear Lever Repair

The steering-gear lever of an automobile broke a short distance above the lower end, and as it was impossible to secure a new one quickly, a repair was made as follows: The portion of the lever at the point of the break was filed off, and a ¾-in. hole drilled in its end to a depth of 2½ in. The ball end was also filed flat, and a ⅝-in. hole drilled through it and countersunk ¼ in. on one end.

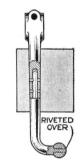

A piece of drill rod of the right length was turned down to ¾ in. on one end, and to ⅝ in. on the other. The rod was then bent to the proper shape, after which the ball was riveted to the ⅝-in. end. The other end of the rod was inserted in the upper portion of the lever, where it was securely riveted.

In making a repair of this kind, be sure to fit the joints tightly and rivet them well, as the lever is subjected to extreme vibrations.

❡A plug tap should never be started in a hole where it is convenient to start the thread with a taper tap.

Measuring Head Thickness of a Gasoline-Engine Piston

The simple device illustrated is very useful in a garage where new pistons are being made for replacement. It

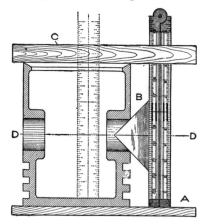

Obtaining the Thickness of a Piston Head with a Surface Plate, Rule, Straightedge, and Triangle

consists of a surface plate, A; a triangle, B; a straightedge, C, and a 2-ft. rule. The straightedge is placed across the top of the head and the rule is inserted in the opening to obtain the inside measurement; then the rule is placed on the outside of the head for the other measurement, the two numbers being subtracted to get the thickness of the head.

The triangle is inserted in the bore of the head, and the rule is placed against the triangle. The center line D on the triangle is the center of the hole, as shown.—Contributed by A. L. Kerbaugh, Allentown, Pa.

Copper-Inlaid Work

The method herein described is suitable for decorating small tool and gauge boxes, instrument cases, etc. Of course, it is just as easy to use any metal, but copper will be the most suitable for the work. Transfer the design, or lettering, with the use of carbon paper to the surface where wanted and engrave it lightly; then go over the engraved design with glue and fill in the depressions with fine copper filings, and when

thoroughly dry, sandpaper it to a nice smooth surface.

This method will provide a lettered inscription or design on instrument cases, tool boxes, and the like, in a nice, durable, copper inlay that will sometimes outlast the article, on the case of which it was placed.

Fitting Tight Rubber Parts

It sometimes happens that a piece of rubber tubing must be stretched over a nipple that is too large. Rubber is so elastic that it offers a great deal of resistance to any tightly fitting part and makes movement well-nigh impossible. Soap is a good lubricant, and about the best kind to use is a glycerin soap, which is melted up and mixed with water. This water is the slipperiest kind of lubricant, and when much of such work is to be done it can be kept on hand ready-mixed. Tubing, hose, tires, gaskets, etc., are some of the parts which may require such treatment.

Planing Gibs on an Angle

The sliding parts of innumerable machines are planed tapering either 45 or 60° and fitted with an adjustable piece, called a gib, to take up the wear. This gib is also planed on one or both edges to the same angle, as shown in the illustration at A. Where large repairs are made, this is a frequent machine-shop job. If a great number of these pieces are to be planed each year,

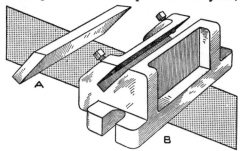

Jig for Use on a Machine Bed to Hold Gibs for Cutting the Angle Surface

it will pay to have a jig for the work, similar to the one shown at B. It consists of a casting having a slot machined in its center length to the angle of the gibs. In this slot the blank is placed and tightened with setscrews. Such a jig can be used on a planer, shaper, or milling machine, as desired. The jig may be bolted to the table of the machine, or it can be held in a vise. With its use the tapered side may be cut by any of the ordinary movements of the machine without tilting the work or setting the cutting head over at an angle. The time saved by its use will soon pay for the fixture.

Unsymmetric Photo Reduction

In copying charts, maps, tabulated sheets, etc., it is often desired to reduce them to a certain height and width to correspond with the page of the report they illustrate. Ordinarily, reduction to the desired height will make the width greater than that of

the image focused on the ground glass C was approximately the measure desired. The width of the image registered as shown by DE and it appeared like the rectangle Fig. 2. The width desired was that shown by DF in Figs. 1 and 2, instead of DE. The side G of the drawing was held in its original position and the side H swung toward the camera, as indicated by the arrow, until the width of the image on the ground glass was that of DJ, the line J being halfway of the distance EF, the amount the image was to be narrowed. This distorted the image so that it appeared as shown in Fig. 3, the side G remaining approximately the desired height. An exposure was then made with the s m a l lest

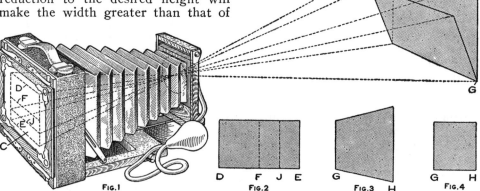

Tilting a Drawing to Reduce Its Size More One Way Than the Other; the Operation being Done Twice to Eliminate the Distortion Caused by the Great Difference in the Focal Plane

the page and a fold must be made in the reduced copy when inserted as a page opposite the description. As an engineer photographer I was requested by the head of the department to reduce the width of a large general drawing of a data sheet for boilers about twice as much as the height, to fit the page of the printed report. The illustration shows how this was accomplished.

The sheet to be copied was fastened to a movable stand, A, Fig. 1, which was set facing the camera and in a vertical position for a plan view. The distance between the camera and the sheet was varied until the height of

stop to give depth of focus, the plate developed, and a print made.

This print was fastened to the board and set in front of the camera, but on a slant with the side G closer than the side H, or reversing the slant shown in Fig. 1. The distance from the camera was varied until the side G showed on the ground glass the exact height required; then the slant was varied until the side H showed the same height as G, and the top and bottom lines showed parallel, the whole appearing as in Fig. 4. A plate was exposed and a print made to the desired size.—Contributed by H. M. Plaisted, Granite City, Ill.

Pattern Gear Teeth Made Quickly

Having a hurry-up job to make a pattern for a special, short sector rack with 18 teeth, and as the two or three

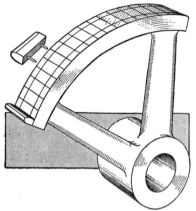

A Sector on Which Eighteen Teeth were Placed to Make a Pattern for a Sand Mold

plans submitted did not appeal to me as being easily and quickly worked out, I set about forming the teeth with an especially prepared metal to make all of them exactly the same size and outline.

This was accomplished by carefully cutting a mold with sufficient draft in hard wood, preparing a good gate and vents, and fitting the cope on the nowel with dowels so that it would register each time the parts were clamped together.

Two holes were accurately drilled

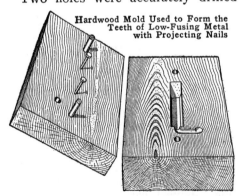

Hardwood Mold Used to Form the Teeth of Low-Fusing Metal with Projecting Nails

into the cope of the mold a certain distance apart, into which nails were inserted so that their heads and a part of the body would extend into the mold.

The holes were of a size to make the nails a snug fit for holding them in place while the metal was poured.

The metal used for making the teeth consisted of lead, 5 parts; tin, 3 parts, and antimony, 1 part. This makes a fine-flowing metal and very hard. After casting the 18 teeth, which were all alike with the points of the nails exactly the same distance apart and projecting equal lengths, as well as being set at exactly the same place relative to the width of the tooth, they were fastened to the sector as follows: The blank was spaced for the 18 teeth and lines drawn on the circumference marking the place to start the nails. It was only necessary to start the nails properly and drive them home to place each tooth where it should be on the sector.

The metal used is very fluid at a low temperature and can be run in wood molds where few pieces are required, but in making a gear with a large number of teeth, it will be found necessary to make an iron mold, which can be quickly cut on a shaper or milling machine. The metal will be found especially adapted for making small patterns, as it is nonshrinkable.—Contributed by W. E. Smisor, Waterloo, Iowa.

Making Blueprints from Heavy Paper

Many times it is desired to make a blueprint from a drawing made on heavy paper, or Bristol board. The main reason for wanting such a print is usually that a copy is desired for filing to provide a temporary reference, or as a duplicate in case the original is lost, in consequence of which a reversal from right to left is no serious objection. If such is the case, place the drawing in the frame with the ink in contact with the sensitized surface of the printing paper. This perfect contact immediately precludes the possibility of blurring due to dispersion of the light in passing through the thick paper; and, to get a clear-cut reproduction, it is merely necessary to increase the length of the exposure sufficiently to compensate for the reduction in the intensity of the light due to passing through the extra thickness.

If the drawing bears considerable lettering and would be very inconvenient in a reversed form, it can be easily read by holding it up to the light and viewing it from the back, or by reading it as reflected in a mirror.

A rather interesting variation of this method of printing that gives an unreversed reading, but with a less degree of sharpness, consists in placing the back of the sensitized paper in contact with the inked surface of the original and then exposing the back of the latter to the sun. In this manner the only dispersion that occurs is that occasioned by the passage of light through the body of the blueprint paper, and when this is of the thin mailing variety, very good results may be secured.

Cleaning a Hardwood Finish

To clean a dirty hardwood finish, apply a coat of kerosene and let it remain until the grime is softened, then wipe it off. Rub with some crude petroleum oil, then polish with felt. An old felt hat will do, or soft, old flannel. Allow it to stand for at least two hours, then polish with a soft linen rag.

Homemade Motorcycle Throttle
Adjustment

Desiring to have a more suitable form of adjustment for a throttle connection on a motorcycle engine, one rider constructed the lever arrangement shown in the illustrations. The mechanism was fastened to the gasoline tank directly above the engine, and a pull rod run to the butterfly valve on the carburetor. The general arrangement is shown in Fig. 1. An assembled sketch of the regulating device is shown in Fig. 2. A segment of an old magneto drive gear was fastened with a setscrew to the shaft A, which in turn was fastened to the gasoline tank, as shown. A lever, B, which freely moves on the shaft A, is provided with a projection, C, permanently soldered to its upper

end. A plunger, D, slides through the projection C and operates against the helical spring E. The device is oper-

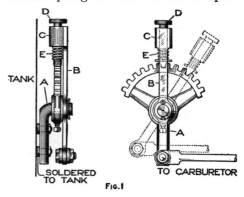

Fig. 1

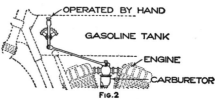

Fig. 2

General Assembly of the Parts After They are Attached to the Tank and Carburetor

ated as follows: The plunger D is pulled out and at the same time the lever B is swung around to any desired angle, depending upon the amount of adjustment required. The hand is then removed from the plunger D, which, engaging with the teeth of the gear, locks the device and makes the adjust-

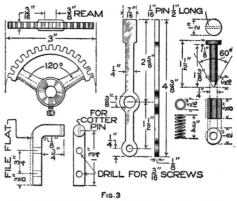

Fig. 3

Detail of Each Piece for the Construction of the Throttle Adjustment for a Motorcycle Engine

ment permanent. A complete set of detail sketches of the various parts is given in Fig. 3.

How to Make a Rubber Stamp

All that is necessary for making rubber stamps that will give excellent results is a few type, some plaster of

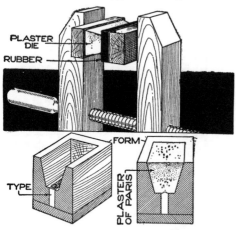

Simple Process of Making Rubber Stamps without the Use of an Expensive Outfit

paris, a strip of vulcanized rubber, and a wood type form. The type can be procured from any printer and comes in almost any style. The block type of letter is very satisfactory for all-around work, while the script type, such as is used for calling cards, makes a nice stamp for signatures. The plaster of paris necessary can be purchased at any drug store for a few cents. The rubber, about $\frac{1}{8}$ in. thick, can be obtained from any rubber-supply house, or the kind used for vulcanizing patches on automobile tires can be used. The vulcanized patching rubber is probably the easiest to obtain, as most motorists and garages keep a supply of it on hand.

First select the style of type desired and make a wood frame, or form, as shown, in which to set the type. The construction of this form is clearly shown. If it is desired to have more than one row of letters, the slot can be made wide enough to accommodate the extra rows. This form should be rather long so that it can be used for stamps containing many letters, as it is an easy matter to block off the extra length when making the short stamp. After the form is completed, set the type in the slot, as shown, and brush lightly with oil. Mix the plaster of paris with water until it has the consistency of thin cream, then pour into the form and allow it to set. After hardening, remove it from the form, and a die will be had from which to make the rubber stamp. Cut a piece of rubber large enough for the stamp and place the plaster die and rubber in a screw clamp, as shown in the sketch. Apply enough heat to soften the rubber and tighten the clamp so as to force the rubber into the depressions in the die. Allow the rubber to become thoroughly cooled before removing the clamp. The pressure can be applied by weights set on the wood block, if a clamp or a vise is not at hand. After the rubber is removed, trim and glue it to a block of wood and the stamp is complete. Very satisfactory rubber stamps can be produced by this method if proper care is taken.—Contributed by Arthur Steed, Swissvale, Pa.

Holding Gear Shaft of an Automobile in Place

In taking the gear box of an automobile apart, it was found that the countershaft had been pushed to one side, due probably to the side thrusts when the gears were shifted and meshed. To avoid this it was necessary to hold the shaft in place at its ends. The repair was made as follows: Two special

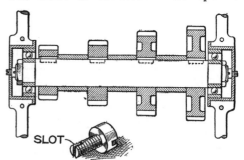

The Screw Heads Resting against the Ends of the Shaft Prevent It from Moving Endways

screws were turned from a good quality of drill rod with large heads, $\frac{3}{4}$ in. in diameter and $\frac{1}{4}$ in. long. The threaded end of each was ⅝ in. long and ½ in. in diameter. A slot was provided at the threaded end. The large ends of these screws were then hardened and ground flat, and inserted into the ball bearings with the heads on the inside, as shown. Then they were adjusted by means of a screwdriver on the outside. The shaft was held between the two screws without end movement.

An Automatic Siphon to Drain Basins below Sewer Level

A number of large water pumps were necessarily located below the surface of the ground and also lower than the sewer-pipe levels of the shop. A drain basin, of course, was left in the flooring of the pump cellar, which was emptied by a siphon lifting the water up into the sewer some distance above it. When the basin filled with water the siphon was set in action by the engineer. On one or two occasions the basin ran over and flooded the cellar. An automatic siphon, as shown in the illustration, was put in which made it impossible to flood the cellar.

The construction of the siphon is simple, and it is easily put into operation. The globe valve furnishing the steam for starting the siphon was removed, and the threads bored out of the bonnet and turned off from the stem. This did not interfere with the function of the stuffing box on the valve stem. The body of the valve was turned so that the stem entered the valve on top of the disk seat, the stem being attached to a long rod extending up to the lever on the solenoid magnet. The construction of the siphon and arrangement of the globe valve supplying steam to it is plainly shown in the illustration. The siphon part was left unchanged. It was made of a ¾-in. pipe tee, a small nozzle being worked back into the steam pipe through the horizontal faces of the tee.

The solenoid was made of an old 4-in. wood packing spool wound with No. 20 gauge insulated copper wire. A piece of ¾-in. soft iron, about 5 in.

long, was used for the magnet core, one end being attached to the long end of the lever.

The make and break of the circuit

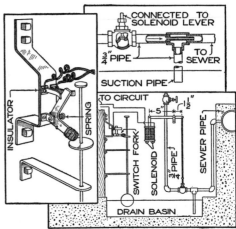

Automatic Valve-Stem Operation for Applying Steam to a Siphon to Remove Water from Low Levels

was accomplished by the sinking and rising of a copper-ball float, to which was soldered a long ¼-in. rod having at its upper end two disks set at a distance apart equal to the depth of the basin.

When the water in the basin accumulates to a certain height, the float, in rising with it, pushes the knife switch in contact, forming a circuit through the solenoid. The pull of the magnet core on the lever bar opens the steam valve and the siphon drains the basin. The sinking of the float brings the upper disk on the rod to a point where it engages the end of the switch crank and the weight of the float pulls the knife switch out, breaking the circuit. The passage of the steam acting on the valve disk from the top immediately closes it tightly to the seat of the valve, thus shutting off the action of the siphon. The electricity in this case was supplied by a 110-volt lighting circuit.—Contributed by F. W. Bentley, Jr., Missouri Valley, Iowa.

⟨Ordinary thumb tacks, such as used by draftsmen, make good fasteners for the ironing-board cover, as they are easily put in place and removed.

Substitute for a Broken Swivel Nut

It being necessary to replace the broken swivel nut of a screw clamp, the following simple substitute was

A Pipe Cap Notched and Fitted over the Ball of the Screw, Then Clinched

made: A pipe cap was secured that fitted the ball of the screw. It was notched to form four prongs. With the cap fitted in place the prongs were bent in, thereby clinching it to the screw, and answering the purpose as well as a regular swivel nut.—Contributed by J. J. Kolar, Maywood, Ill.

Handle for Holding Light Tools for Hammer Heads

Many times a mechanic needs a hammer of a different shape than any in the kit of tools. With a handle or holding device, as shown in the sketch, a

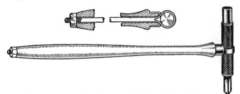

A Detachable Handle for Holding Small Punches to Use as a Hammer Head

nail set, a center punch, small cold chisel, or any convenient piece of metal or small tool, may be converted into a hammer exactly suited for the work at hand.—Contributed by Floyd B. McElroy, Indianapolis, Ind.

To Make Carbon Granules for Telephone Repairing

It is almost impossible to obtain fine carbon granules for use in telephone repairing, but the following method is one that I have used with good results. Remove the lead from a hard pencil and cut it into pieces about $\frac{1}{16}$ in. long. Prepare two small boards, about 4 in. square, and glue a piece of fine sandpaper to one surface of each board. Place a few pieces of the pencil lead between the sandpaper surfaces and roll them gently with a circular motion. When the grains have become round and of the right size, they can be polished by rolling between the uncovered sides of the boards. I have found that granules prepared in this way are superior to some I have bought.—Contributed by C. C. Heyder, Hansford, W. Va.

Automobile Number-Plate Bracket

A simple and quickly made bracket for holding the number plate of an au-

tomobile on the front of the radiator is shown in the illustration. A piece of $\frac{5}{16}$ by $1\frac{1}{4}$-in. cold-rolled steel rod is first annealed by heating it to a red heat and then allowing it to cool slowly in the open air. It is then forged into the necessary shape and size, after which the holes for the clamping screw and for the number plate are drilled and tapped.

An Emergency Valve Spring

A case of missing-cylinder trouble developed on the engine of an automobile one day, and the cause was laid

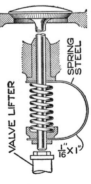

to a weak and defective spring on the inlet valve. The following temporary repair was made by the roadside, and the car was finally driven back to the garage under its own power. A piece of good-quality spring steel, which had been at one time used on the magneto clamp, was cut to a length of 6 in., and two holes were drilled in it, one at each end, of sufficient size to clear the valve stem. This piece of steel was then placed in position as shown, and upon starting the engine the cylinders all fired regularly.

Centers for a Machine Vise

Centers have many uses in machine work and are generally a part of the equipment on every milling machine. Such work as cutting flutes in taps and reamers, cutting squares and hexagons, and a variety of similar work on pieces having center holes in the ends, can be best accomplished on centers. If a milling machine is not a part of the equipment, or there are no centers at hand, very good work can be done on the planer, or shaper, by the aid of a vise with a pair of plain centers added.

The sketch illustrates two pieces of square tool steel turned to the regular 60° angle, shouldered out on the lower side and drilled for cap screws. They are then hardened and tempered. The work should be carefully done and the

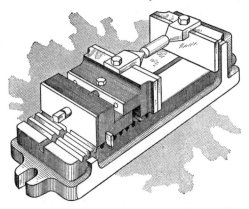

Centers Made of Tool Steel Fitted to Machine-Vise Jaws, Then Hardened and Tempered

position on the vise jaws accurately located so that any work done on the centers will be true.

⊄Before starting to fill a fountain pen, or otherwise to work with ink, wet the hands thoroughly in water, and the ink will not enter the pores, and it can be washed off readily.

Substantial Stepladder Brace

The ordinary stepladder braces are apt to become loose and cause a rickety affair, unsafe to mount on the top step.

The Buggy-Top Joint Placed between the Stepladder Supports to Hold Them Rigidly

One workman, having a great deal to do on a stepladder, made a much more substantial brace by using a buggy-top joint, as shown. When locked in position, it makes the parts of the ladder very rigid.—Contributed by James M. Kane, Doylestown, Pa.

Hardening Steel without Scaling

To harden polished steel articles without producing a scale, proceed as follows: A mixture of equal parts of table salt and finely ground cornmeal is prepared, and the article to be hardened is first dipped in water and then into the mixture. Place in a fire, and when hot enough to melt the particles adhering to the surface, take it from the fire and roll in the mixture. When all covered, place in the fire again and heat sufficiently for hardening. Be sure to see that no part shows signs of becoming dry. If such spots show up, cover them with the mixture.

This mixture forms a coating that keeps the air from striking the metal, thus preventing oxidation. When cooled in water, the coating readily comes off, leaving the surface smooth.

Attaching Auxiliary Automobile Springs

A touring car that had been converted into a commercial vehicle had a set of light springs which had lost

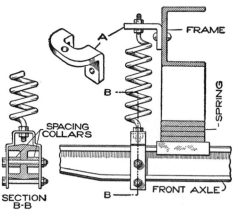

Auxiliary Springs Attached to Support Part of the Load of an Automobile Body

their flexibility, due to constant wear, and it was practically impossible to ride in the car with any comfort. The proper solution would have been to insert a complete set of springs, but this being too expensive, it was decided to try out a set of auxiliary helical springs.

The springs were fastened to the frame side member, at one of its ends, and to the front-axle center forging, at its other end. For the upper connection a bracket was forged, as shown in sketch, at A. A ½-in. hole was drilled in the center, after which it was riveted to the frame side member.

For the lower connection, a U-shaped piece of metal was forged to fit over the front axle, where it was held with two bolts.

The springs were made of ½-in. spring steel, having a 2-in. pitch diameter with a distance of 1 in. between each coil when the spring was without load. The ends were threaded for nuts. The job took considerable time, but there was a notable difference in the riding qualities.—Contributed by Adolph Kline, New York City.

A Bronze Surface on Yellow-Brass Castings

Yellow-brass castings may be given a bronze surface in the following manner: Mix together equal parts of sulphuric acid, nitric acid, and water, mixing first the nitric acid and water, then adding slowly the sulphuric acid. The brass castings are first dipped in boiling water, then into the acid solution and back quickly into the boiling water, after which they are thoroughly rinsed in clean water. They are then dried in sawdust. The castings must be clean and free from soldering fluxes. The surface will present the appearance of gas fixtures and will remain so indefinitely if it is given a coat of lacquer.

Locating Water Level in a Locomotive Glass Gauge

It is quite difficult to locate the water level in the gauge glass of a locomotive when on the road, as the constant jostling of the engine keeps the water jumping in the gauge. It happens quite often that the fireman must look for a considerable length of time to determine the water level. To overcome this difficulty I inserted a light silver bead in the gauge glass. The bead will stay at the water level and is easily seen.—Contributed by William Frost, Marathon, Fla.

Oil and Waterproofing Cork Floats

To waterproof a cork float, coat it with a rubber solution made by cutting crude rubber into small pieces and dissolving it in gasoline. If it is desired to make it proof against oil also, soak the cork in a glue solution made of 2 oz. glue, ½ oz. glycerin, and 6 oz. water. To keep this solution from spoiling, add a little oil of wintergreen.

⊄A very effective way to prevent a thief from taking an automobile is to remove the timer cap from the magneto.

Powdered Wax for Ballroom Floors

To make a powdered wax for a ball-room floor, melt in benzine as much wax—paraffin will do—as the liquid will take up, then stir in some talcum powder to form a fairly stiff paste. Rub this through a No. 1 sieve, then spread it out thinly on trays to permit the evaporation of the benzine. Be careful to keep it away from a flame. When the mass has become per-fectly dry, pulverize it and place in tin cans with perfor-ated tops. Use it by sifting the powder on the floor. — Contrib-uted by A. Kelly, Malvern, Pa.

An Emergency Eye Dropper

The value of a saturated solution of boric acid as an eye-wash is now quite generally known. The small glass dropper with which to apply this and other eye remedies is so fragile that it is nearly always found chipped or broken ; and if it has escaped unharmed, it is usually discovered that some one has been filling a fountain pen with it. When confronted by such a con-tingency, simply take an ordinary drafting or ruling pen, and, after wiping it clean, dip it into the solution and with the points well separated touch the moist eyelid, which will instantly cause the liquid to flow in.—Con-tributed by John D. Adams, Phoenix, Arizona.

A Carpenter's Tool-Chest Cart

In my carpenter work I have many odd jobs, which makes it necessary to call a drayman for hauling the chest of tools each way, and this added expense on small jobs makes them unprofitable. To eliminate this expense I constructed a tool-chest cart that can be easily pushed along on a sidewalk, paved street, or smooth road-way, by hand.

The frame of the cart is made of ½-in. pipe set on 20-in. bicycle wheels using pneu-matic tires. The

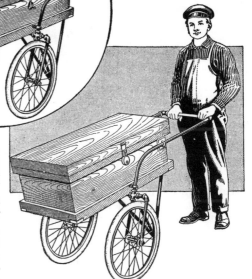

The Tool Chest can be Easily Carted to Any Place and the Workman Is Sure to Have All Tools at Hand

wheels are set far enough forward so that there is considerable weight on the post at the rear when standing still. When lifted, the handle is of convenient height for pushing, and it balances well on the wheels.

It is much easier to push the cart than to carry a few tools in a hand box on the shoulder, and when I arrive at the work I have everything I need, including screws, brads, and nails of various sizes.—Contributed by Sim Goddard, Sheridan, Wyo.

A Floating Boat Landing

Where the tide rises and falls the float shown makes a convenient landing for a small boat. Four posts are set, one at each corner of a suitable-

The Floating Platform Makes an Excellent Landing Place for Small Boats in Tidewaters

size platform, allowing some space to make the platform free. The structure should be built near a dock or stationary high landing. Make up the platform strongly and bend a loop of heavy iron rod around each post and flatten the ends for bolt holes. Drill two holes in each end for bolts and fasten them to the platform.

Steps, or a stairway, are constructed and hinged to the dock so that the lower end will rise and fall with the movements of the platform.—Contributed by Fred L. King, Islip, N. Y.

❏When mounting an emery wheel, tap it lightly to see whether it is sound or cracked.

Easily Made Name Plates

Brass or copper-faced name plates for machinery, doorplates, etc., can be made easily and cheaply as follows: Set up the desired lettering in rubber, or metal, type and make a plaster-of-paris impression. Then inclose it in a small frame the size of the desired plate and $\frac{1}{16}$ in. deep. Use either copper or brass filings for the facing material. These must be thoroughly washed in soldering flux and allowed to dry, after which they are well sprinkled in the impression left by the type.

Fuse a compound of seven parts lead to three parts of block tin and pour it into the open mold. When the metal becomes a little cool, but is still soft, press it with a flatiron, or a similar object, to force the metal well into the corners and to remove all air. When cool remove carefully, trim and finish on the face with a piece of emery cloth laid flat on a board.

Before pouring, or before applying the filings, the mold should be carefully dusted with black lead. If this precaution is not observed, the mold is liable to be damaged when the casting is removed. If only one plate is to be made, this caution need not be considered.

Spring Shock Absorber for Crutches

The jarring experienced when using crutches can be greatly reduced if spring shock absorbers, as shown in the illustration, are fastened at the bottom. The device consists of a metal tube, open at both ends, but provided with a solid partition in the center. The lower end contains a shock-absorbing spring, and a loosely fitting reciprocating plug, to one end of which is attached a rubber tip, while the other end is provided with a stud, threaded on the end for an adjusting nut. The partition should be drilled to fit the stud. With spring and plug in place,

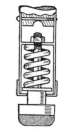

the nut should be put on, and the spring adjusted for the desired amount of compression. The shock absorber can then be fastened on the crutch with a small bolt and nut, allowing sufficient clearance between the end of the crutch and the top of the reciprocating plug, so these will not strike together.—Contributed by M. Morris, Toronto, Canada.

Automatic Condensation-Discharge Trap for Compressed-Air Tanks

Considerable difficulty was experienced from water condensation in the compressed-air tanks passing up through the return pipes and into the pneumatic tools that were used in the shop. A large number of such tools as motor drills, pneumatic hammers, etc., were used by the men in the erecting shop, and the presence of water in any of these tools did not take long in making itself known, which caused damage to the sensitive parts. As the condensation of water in any like case is irregular, depending on the condition of the atmosphere drawn by the compressors, it is hard to keep a tank drained and free from water at all times.

The sketch is descriptive of the manner in which an automatic condensation-discharge trap for this water was inexpensively constructed and operated in connection with the tank and pipe lines. An old 10-in. air cylinder was utilized, with two heads to fasten tightly on the top and bottom. The 8-in. copper ball, or float, pulls the valve from its seat when the water lifts it. When the least amount of air begins to escape the valve is instantly drawn to its seat. The valve seat and guide spindle worked very nicely soldered directly on the copper ball, or float. One of the traps was worked in connection with the large storage tanks and another installed at the end of the air pipe line in the erecting shop.

In the case mentioned the traps at once made their value apparent, for no further difficulty was experienced by the men using pneumatic tools in the erecting shop, and also the automatic draining of the storage tanks relieved

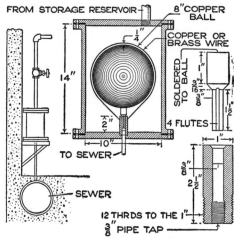

Trap for Use in a Pipe Line or at a Tank to Remove Water from Condensation

the engineer's mind of a matter which had previously been of no little concern.—Contributed by F. W. Bentley, Jr., Missouri Valley, Iowa.

Substitute for a Broken Automobile-Spring Clip

A clever substitute for a broken spring clip is shown in the illustration. The clip broke at the point indicated in Fig. 1, and to repair it was practically out of the question. A piece of cold-rolled stock, 3/8 in. thick and 1¼ in. wide, was cut to the proper shape to fit over the spring; two bolts of the proper size and length were procured, and the assembling was made as shown

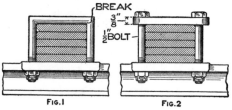

Substitute for a U-Bolt Clip, to Hold an Automobile Spring on the Axle

in Fig. 2. The job was quickly done, and a great deal of time saved, as it would have taken several days to procure a new clip.

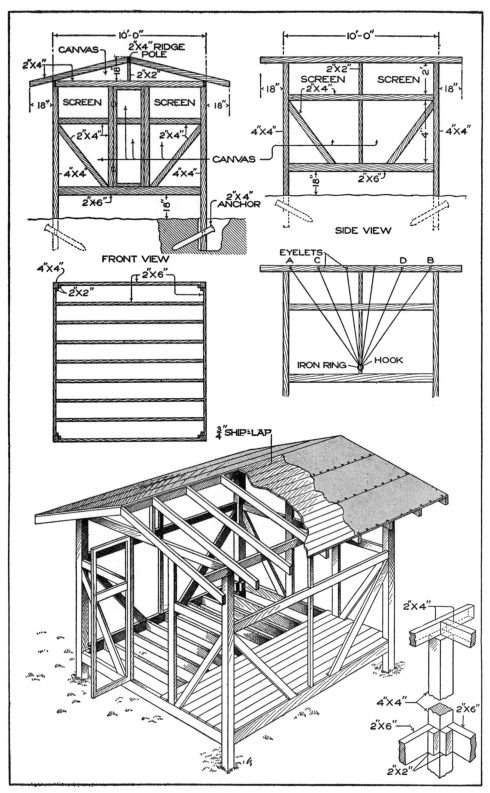

CANVAS
2"X4" RIDGE POLE
2"X4"
10'-0"
2"X2"
SCREEN
SCREEN
18"
18"
2"X4"
2"X4"
CANVAS
4"X4"
4"X4"
2"X6"
18"
2"X4" ANCHOR

FRONT VIEW

10'-0"
2"X2"
SCREEN
SCREEN
2"
18"
2"X4"
18"
4"X4"
4"X4"
4"
18"
2"X6"

SIDE VIEW

4"X4"
2"X6"
2"X2"

EYELETS
A   C   D   B

IRON RING   HOOK

3/4" SHIP LAP

2"X4"

4"X4"
2"X6"
2"X6"
2"X2"

A Tent House

By L. P. PASEWALK

THIS tent house, or sleeping bunga-low, was the result of an urgent need of a place for sleeping out in the open, which would afford the advantages of a house. It was built in a convenient place in the yard on four posts, 9 ft. long and 4 in. square. These posts were set in the ground in a perfect square, 10 ft. on the sides, and to a depth of about 18 in., then anchored with pieces of 2 by 4-in. material nailed across their ends. Before tamping in the dirt, however, the posts were merely set in the holes dug for them, then the framework was joined to the posts.

The floor sills were first cut to length to fit in between the posts, each being 9 ft. 4 in. long and squared to make a good joint. These were fastened to the posts with toenails, and further strength-

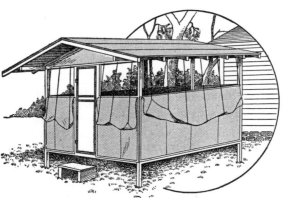

The Tent House Has All the Comforts of a Home and the Advantages of Sleeping in the Open Air, Protected from Rain and Bad Weather

ened with blocks, as shown in the ground plan. At a point 4 ft. above the sills, pieces of 2 by 4-in. material, in the same lengths and attached in the same manner, were placed between the posts.

The plate for the rafters to rest on consists of 2 by 4-in. material, set on edge so that their outside surfaces were flush with the outside of the posts, two pieces being 13 ft., and two pieces, 9 ft. 4 in. long.

The rafters were cut from 2 by 4-in. material, 6 ft. long, this length being sufficient to cut the angles on the ends to make the fit at the ridge. Studs were set in at one end to provide an opening for the door, which was merely a frame covered with canvas.

After the framework was fastened together solidly, the dirt was tamped into the holes about the posts.

Sheathing boards were laid closely together on the rafters and prepared-roofing material placed on them. The sides were covered with canvas up to the noggin, or rail, set in 4 ft. from the sills. An ordinary floor was laid on the joists, set in between the sills. The 2-ft. space above this point was left open, except that it was covered with screen, and an adjustable cover-ing, operated by cords, provided a means of closing up one or all of the openings at will, the several cords con-trolling one covering being operated by one common point at a ring.

The arrange-ment of this covering is shown. It was constructed of canvas, of a size to fit the opening, fast-ened to the lower edge of the rail and allowed to hang down on the outside. The cords controlling the coverings, or flaps, were at-tached to the loose end of the canvas and run through eyeleted holes in the plate. The cord from A runs to a ring, then to B; from C to the ring and to D, and so on. When the ring is drawn down and hooked over a nail at the bottom on the inside, the flap is pulled up over the screened opening.

This made an excellent sleeping place, like a tent and outside, yet it provided a comfortable place when a storm came up during the night.

⟪If an automobile is left standing in a garage for any length of time, raise the axles on supports to remove the weight from the tires. Weight flattens the tire in one place, causing a crease in the fabric which weakens it to some extent.

Support for Hose Connection between Engine and Radiator

In certain types of automobiles the radiator is supported at the top by the

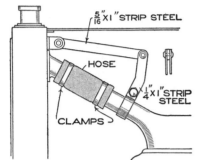

Supporting Bar to Take Up Vibrations of the Radiator to Prevent Strains on the Hose Connection

rubber hose which connects the manifold to the radiator. The constant vibration of the radiator and its forward and backward movements are all imparted to the rubber hose with the result that it becomes badly warped and twisted, and it does not take long before the hose is useless. Trouble of this nature can be eliminated to a great extent by introducing a connection between the radiator and manifold so that the latter, being made of cast iron, will more readily stand the strains than the rubber hose. A piece of steel is firmly clamped to the manifold and is in turn connected to the radiator by another piece of steel. Such a connection is very flexible and therefore is capable of withstanding high strains and vibrations.

❡A shaft bearing will take only so much oil, and it is a waste to use more.

Cableway to Procure Water for a Mountain Lodge

The water used in my mountain lodge was procured from a stream 50 ft. below, and not being acclimatized, the lightness of the air made it an exceedingly hard task for

A Cableway Run from a Mountain Lodge to a Stream Below on Which a Trolley is Operated with a Windlass, to Obtain Water

me to carry it up in pails. To do away with this old-time method, I constructed a cableway with a trolley operated by a windlass, which served the purpose well and required very little effort. I first secured a strong telegraph wire for the cable and fastened one end to the eave of the veranda and the other to the base of a tree at the opposite side of the stream. Two pieces of board and two old iron pulleys were procured and fashioned into a trolley to run on the wire. A block and pulley was then hung to the lower edges of the boards. A rope was fastened to a pail and run up through the pulley block and to a windlass drum placed between two posts of the veranda.

A bumper was attached to the wire at a point over the stream, and a coil spring run on the wire in front of the bumper block. A knot was tied into the rope 4 ft. from the pail. To obtain a pail of water it is only necessary to let out the rope on the windlass until the trolley strikes the bumper and it is lowered

into the stream until filled. When the windlass is turned the pail is drawn up until the knot strikes the pulley block, and then it travels up the cableway until it can be taken in by hand.—Contributed by P. E. Ogilvie, Glace Bay, Cape Breton.

Cutting Tool for Packing

To cut packing in some of the shapes necessary for gasoline-engine heads is quite a difficult task. The irregular shape can be easily cut by the use of two tools, made similar to the regular cold chisel, as shown in the illustration. The tools are forged just like making a cold chisel, after which the flattened edge is made rounding on a ⅜-in. radius for the larger tool and a 3/16-in. radius for the smaller, the widths being 9/16 in. and ¼ in., respectively.

The large one will cut out circles or holes, of any shape, from 9/16 in. up;

The Curved Edge of the Chisels Makes It Easy to Cut a Curved Opening

and the small one from ¼ in. to 9/16 in. in any kind of packing.—Contributed by John P. Kolar, Ithaca, N. Y.

A Homemade Cradle

The cradle illustrated has all the advantages of any rocker cradle, and besides it is much easier for the mother to take the baby from it while lying in bed, as the supports run under and cause the basket to tip toward the bed.

It is constructed of a clothes basket, several pieces of ¾-in. pipe and 2 two-way side-outlet tees. The standards are 38 in. long, ornamented on their upper ends with brass bedpost balls. The spreader is 44 in. long. Each extension for the supports is 13 in. long, bent as shown, and fitted with a caster on the lower end. About 6½ in. from the upper ends of the standards holes

are drilled and hooks fastened by riveting the ends of the hook material. These hooks hold the ends of the ropes

A Clothes Basket Swung between Standards Made of Gas Pipe for a Cradle

attached to the sides of the basket. The inside of the basket is upholstered, and the whole frame and basket is given a coat of white-enamel paint.

Tool for Removing Old Tin from Roofs

An effective tool for removing old tin from roofs can be made from a piece of steel and a 3-ft. length of ¾-in. pipe. The steel is formed into the shape of a hook and welded to one end of the pipe, the other end being fitted with a spade handle. To use the tool, the roof is marked off into strips, about 10 ft. wide, with a chalk line, and the hook is pulled along on the line, cutting up the tin into large sheets ready to be rolled up. When a soldered joint is

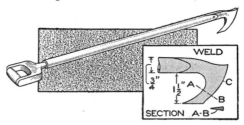

Tool for Cutting Old Tin Roofing into Strips So That It can be Rolled

encountered the workman strikes the boss C with a hammer to drive the blade through it.—Contributed by Wilbert Bernhardt, South Bend, Ind.

Electric-Heating Coil for an Ordinary Soldering Iron

An ordinary soldering copper may be easily converted into an electrically heated one by placing a heating element about the body of the iron. Proper means, of course, must be provided for

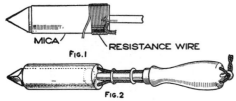

MICA **FIG. 1** **RESISTANCE WIRE**

FIG. 2

A Coil of Resistance Wire Built Up about an Ordinary Soldering Copper for Heating by Electricity

connecting the heating element to a source of electrical energy. The size and amount of wire for the heating element will depend upon the degree of heat required and the weight of iron being heated. A soldering iron weighing about 2 lb. is a very common and useful size, and it will be assumed that such an iron is to be supplied with a heating coil.

Place several thin layers of mica, about .002 in. in thickness, around the body of the iron, and fasten it in place temporarily with several turns of small wire. Procure 20 ft. of No. 26 gauge nichrome resistance wire. Attach one end of the resistance wire to a piece of asbestos-insulated copper wire, of at least No. 16 gauge and about 15 in. long. Anchor the junction of the resistance wire and copper wire to the soldering iron a short distance from the end nearest to the handle, making sure they are well insulated from the metal part of the iron. Wind the resistance wire around the iron, separating the various layers from each other, to within a short distance of the other end of the iron, as shown in Fig. 1. Place a layer of thin mica around the iron and wind on another layer of the resistance wire in the reverse direction from the first layer. This will give a noninductive winding, or one that can be used on either a direct or alternating-current circuit. Continue in this manner until all the resistance wire is placed about the iron, and then attach a piece of copper wire to the outside end, just the same as for the inside end. A layer of mica is then placed on the outside of the completed winding and fastened with several turns of wire.

The iron is now ready for a trial test, and this should be made before proceeding with the construction. Connect the free ends of the two pieces of copper wire to the terminals of a 110-volt circuit, and allow the current to flow through the iron for four or five minutes. If the iron becomes too hot, the resistance of the heating element is not high enough. If it does not heat up sufficiently, its resistance is too large. To decrease the temperature, add more resistance, and to increase it, remove some of the wire. If either of these changes is required, it must be made before the iron is completed.

The mica covering will not stand very much rough usage and a protection must be provided for it. A cover for the mica can be made from a piece of thin sheet iron, formed into a tube of proper length and diameter to completely envelop the heating element over the mica insulation. The joint in this tube is formed by bending the edges together. Two holes are drilled lengthwise through the handle for the copper wires attached to the heating element. The free ends of these copper wires are soldered to the ends of a piece of lamp cord. If the holes in the handle are drilled large enough, the joints where the copper wires are attached are placed within the handle. A screw eye is fastened in the end of the handle, into which the lamp cord is anchored to prevent any strain coming on the wires attached to the heating element. In Fig. 2 is illustrated the completed iron.

Temporary Reflector for a Headlight

New reflectors or lenses for automobiles are seldom found in stock, and when one is broken, a lamp may be useless for some time before replacement can be made. For temporary service, cut out a disk of bright tin of the proper diameter, insert it and hold in place with small wedges. A bright bottom from a nonfluid-oil pail will do as well, if one is at hand. A prevention is better than a cure, and barring accidents, broken lenses usually are caused by the flame being blown backward by a leak around the door. The owner should occasionally examine the fit of the lamp doors and see that they are tight.

A Grinding Gauge

A very efficient and easily made grinding gauge for tool and gauge grinders can be made from a piece of machine steel, $2\frac{1}{8}$ in. square by $\frac{3}{32}$ in. thick. The 60° angle is for grinding or turning lathe centers, and similar work. The 59° angle is for drills, countersinks, center drills, etc., while the 45° angle gives the correct slope for the chamfers on reamers and taps.

The 45° angle should be large, as shown, so that reamers up to 2-in. may be gauged. The surface forms a square

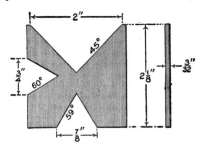

Gauge for Toolmakers and Grinders to Determine the Proper Angles for Tools

and also a straightedge for showing clearance. This tool, unlike protractors, is always set and never slips.

Screen for a Motor-Truck Radiator

Radiator accidents of a serious nature usually can be avoided by providing a protecting screen. The one illustrated is inexpensive and is readily attached to a truck frame in front of the radiator. It consists of an angle-iron frame with a screen made of strips of metal, $\frac{3}{4}$ in. wide by $\frac{3}{16}$ in. thick.

The entire frame is held firmly to the truck frame by means of four braces,

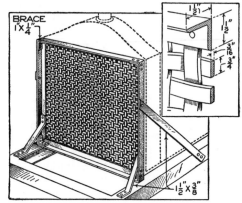

A Protecting Screen Made of Steel Strips to Avoid Serious Damage to Truck Radiators

two on each side, all made of flat steel $1\frac{1}{2}$ in. wide and $\frac{3}{8}$ in. thick.

Iron Cement for Steam Pipes

To make a permanent cement to be used for stopping leaks in steam pipes, where calking or plugging is impossible, mix black oxide of manganese and raw linseed oil, using enough oil with the manganese to bring it to a thick paste. Apply this to the pipe joint or leak. It is best to remove pressure from the pipe and keep it sufficiently warm to absorb the oil from the manganese. In about a day the cement will be as hard as the pipe.

Protecting the Gas Mantle

"One fly-power" is not much force, but when these pests make a thoroughfare of the gas chimney the incandescent mantle is liable to suffer breakage during the procession. To avoid this, slip a paper bag over the chimney and 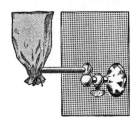 secure it at the bottom with a rubber band. This will effectively shut out the flies and keep the chimney clean as well.

Waterproof Joint for a French Window

To make a French or swing-in window strictly waterproof, set the stool in so that when the window is hung, it will project out over the stool about ⅜ in. Make a weather stop, ⅞ by 1 in., beveled on top to shed the water, and as long as the window is wide. Procure some pieces of ¼ by 1¼-in. lattice, about 1¼ in. long, and fasten them with nails on top of the window sill just outside of the stool. Nail the weather stop on top of these pieces, and any water that gets in between it and the window will run off the drip formed by the V-shaped notch, or rabbet, in the bottom of the window, down the weather stop, and out under it. This makes the window waterproof in any storm.—Contributed by Bert Fish, E. Rochester, N. Y.

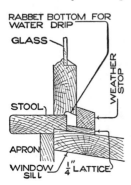

RABBET BOTTOM FOR WATER DRIP
GLASS
WEATHER STOP
STOOL
APRON
WINDOW SILL
¼" LATTICE

Oilers for a Small Dynamo

A dynamo installed for lighting only in an automobile had no provision for oiling except an oil hole in each journal. The owner neglecting the oiling, frequent trouble occurred from hot bearings, which finally had to be renewed. To prevent this semiannual expense, a pair of self-feeding oilers were made as shown. The lower side of the frame and the bushing were drilled and tapped, and a piece of ⅜-in. brass was screwed into the hole. This piece of brass was threaded on the projecting end and had a ⁷⁄₃₂-in. hole drilled through it. A piece of

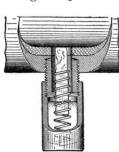

⁷⁄₁₆-in. brass was tapped to screw on the outside of the projecting plug and drilled out for almost its entire length. This gave an oil-storage space.

To carry the oil to the shaft, a piece of belt leather was shaped to make a sort of round pin, ³⁄₁₆ in. in diameter. This was screwed into a light compression spring which kept it constantly up against the shaft and its lower end dipped into the oil. While the leather did not act as a wick, it served the same purpose and carried up sufficient oil to the shaft to keep it well lubricated. Filling was only necessary at long intervals.

Substitutes for Staples to Hold Door Hasps

The ordinary hasp for a door attached with staples does not provide a very secure fastening when used in connection with a padlock. A much safer holding device than the staples is obtained by the use of carriage bolts. The bolts are bent, as shown, the threaded end is run through the door, and a nut is turned on the threaded end. The bolt cannot be pulled out like a staple.—Contributed by Chas. H. McElroy, Indianapolis, Indiana.

Using Glass to Grind Glass

It is not generally known that glass will cut glass. If a little work on smoothing the edge of some glass object is desired, procure a circular disk of glass, such as a round eyeglass or watch crystal, and mount it as follows: Turn a wood base to fit in the chuck of a jeweler's, or other, lathe and fasten the glass with the concave side against the wood by using some shellac as a cement. If it is properly centered and made to revolve rapidly, the edge can be used to grind and smooth other glass pieces.

Dividing Tool for Graduating Scales

A tool designed for graduating any flat surface in any number of parts, up to $\frac{1}{64}$ in., is shown in the illustration. By changing the feed screw and nut to the metric system, graduations for these scales can also be made. The frame consists of a length of machine steel, $\frac{9}{16}$ in. square, drilled for the feed screw A and the guide rod B, then tapped for $\frac{1}{4}$-in. clamp screws, as shown. The two collars C and D serve to prevent longitudinal play, and the latter also serves as an indicator, being divided into four equal parts, as shown, and graduated accurately, then marked 0, 1, 2, and 3. The feed screw has 16 threads to the inch, so that one turn makes the marking guide E move $\frac{1}{16}$ in., while a half turn moves the guide $\frac{1}{32}$ in., and so on. The threads on the screw should be carefully cut and lapped to fit snugly in the threads of the guide E. The beveled face of the collar D being divided into four parts, the screw may be accurately moved quarter turns, thus spacing to $\frac{1}{64}$ in., which is usually fine enough for any scale.

While the instrument is small, it will accurately graduate a scale, rule, or tape of any length. In use, the surface to be graduated must be cleaned and coated with copperas, then lines must be made with a scriber lengthwise of the scale, the first $\frac{3}{32}$ in. from the edge, the next $\frac{1}{8}$ in. from the edge, and so on. Place the work on the frame F, and fasten it down with the clamps G. The marking guide E is run up to the head of the tool and set flush with the end of the scale to be graduated, and the tool is ready.

Give the thumbscrew H one quarter turn, then make a clear scratch on the prepared surface, drawing the scriber along the side of the guide E; give the screw H another quarter turn, and repeat until the whole length is marked. This spaces the marks $\frac{1}{64}$ in. When the length of the lead screw has been graduated, return and space a half turn for $\frac{1}{32}$ in., and continue so until the scale is graduated as desired.

In case of a long scale, graduate each length at a time, setting the last graduation for the first mark and repeating

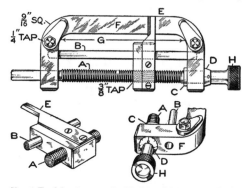

Hand Tool for Accurately Marking Divisions on Scales and Rules of Special Construction

each operation. With this tool many novel, useful, and accurate forms of scales may be easily made. While this instrument will not compare with machine-made tools of the latest patterns, or with the automatic dividing engines, it is quite rapid and is absolutely accurate.—Contributed by J. B. Murphy, Plainfield, N. J.

A Quickly Made Wrench

The illustration shows how a wrench for a hexagonal nut can be quickly made. A piece of ordinary tubing, with an outside diameter equal to the dimension across the flats of the nut and about 5 in. long, is thoroughly annealed. The nut which the wrench is to fit is heated to a red heat, and the tube is hammered down over it to make the shape as shown. The nut will

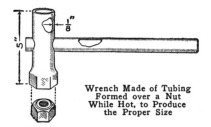

Wrench Made of Tubing Formed over a Nut While Hot, to Produce the Proper Size

contract a little in cooling, sufficiently to allow the wrench to slip over it freely. Another piece of tubing is used as a handle.

Painting Wire Screen

Procure a board, about 10 in. long, 8 in. wide, and ¾ in. thick, that is slightly curved as shown. Fasten a piece of round wood, 2 in. in diameter and 6 in. long, to its center on one side for a handle. Hold the board under the screen the same as holding a plasterer's trowel and paint on the upper side, applying the paint quite freely. Allow the screen to stand for a time, then brush dry to remove the surplus paint.—Contributed by J. L. Riley, Dallas, Tex.

Makeshift Grabhook for a Well Bucket

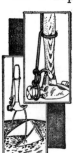

As I happened to lose the water bucket from the rope in the cistern and had no grabhook, I managed to get the bucket out very easily as follows: A rope was tied to a claw hammer, as shown in the illustration, which served as a hook that was easily passed into the bucket bail, so the bucket could be drawn out.—Contributed by A. Jaminet, Denver, Colorado.

Handle to Hold Setscrew While Smoothing Head

As it was necessary to smooth down the edges on the head of a short case-hardened setscrew, and I found that a file made no impression on the hardened surfaces, the only other thing to do was to use a grinder. To facilitate holding the screws while grinding I made a short handle of hard

wood, bored a hole of sufficient size for the threads to cut their way in, and turned the setscrew into the hole. This held the screw firmly so the grinding could be done with ease.—Contributed by James M. Kane, Doylestown, Pa.

Protecting the Eyes When Making Hole in Concrete Ceiling

In making some holes in a concrete ceiling for bolts, a millwright experienced considerable trouble with particles falling in his face and eyes. To protect the eyes, a piece of celluloid was slipped over the chisel. This did not obstruct the view or prevent particles from falling to one side.—Contributed by J. J. Kolar, Maywood, Ill.

Waterproofing Hinge Joints on Automobile Hoods

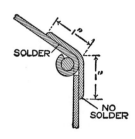

Automobiles of the cheaper grades, of which there are many, never are supplied with a covering on the hood hinges to keep out the rain. This trouble may be overcome by placing a bent strip of metal over the hinges, the upper part being soldered to the top of the hood while the lower part is bent to form a close fit with the vertical side, but left unsoldered to permit the opening of the hood.

❡Prestolite gas run too low for lighting the lamps can be revived temporarily to finish a run by heating the tank, which releases some of the gas from the absorbent.

Reading Performance Curves of Motors and Generators

It is quite essential that persons owning, or expecting to own or have charge of, electric motors or generators, should be sufficiently familiar with the performance curves of the machine in use to determine its main characteristics. These performance curves tell, graphically, the whole story of the capabilities of the machine, and it is an easy matter for one experienced in reading such curves, or familiar with them, to determine these capabilities almost at a glance.

Machines, more than ever before, are sold on their performance characteristics, as shown by curves, and the prospective customer usually demands certain characteristics of the selling company. It is no longer possible for the salesman merely to give the horsepower and voltage of a motor, and expect the purchaser to make a selection from this information alone. Characteristic curves are usually demanded. The same is true with generators.

The sketch shows the performance curves of an 80-volt direct-current series motor, such as is used on electric vehicles, and the complete behavior of the motor in operation may be determined from an inspection of these curves. In this case the various curves are all drawn with reference to the current taken by the motor, the current being plotted along the horizontal and the other quantities on the vertical lines.

The "torque" is the turning effort of the machine measured in pounds at a distance of 1 ft. from the center of the shaft. The efficiency is the output of the machine, expressed as a percentage of the input and abbreviated "eff." The "R. P. M." is the revolutions of the armature shaft per minute, and "B. H. P." is the brake horsepower.

When this motor is taking a current of 40 amperes it is operating at a speed of 460 revolutions per minute; developing a torque of 37 lb. at a radius of 1 ft.; the horsepower output is 3.25, and the efficiency is about 77 per cent. The

above values of speed, torque, horsepower, and efficiency are determined by following the vertical line corresponding to 40 amperes upward until the various curves are encountered,

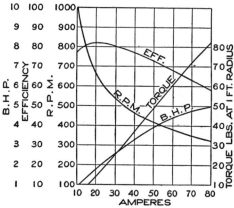

A Performance Curve of an Eighty-Volt Direct-Current Series Motor Used on Automobiles

and then along horizontal lines from the points of intersection to the various vertical scales where the values can be read. If any one of these quantities is given, all the others may be determined in a manner similar to that indicated above. Thus, if a machine is operating at a speed of 400 revolutions per minute, it will take a current of 53.5 amperes, the efficiency will be 71 per cent, the torque will be 53 lb. at a radius of 1 ft., and the horsepower will be a little less than 4.1.

The Proper Way to Place Ice in a Refrigerator

As heat always travels to the top of an inclosure, it does so also within the walls of a refrigerator; hence, if a piece of ice is not large enough to fill the ice space, lay it in such a position that the largest portion is at the bottom of the cavity. This will save considerable ice where a small quantity is used at a time.

⟨The presence of sulphur in a silver-plating solution will cause patchy deposits. The sulphur comes from the rubber used about the plating solutions.

Proportioning Anchor Plates for Machinery Foundations

It is frequently necessary for the mechanic installing machinery to make the foundation anchor plates in the field. This is

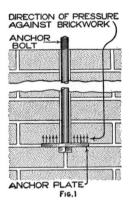

DIRECTION OF PRESSURE AGAINST BRICKWORK

ANCHOR BOLT

ANCHOR PLATE

Fig. 1

particularly true when an installation is in a small town or city where standard anchor-plate castings are not available. The following tells how satisfactory anchor plates can be proportioned and made from wrought-iron plate.

The function of an anchor plate is to prevent the withdrawal of the anchor bolt from the foundation, or to anchor the holding-down bolt in the masonry. An anchor bolt and plate in position in a brick foundation is shown in Fig. 1. The strains which are imposed upon an anchor plate are indicated by the arrows. When the nut on an anchor bolt is screwed down to clamp the machine bedplate in position, the force is transmitted through the bolt to the anchor plate and then presses up against the masonry in which it is imbedded. The total force in pounds with which an anchor plate bears upwardly against the foundation masonry is equal to the tension in pounds to which the anchor bolt is subjected by screwing down the nut. In proportioning an anchor plate, it can be assumed that this load is equally distributed on the portion of the upper surface of the anchor plate.

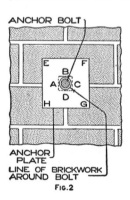

ANCHOR BOLT

E F
B
A   C
D
H   G

ANCHOR PLATE
LINE OF BRICKWORK AROUND BOLT

Fig. 2

In proportioning the bearing area of the anchor plate—that is, the area of the plate that pushes, or rests, against the masonry—the following rule should be observed: The area, in square inches, of the anchor plate that bears against the foundation multiplied by the safe compressive strength of the material of the foundation, in pounds per square inch, should at least equal the tension which the bolt is capable of sustaining. For example, the tensile strength of wrought iron is about 20 times the compressive strength of brick, hence the bearing area of a plate resting against a brick foundation should be at least 20 times the cross-sectional area of the bolt.

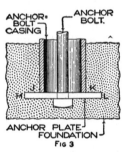

ANCHOR BOLT CASING

ANCHOR BOLT

H   J   K   L

ANCHOR PLATE
FOUNDATION

Fig. 3

Observing the foregoing rule and referring to the case of the anchor plate in question, the area EFGH, in Fig. 2, which shows a top view of the anchor plate, should be equal to at least 20 times the area of the bolt for a brick foundation. Obviously, in figuring the effective area of the plate, the area of the circular surface ABCD must be subtracted because this area does not bear against the brick of the foundation. For materials other than brick, the ratio between the bearing area of the plate and the cross-sectional area of the anchor bolt will, of course, be different than 20 to 1. The reason for this is that other materials have different compressive strengths than brick. The compressive strengths of the various masonry materials can be found in some of the many handbooks and will not be given here.

From the description the procedure

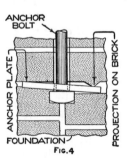

ANCHOR BOLT

ANCHOR PLATE

PROJECTION ON BRICK

FOUNDATION

Fig. 4

in determining the area desirable for an anchor plate that is to be used in any kind of masonry will be obvious. In determining the effective bearing area of an anchor placed in a casing, as shown in Fig. 3, certain precautions must be observed. For example, only a portion of the anchor plate, indicated by HJ and KL, is effective in pushing against the masonry. The effective area of the plate is greatly reduced, due to the presence of the casing. Corrections for this condition can be readily made and the proper area of the plate computed from the suggestions which have been given.

The thickness of the anchor plate must be such that it will not bend or buckle when the bolt impresses a strain upon it. For a rough and ready rule, the thickness of a steel or iron-plate anchor may be taken as equal to .4, or possibly .5, of the diameter of the foundation bolt with which it is to be used. For example, if the foundation bolt is 1 in. in diameter the thickness of an anchor plate, in iron or steel, should be at least .4 in., or possibly .55 in. This rule is obviously a rough and ready one, and cannot be followed in all instances, although it will give safe results in the average case.

The transverse strains that are imposed on an anchor plate, due to unequal loading, may be very great. It sometimes occurs, due to the inequalities in the surfaces of bricks or stones used in a foundation, that an anchor plate will bear against the masonry at only two or three points, as shown in Fig. 4. In such a case the load is not uniformly distributed, and extensive strains are therefore imposed on the anchor plate and on the masonry. To protect against such conditions, it is well to so proportion anchor plates that their factors of safety will be ample.

❡The presence of boracic acid in a nickelplating solution will cause the whitening of the deposit, and also makes it softer and eliminates the tendency to pit.

Attaching Steam Sterilizer to Hot-Water Tank

If a hot-water tank be connected up as shown, it can be used not only for its regular service to furnish hot water, but, by a proper manipulation of valves,

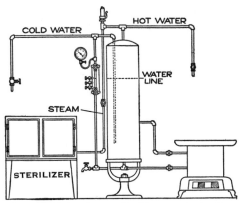

Obtaining Steam from a Hot-Water Boiler for Use in a Sterilizer

will serve also as a boiler in furnishing steam for sterilizing purposes.

To this end, the regular connection of the stove water back to the tank should remain unchanged except for a tee in the drain pipe of the tank. This tee should have its side outlet turned vertically, so that a connection can be made with the lower end of a boiler water column, which should be placed to indicate both steam and water when about one-quarter of the tank's capacity is filled with steam. The upper end of the water column connects with the side outlet of a tee provided in the cold-water supply line. On the regular hot-water outlet at the top of the tank is connected a cross fitting. To one of its horizontal outlets is connected a short length of pipe, provided with a stop valve at the extreme end, for the purpose of relieving the vacuum when draining the tank, or permitting the escape of air when filling it with water. The opposite outlet of the cross is connected through a stop valve, conveniently placed, with the sterilizer. In order to prevent excessive pressure caused by the generation of steam, a safety valve must be provided, which should be connected in the main outlet line so as to have no valve between it and the tank, thereby preventing any possibility of an explosion by carelessly shutting off the operation of the safety valve. The steam pressure should at all times be indicated, and for this purpose a steam gauge should be attached to the water column through a circular or U-loop, which is for the purpose of retaining water at all times so the steam cannot come in direct contact with the gauge and injure it.

When using the heater for regular service, the sterilizer stop valve should first be shut off. Then the cold-water valve can be opened to fill the tank, the air of the tank meanwhile being relieved by the valve at the end of the short pipe.

In using the sterilizer in connection with the tank, the cold-water supply should first be shut off. Then the water in the tank may be drained off until the water level shows about halfway in the water column, the vacuum in the tank meanwhile being relieved by the valve at the end of the short pipe line. When the proper level has been obtained, the vacuum-relieving valve should be shut off and steam may be raised as required. Should the amount of steam become excessive, part of the tank water may be drained off, and an equal amount of cold water added; this will tend to condense the steam and relieve the pressure. The water level should be regulated so it can always be seen in the gauge glass; if it is too high, part of it should be drained off; if too low, an extra amount must be added from the cold-water supply.—Contributed by W. N. House, Great Neck, N. Y.

To Make a Cone Clutch Engage Smoothly

A cone clutch that cannot be made to engage smoothly, can be remedied to some extent as follows: Make six or

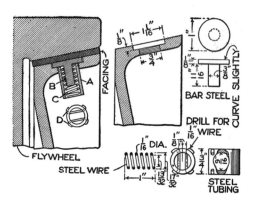

Pressure Buttons to Raise the Surface of a Clutch, to Make It Take Hold Slowly

more sets of pressure springs and place them in the clutch face, as shown. Each set consists of a collar, A, which is screwed into the face of the clutch; a plunger, B, operating in the collar and against the action of a coil spring, C, which is held in position by means of two pins, D. The shape and dimen-sions of these various parts are shown in the sketch.

The position of the clutch facing, directly above the plunger B, is raised a trifle higher than its normal height, due to the pressure of the spring, with the result that the entire surface of the facing does not come in contact when the clutch is engaged, and the sudden gripping is entirely eliminated.

Etching Fluid

An excellent fluid for etching steel, either for making a beautiful frosted effect, or for deep etching of names and trade-marks, is made up as follows: Mix together ¼ oz. of powdered table salt and 2 oz. of copper sulphate with ½ pt. of vinegar and 40 drops of nitric acid. The parts not to be etched are covered with paraffin or beeswax. Deep etching or frosting is effected by leaving the article to the action of the fluid for a longer or shorter time.

⁋It is dangerous to put a large washer on one side and a small one on the other of an emery wheel.

Shop Notes

Spark Test for Steels

By NEIL W. FRENCH

MANY times during the day, in almost every shop, there arises the necessity to judge accurately and speedily the grade, or carbon content, of a chance bit of metal. Especially is this true where a considerable scrap heap accumulates, from which the workman, searching for an odd piece to fit an emergency, could satisfy his wants if he had some knowledge of just what kind of iron or steel he had in hand. For this purpose the spark test, as charted below, is unerringly accurate, and is always quickly available.

Of course, it must be admitted that veterans in the service of the machine shop many times are able to tell the composition of a piece of metal by the "heft" or the "feel" of it; or by some other more or less intuitive sense which one may acquire by long experience. Although many times in the right, a decision by this method cannot entirely satisfy a critical workman, or prove reliable in an unfamiliar case. Furthermore, it generally falls to the lot of the apprentice or the unskilled helper to run to the scrap heap for the desired piece. The judgment of this person is entirely untrustworthy, and he should be given a sure and definite system of selecting the metal.

The spark test answers all the requirements to a marked degree. The variations in the sparks from the different metals, when held to a grindstone, are pronounced and easily evident to the veriest novice with the aid of the chart. To the man of experience, the spark test forms a prolific field of study, as the appearance of the sparks follow closely any change in the constituents of the metal, and with close observation, the qualities of the iron or steel may be told with a high degree of exactness.

Another point in favor of the spark test is its ready availability. Other

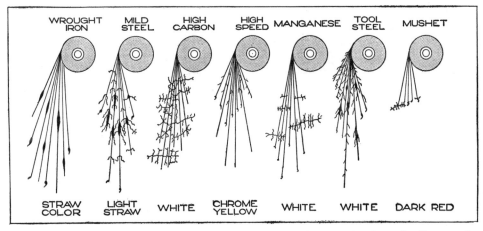

The Variations in the Sparks from the Different Metals When Held to a Grindstone Are Pronounced and Easily Evident to the Latest Apprentice with the Aid of the Chart

accurate and definite methods of test, the fracture test and the chemical analysis, involve a large expenditure of time, and in many cases, the mutilation of the piece. A grindstone will be found in any shop, and to touch a small portion of the sample to it requires but a second, and does not damage the piece, as a glance often suffices to decide the quality of the metal. Then, too, comes the added advantage that the apprentice can do the job without wasting the more valuable time of the machinist.

Wrought iron, with its low amount of carbon, gives a straw-colored spark, coming off the wheel in light lines with enlargements at certain points where a particle of iron burns in the air. The lines and sparks are quite regular and quiet, and may be readily recognized. Carbon produces the phenomena which might be expected, a miniature explosion, which sends little white lines at right angles to the heavier iron lines. In the case of the high-carbon steel the carbon sparks overcome the iron ones and the wheel seems to send off a shower of twinkling little stars, very similar to the "flowerpot" fireworks. These explosive particles are characteristic of carbon.

The alloy steels present quite an array of distinguishing sparks, each varying with the alloy. These may be best studied with the actual known specimens, but some of the more common alloys may be mentioned. Chromium produces a chrome-yellow color, which may be easily recognized after once having been seen. Manganese makes very white lines, with explosions like the carbon, except that the bursts are less in number and apparently more violent. Mushet steel shows a few dark-red lines under the wheel. The harder steels naturally make a shorter spark, and it requires closer observation to become familiar with them.

The chief advantage of this method is its simplicity and adaptability. Each shop is likely to carry standard qualities of iron, and to chart them would be a simple task. Then the latest apprentice could select from the scrap heap the blackest and dirtiest piece of iron and quickly tell its qualities.

An Emergency Ruby Lamp for Photographers

A railway photographer, securing pictures of the manner in which the engineers were placing a certain man-

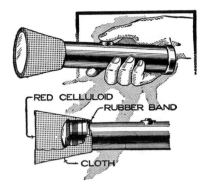

A Light-Proof End Having a Piece of Red Celluloid is Fastened over the Flash-Lamp Bull's-Eye

ufactured tiling, found that the ordinary camp life provided no dark-room facilities, which is necessary in transferring the plates and loading the plate holders, as the exposed plates were sent to the city for finishing. A piece of light-proof hood canvas served the purpose of the field dark room, but the dark lantern was provided for in a manner which can be applied in many ways.

A circular piece of red celluloid, about 1¼ in. in diameter, was glued to a strip of light-proof focusing cloth, cut in the manner shown in the sketch. The outer end of it had an elastic band which was slipped over the lens of a small electric pocket torch. The device was very useful on the field, as plate holders could be safely loaded and the exposed plates securely packed at any place where views of interest might be taken. The cap was slipped from the end of the torch after using it as a dark lantern, and carried in the vest pocket.

A Hook for Idle Belts

It is the practice in a great many shops, where belts are thrown from driving pulleys of main shafts to check indefinitely the motion of the counter-shaft for repairs, etc., to tie the belt to the ceiling or roof at some point near the shaft. This is, of course, to prevent the belt from dropping on the main shaft when thrown from the pulley. If a joist, or some other means of securing the rope, is at hand, this is perhaps as good a way as any, but convenient anchorage is not always available.

The sketch shows an anchor hook, of which several were placed along the main-shaft pulleys in a paper mill. When it was necessary to throw out a set of countershafting from the main-shaft pulley, the belt was simply thrown over the hook, which was so placed back of and to one side of the

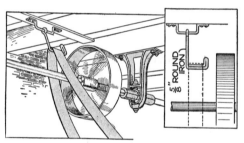

Hook Fastened to an Overhead Support to Hold a Belt Away from a Turning Shaft

main-shaft pulley as to afford a good spread of the belt over the shaft.

The hooks are easy to bend and fasten to joists and beams, and their value lies in always being ready and in place, which can be appreciated only when trouble unexpectedly occurs in a set of countershafting.

Card-File Guide to Advertise Rooms for Rent

These card files are made up and placed in drug stores of a locality for giving information in regard to rooms for rent, apartments, or hotels, with description and rates, a small photograph of the place, and directions how

to reach it by car. Each card slides on a rod and may be raised for inspection. The outside box is made of light

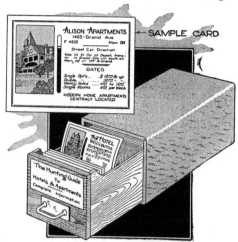

File Holding Cards Descriptive of Rooms, Apartments, or Hotels, and Where Located in the Vicinity

wood just large enough to admit a drawer for holding 5 by 8-in. cards.— Contributed by Mrs. J. E. McLaughlin, Los Angeles, Cal.

To Repair a Clutch Lever

The three operating levers on the dry-plate clutch of a rather old type of automobile became worn so badly that adjustment was impossible. A new set of levers could not be procured, and a repair was necessary. A hole was drilled and then tapped through the operating boss where the wear had taken place. An ordinary round-end setscrew with locknut was then inserted, and as the end became worn, it was screwed forward to maintain the proper adjustment.

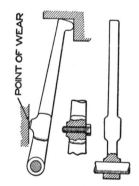

¶Never use machine oil on cutting tools, nor lard oil for lubrication.

Fruit Racks for Display Purposes

The problem of displaying fruit as well as keeping it in stock is sometimes a puzzle to fruit dealers, espe-

The Fronts of the Original Fruit Cases, or Boxes, Fitted with Display Racks

cially when bad weather will not permit a display in front of the store, as is usually the custom. This compels the dealer to use a great deal of floor space to display the fruit well on the inside.

A few racks, as shown in the illustration, will not only take care of the stock, but will display it as well. A rack, fastened to the box as shown, will permit the boxes to be set sideways on top of each other, thus affording a good display for the fruit as well as taking up very little space. The fruit can be handled much easier, and the loss by rot will be reduced to a minimum, as sufficient exposure to the air is provided.

When all the fruit is removed from a box, the rack can be removed and fastened to another box. The end pieces of the racks are constructed of boards 1 in. thick, to which are fastened strips of wood about one inch apart. The strips should be about one inch wide. These may be fastened with nails, or mortised in the end pieces; or they can be made adjustable by cutting slots in the end board large enough for the pieces to slide in them. In this case pins are placed through the ends of the slats to prevent them from slipping out.—Contributed by Harry Slosower, Pittsburgh, Pa.

Finishing Work Too High for a Planer

A job came along to plane off one face of several castings that were too high to pass under the cross rail of the planer. For various reasons it was not advisable to lay them down and use the vertical feed, so it became necessary to do the work in some other way. They were finally placed in their natural upright position on the planer bed, then an extension tool, A, such as is used for cutting keyways in pulleys, was put in the tool post, but in an inverted position, as shown. With the cross rail B raised to its limit, this tool was just high enough to do the cutting, and it did the work nicely and without special outlay to add to the cost of the work. With the tool thus inverted, it had a tendency to lift and slide along without cut-

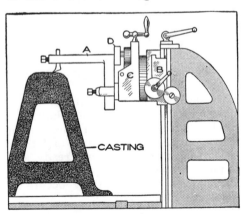

Cutting Down the Upper Surfaces of Castings Too High for Regular Planer Work

ting, because the cut caused the clapper to lift about the center C instead of holding it down as in using it in a normal position. This lifting up was prevented by the block D.—Contributed by Donald A. Hampson, Middletown, N. Y.

Electric Water Heater and Time Switch

By JOHN D. ADAMS

WHEN boiling water on the usual electric stove or hot plate, the current first heats the resistance wire, then the enamel in which it is imbedded, and finally the outer surface of the iron, top, bottom, and sides. A portion of the heat is conducted through the container into the water; the remainder is all loss. Why not, therefore, use the water itself as a resistance and generate the heat directly in the water and thus practically eliminate all these losses of conduction and radiation?

To apply this principle in its most convenient form, a neat little white-enamel pail of the proper capacity should be procured. For electrodes, carbon suggests itself as the cheapest and most inert conductor. With it rust and corrosion need not be feared, and an ample supply may be had from the center element of a discarded dry cell. Saw off two blocks, flatten the bottom surfaces by rubbing them on a smooth sheet of sandpaper, and then round off and smooth the tops. In the center of the bottom of each, drill a hole with a $\frac{3}{16}$-in. drill, and then work the drill around at an angle so as to widen the hole at the bottom. This process should be continued until the knurled nut from a dry-cell connection can be nicely accommodated, in the manner indicated in the sketch. The carbon should be heated for some time over a gas or Bunsen flame to burn out all the impurities and chemicals. While this is going on, the brass nut should be tinned all over the outside and the center plugged up tightly with a piece of soft wood. When the carbon ceases to smoke or steam, place the nut in the tapering hole and melt enough solder to fill the remaining space. Arrange some little fastening to hold the nut down until set, as it will float on the melted solder if left alone. When cold, remove the wood plug and clean out the threads.

Having treated both carbons in this manner, a preliminary test should be made to determine the proper distance

apart at which they may be best operated. Fasten them with screws to a hard piece of rubber or fiber, allowing about $\frac{1}{2}$ in. space between them. Connect them up with two pieces of wire having waterproof insulation so that they will be directly across the

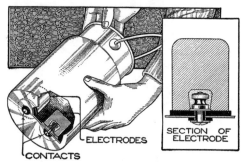

SECTION OF ELECTRODE
ELECTRODES
CONTACTS

Carbon Electrodes Fastened in a Pail to Cause the Water to Heat by Its Own Resistance

110-volt circuit, placing a five-ampere fuse in series. Completely immerse in water and observe the heating effect. If not sufficiently rapid, decrease the intervening distance to $\frac{3}{8}$ in. and then allow the water to boil before making a further change. If the fuse is not then blown, another reduction may be made.

When the proper distance is determined, two holes are to be drilled in the bottom of the enameled pail, and to avoid chipping or cracking the enamel, they must be drilled in the same manner as drilling glass, that is, with a piece of brass or copper tubing for a drill, which is fed with turpentine and emery dust. To keep such a drill from slipping around at the start, a piece of cigar-box wood, or hard wax, should be placed over the spot to be drilled. To gain access to the enamel, an ordinary drill may be used, after which the copper tube and emery dust are necessary.

Two large rubber washers and two smaller ones of fiber, all indicated in heavy lines in the sketch, are to be made. The center holes in these should be large enough to receive the brass bolt from a dry cell when covered with a piece of rubber tubing for insulation. Having cut off two of these bolts to the proper length, place the electrodes and the large washers inside the container and fasten them

Time Switch to be Used in Connection with the Heater for Heating Shaving Water

down tightly, all as indicated in the sketch.

This water heater requires no stove, merely a block of wood with two contact plates. When the water is sufficiently heated, it is only necessary to lift it up by the bail and carry it wherever required—no connecting or disconnecting. If it is forgotten, the water is boiled down, and the circuit is thereby broken and the consumption of the current automatically ceases.

At a predetermined hour the device illustrated turns on the light and heats two or three quarts of water for shaving. The object in having the light turned on is to make it serve in lieu of the disturbing alarm clock, the light alarm being very satisfactory when one is fairly regular in his habits.

All dimensions have been omitted, as they are, for the greater part, either immaterial or else must be adapted to the size of the watch or the heating pail. Most of the parts may be made from such scraps of brass or copper as usually accumulate around the experimenter's bench. For the timepiece, I used one of the standard dollar watches, and for the actuating magnet, a high-resistance coil taken from an old telephone bell. The long hand is removed from the watch and the watch secured in place by means of three brass fingers, which are screwed to the

baseboard and are so shaped that they permit the watch to be rotated in a horizontal plane about a third of a turn. A narrow strip of copper foil is next arranged so as to overhang the face of the watch and intercept the hour hand once every 12 hours.

The coil with its iron core is then fastened to the base block by means of a bracket at the rear and a narrow band in front, or in any other suitable way that will suggest itself. The armature consists of a small soft-iron block, pivoted to the base at the lower edge and provided with a small projection on its back for the purpose of holding up the switch blade. A light spring holds it back from the magnet and a stop keeps it from going farther back than indicated in the sketch. The blade consists of a small strip of brass or copper swung in a suitable standard and provided with a tension spring that will cause it to drop, when the armature is attracted, into a U-shaped contact below. As the carrying capacity will only be from three to five amperes, the U-shaped connection into which the blade drops should be of light spring brass or copper. By providing the blade with a small handle, shown projecting upward at an angle of 45 deg., the timing feature may be thrown out of action by depressing it, in which position the tension spring will tend to keep the blade up instead of down.

For the heating contacts, two semicircular plates are secured in place with countersunk screws and at such a distance apart that it will be impossible for either of the contact screws on the bottom of the pail to short-circuit them. For holding the lamp, a neat-trimmed hole will answer every purpose, if the base is of hard wood. The center contact may be made by means of a spring from below, while a small strip of metal, or piece of wire, bent over the edge into the hole will make the outside connection. If the lamp base fits closely, a decided screw action may be had, even though no threads were made in the wood. Two brass bolts from discarded dry cells, let up through the bottom of the base, will make a satisfactory fuse block if a piece of heavy mica is placed on the wood before the nuts are screwed down.

The method of operation is simple. Connection is made with the watch through one of the three fingers that hold it in place, and as soon as the hand makes contact with the overhanging strip the current passes through the coil to the armature and into the switch blade. The instant the magnet coil operates, it breaks its own circuit and the blade drops into its contact piece below and closes the circuit through the heater and the lamp. The flash of alternating current through the watch does not affect it in any way. All connections are indicated in the sketch and may be readily concealed in grooves cut in the bottom.

Bracing a Strained Running-Board Bracket

The bracket supporting the running board of an automobile was strained, and the board started to sag to one side very badly. To replace the bracket with a new one was quite a job, as it was fastened to the frame with rivets. In making the repair, two pieces were cut from $\frac{3}{16}$-in. sheet steel to the proper shape, which were then riveted to the bracket, as shown. The reason for making the portion at the bend very large was that this part of the bracket

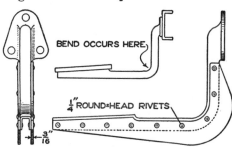

Strips of Sheet Metal Placed on Each Side of the Bracket to Reinforce It

carried the greatest strain. The job, while it entailed a little work, entirely eliminated the trouble.

Jack for Unloading Lumber from Car Doors

In unloading cars of lumber, the boards must be slid out of the doors no matter whether they are loaded on

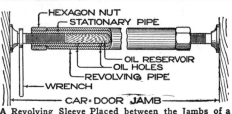

A Revolving Sleeve Placed between the Jambs of a Car Door for Rolling Out Boards

trucks or on a conveyor. The sliding of the boards is not easily accomplished, and in a close place a person finds it quite difficult to shove the rougher material over the edges of the other boards to get them out of the car. Where a large quantity of lumber had to be taken from the cars, a jack was made as shown for rolling the boards out of the door.

The jack is adjustable so that it can be set in any-width door and at any height. It consists of two screw ends, with right and left threads, fitted into the threaded ends of a pipe. Another pipe is fitted loosely over the first one so that it will revolve freely. To keep the revolving pipe from slipping endways, nuts are turned on the ends of the stationary pipe. It is readily seen how this jack may be quickly fitted in the car door to provide a moving surface over which the boards are easily pushed.—Contributed by Frank P. Reidhaar, Connersville, Ind.

❡In setting a pulley tighten all bolts alike.

Substitute for a Hook to Lower Pipe

Having some heavy pipe to lower into a shaft to a mine, I rigged up the device shown. It was made of ⅝-in. iron rod. The threaded ends were placed in the holes in the pipe flange, and nuts turned on the under side. Locknuts could be used to insure greater safety in lowering the pipe. For very heavy pipe, heavier material than ⅝-in. stock should be used. The lowering rope was attached to a large ring at the top.—Contributed by H. V. Olson, Hibbing, Minn.

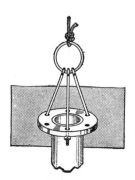

To Prevent Gas Explosions

Acetylene and other gas explosions are sometimes caused by the flame following the gas in the tubing back to the generator, or tank, and there exploding the stored-up gas, causing considerable damage. This is especially true when starting a new plant in which there is a proper mixture of air and gas to cause this "back-firing." Pure gas cannot be exploded in a tank. In order to prevent an explosion from this cause, the device shown should be connected between the supply and the burners, as near the generator as possible.

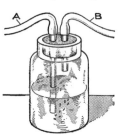

The tubing A is connected to the generator and to a tube passing through a hole in the cork of the bottle almost to the bottom. The tube B supplies the gas to the burners and is connected to a short piece of brass tubing just passing through the cork. The holes are drilled through the cork with a thin-walled tube that has been sharpened from the outer edge, so as to make the tubes fit tightly and prevent the gas from escaping. The bottle is filled one-third full of water; then the cork is inserted and the tubes squeezed in tightly, with the long tube immersed in the water.

The gas is forced through the water and then it follows the tube B to the burners. If the flame follows the tubing it cannot pass the bottle, as the water stops it and thus prevents an explosion.—Contributed by Chas. I. Reid, Millersburg, Pa.

Rubber-Stamp Rack

A simple and convenient rack for supporting rubber stamps on a flat table-top desk can be made as shown in the illustration. Two angle brackets of metal strips, about ⅛ by ½-in. stock, are made with one end about 2 in. long and the other about 5 in. The short ends are drilled for screws to attach them to the lower side of the table top. The long ends are 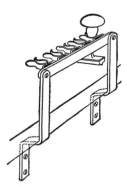 drilled near the top for fastening the stamp rack. The rack can be bought in any suitable length from a local stationery or hardware dealer, and, after being provided with a hole at each end, can be attached to the upper ends of the angle brackets with small stove bolts, or wire. The assembled rack may then be fastened in the place selected for it on the table. With this arrangement, any desired number of stamps can be provided for.—Contributed by C. Currier, Port Elgin, Canada.

❈An all-steel wheelbarrow makes a good place for a fire on contract plumbing jobs. It can be taken to the spot where the melted lead is wanted.

Boxing Pressure Gauges for Shipment

It is the custom of a great many establishments having numerous pressure gauges in the various power plants to send the gauges to a central point, or shop, for repair and adjustment. It is, of course, necessary to properly box, or crate, them to prevent damage through rough handling in shipment, and it takes considerable time to make boxes suitable for one or two gauges at a time.

The sketch shows how an inexpensive and permanent shipping box can be made for the gauge, which can be used many times, even for gauges of varying thickness and diameter. The round top pieces are of wood, to which is tacked the side piece or circular strip of tin. By packing a little excelsior or waste around a small gauge it can be sent in the same box. All that is necessary is to bend over the

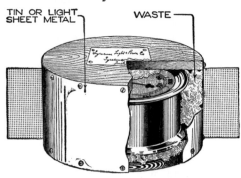

A Quickly Made Packing Box to Hold and Safely Carry a Pressure Gauge

tin sides and fasten them, and the gauge is ready to ship. One or two of these kept on hand in the plant will be found very convenient when a gauge suddenly requires shipment to the central point for repairs.

Handle Lock for Secret Compartment in Fancy Box

An ingenious opening and locking device, made in a cover of a fancy jewel box, is shown in the illustration. The handle of the box constitutes the locking device. The handle holder B is made to turn in the secret cover, its under side having a brass extension that passes under the box cover and holds the secret cover firmly in place.

It is only necessary to press the

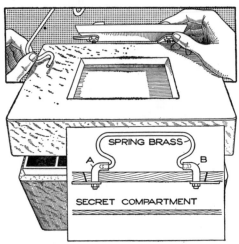

Secret-Compartment Cover on a Fancy Jewel Box Locked by the Handle

handle ends out of the holes in the holders A and B, turn the piece B until the lock piece clears the cover top, then the secret cover is free to be lifted away from the box cover.

How to Tag Bags

A quick way to tag bags is to run the wire, or string, through an ordinary sack needle, then drawing it through the bag and tying it. This

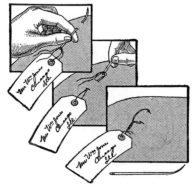

The Sack Needle is Threaded with the Fastenings of the Tag, Then Run through the Sack

is much easier than working it through with the fingers.—Contributed by Louis Wahrer, Tiffin, O.

Warehouse Steps for Trucks

Steps used in warehouses or places where one floor is only a few feet above another floor are usually bother-

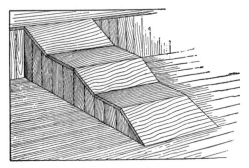

The Rise on Each Step is Made Slanting with a Width Narrower than the Tread

some, for in such a place trucks are used to cart large objects from one point to another. In a certain warehouse where the steps were used as much to walk on as for the trucks, the owner made the rise as shown in the sketch. The rise on each step was made slanting so that the wheels of the trucks would run over them.

How to Make a Gasoline Strainer

A good feature to incorporate in the fuel system of an automobile is the placing of a gasoline strainer in the line between the tank and the carburetor. Those who wish to install a strainer

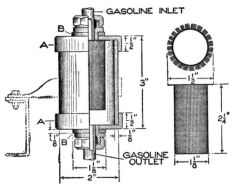

Gasoline Strainer Placed in a Pipe Line on an Automobile to Catch Particles of Dirt

and are somewhat mechanically inclined will be enabled to construct a

very efficient and at the same time inexpensive one by the following description:

The body consists of a piece of brass, or bronze, pipe, threaded at both ends and provided with a closing plate, A, at either end. These end pieces are ordinary pipe caps and are provided with collars, B, which are soldered to them. The strainer part is made cylindrical in shape, of fine brass screen, and has a flange at its top for the purpose of fastening it to the top cover to which it is soldered. The pipe connections consist of ordinary pipe unions. These unions are screwed into the top and bottom caps, white lead being placed in the threads to avoid leakage. The complete strainer is fastened to the frame side rail with a piece of flat steel soldered to the body and in turn bolted to the frame.

A Flexible Rubber Washer

For a washer that combines elasticity with water-resisting qualities there is nothing to equal one cut from a piece of automobile tire. As it is live rubber, it is almost impossible to cut it with a knife. Use a pair of scissors to cut out the disk, and a belt punch to cut out the screw hole.

Since the washer is very flexible it is best to use a brass, or copper, washer between the screw head and the rubber, as the screw alone will not hold it very well. If the fabric is left on the rubber it will increase the life of the washer.

Lubricant for Tapping Boiler Plates

Boilermakers, when tapping sheet-steel plates, dip their taps in a solution of white lead and lard oil, thinned to the consistency of cream. This also makes the best and easiest-cutting lubricant obtainable for tapping in machine steel.—Contributed by Joe V. Romig, Allentown, Pa.

Arm Flash Lamp for Repairmen

In my work at night I have often felt the need of a helper to hold the flash lamp while making a repair. To use the ordinary flash lamp is very difficult when the occasion requires quick action. Having no helper, I contrived to overcome the trouble by placing the flash lamp on my left arm; the front near my wrist, and the back close to my elbow. With two small bands of copper wire fastened around each end and over my arm I can hold the light permanently in instant readiness. In this manner I have the use of both hands and can throw the light on any object at will while I remedy or find the trouble.—Contributed by Max J. James, Collinsville, Okla.

Adjustable Store Shelving

Retail stores, where the commodities are small and many times kept in small boxes or packages like groceries and hardware, can be arranged so that the shelving is adjustable to take any new-size package without the waste of space, as shown in the illustration. The stiles are scored with saw cuts at intervals of 1 or 2 in., and where necessary, they can be spaced every ½ in. The shelving consists of galvanized metal of about No. 16 gauge. By inserting the shelves in the proper saw cuts, the sizes of the various compartments can be adjusted to suit the various packages to be stored in them.

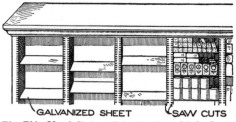

GALVANIZED SHEET   SAW CUTS

The Thin Metal Shelves Take Up Very Little Space between the Packages

This eliminates the waste space and permits a great deal of material to be stored in a small space.—Contributed by J. J. O'Brien, Buffalo, N. Y.

To Make a Curved Rack for a Lever

In building an experimental device, a lever was to be set in different positions much as a brake is set on an

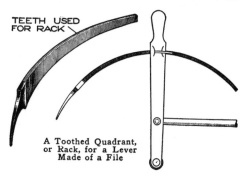

TEETH USED FOR RACK

A Toothed Quadrant, or Rack, for a Lever Made of a File

automobile with a dog engaging a toothed rack or quadrant, only in this case the teeth were to be on the side of the rack. This seemed rather expensive to make, as the rack had to be 12 in. long with approximately 20 teeth to the inch.

The method adopted was to heat a 14-in. file and bend it to the desired curve. This made a rack already cut on the edge with material of the best quality, and the entire cost was the price of the file. In bending, the teeth of the file assumed a position almost radial, as required. With the tang cut off it made an ideal quadrant.

Spikes on Shoes for Roof Workers

A person working on a shingle roof is much safer—in fact he can walk all over a roof of ordinary pitch without fear—with a three-penny shingle, or lath, nail driven through each edge of the shoe soles just outside of the uppers, and one slantingly through each side of the heels. The points should stick through about $\frac{3}{32}$ in., or far enough to stick into the shingles without bending. When through working on the roof, the nails can be withdrawn without injury to the shoes.—Contributed by L. M. Hodge, Wilmington, California.

❁Do not use a fine file on babbitt metal or lead.

A Wood Gouge

A good emergency gouge can be made from a
piece of bicycle tubing, as shown in the sketch. Of course, it will not have the temper of the real gouge, but it will hold the edge long enough to serve in an emergency case. It is only necessary to fit on a wood handle to make it quite convenient for use.

Putting in Water or Lubricator Glasses Easily

When putting in a new water or lubricator glass it is a very difficult job to get the glass through the rubber packing. To make this easy, simply give the glass and rubber packing a coat of machine oil. No matter how tight the packing fits, the glass will slide easily into place. This will prevent breaking many glasses when putting them in the fittings.—Contributed by John P. Kolar, Ithaca, N. Y.

A Bottle Washer

A cheap bottle and glass washer for soda fountains and bars can be made as illustrated. A cast-iron base is
made with a tapered hole, into which is driven the end of the brush handle. This construction permits easy removal of the brush when it is worn out. The bottom of the base is formed cupping and a rubber flap is fastened in it with a screw. With the hollow base and the rubber flap, the washer can be set on the pan of the washing rack, and the cup-shaped rubber will produce a suction that will hold it in place without any fastening, so that glasses and bottles can be washed without any trouble of disturbing it. The rubber will last for some time and the iron base is indestructible, while the brush may be easily renewed.

Tool to Hold Joint Edges while Welding

In welding the seams of heavy shells, a helper is usually necessary to hold the seams level and apart. The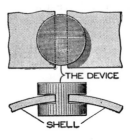
helper uses chisel bars for this purpose and he must be on the job while the seams are being welded. A small and simple device, shown in the sketch, saves the time of the helper. It holds the seam apart and level and all the welder has to do is to hammer it back as the welding is advanced.

The device is very simple in construction and in operation. It is made of a 4-in. cold-rolled steel bar, about 3 in. long. Slots are milled, as shown, leaving a strip of metal along its diameter. The slots are made just large enough so that it can be easily slipped on the end of the shell. These slots keep the seams from twisting and hold them level. The strip of metal between the slots holds the seam apart. —Contributed by George Marks, York, Pennsylvania.

How to Preserve Reference Tables

Reference tables are very convenient to use, but they soon become dirty and torn in constant use. This may be prevented by dipping them in lacquer. Use a shallow tray, place the lacquer in it and lay in the prints, then remove and hang them up to dry. This makes the paper dirt-proof and also toughens it.

Cause of Water-Tank Explosion

Almost all tanks supplying water to railway engines are so located that they are filled by gravity. For this reason all tanks are similarly built, that is, with a roof, and made practically air-tight with the exception of a vent in the shape of an overflow pipe. In one instance, one of these tanks was filled with the aid of a power pump. During a cold snap the overflow pipe became frozen and very little space was left for the air to escape. The pump was started and a burst tank was the result.

Turning a Ball in a Milling Machine

To turn a ball perfectly round is a very difficult job for any machinist using a lathe, unless the lathe is fitted with a special attachment designed for the purpose. Few machinists know that the job may be easily and accurately done in a milling machine without any special fixtures except to make a simple tool to fit the fly cutter head.

Such a tool is made from a bar of square steel having the proper dimensions to fit the hole in the head, by bending a portion at right angles to the main body to make a cutting tool, as shown. Place the material in the centers so that it is held by the lugs A. The tool is revolved in the regular way and the ball slowly fed around in the direction of the arrow.

A perfect ball can be turned, excepting the center lugs A, which can be easily finished off by hand. The lugs can be turned down very small by the same tool after finishing the other part

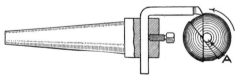

Simple Tool for the Fly Cutter Head of a Milling Machine to Turn Balls

of the surface. It will be readily seen that a perfect ball can be easily turned by this method —Contributed by J. A. Brearley, Washington, D. C.

Sprag for an Automobile Truck

Considerable trouble was encountered by the owner of an automobile delivery truck, in an extremely hilly

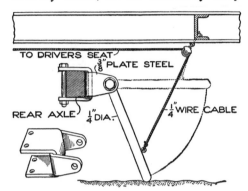

Sprag Attached to the Rear End of an Automobile Truck for Relieving the Brakes

country, in keeping the truck stopped without locking the brakes. This caused a great deal of wear and expense, and some person suggested that a sprag should be installed. The sketch shows the manner in which it was attached. The sprag rod was made of a piece of 1¼-in. cold-rolled steel, and was hinged at its upper end on a U-shaped bracket. The rise and fall of the sprag was controlled by the driver at the front by means of a foot button and cable.

To Blacken Brass

Brass having surfaces that require a dead black can be treated as follows with good results: Heat the brass over a fire that is clear, such as charcoal, and do not allow the sparks to come in contact with it, or else red spots will appear. When the metal becomes slightly red, dip it in nitric acid, then heat again, but not to a red heat. Give the surface a good rubbing with a bristle brush, and clean with a cloth slightly greasy. A fairly permanent dead black will be the result.

❡When putting up a line or jackshaft, be sure to make a liberal allowance for expansion and contraction.

An Emergency "Woodruff" Key

While driving over some very rough country in a car, I had the misfortune

to shear off the "Woodruff" key in the drive pinion. Being 30 miles from home, this placed me in a difficult position. In looking through the tools in my kit, trying to think of some remedy, my eyes fell on an open-end wrench, and the shape of one of its jaws gave the idea of making a key, which I proceeded to do by cutting it off on the dotted line. It happened to be the right size and a good fit.—Contributed by Ellis Johnson, Maple Creek, Sask.

A Grind Finish on Rivet Heads Made with a Hammer

A quantity of brass parts were to be put together as shown in the sketch, the shouldered ends of the rods passing through the drilled bars and being headed over. A hammered finish was

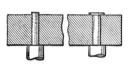

prohibited, and there was not money enough in the job to rivet and then finish with a set, or to do any hand-finishing after the hammering had been done.

To do the work quickly and make it look neat, a piece of steel was drilled the size of the rods, to be used for a riveting block. The face of a hammer was then ground on a 36-grain emery wheel just enough to leave the marks of the wheel on the metal. This hammer was then used for riveting. When finishing the rivet head, the final heavy blow was made with the ground face so as to obliterate all other marks and leave the imprint of the ground surface. The finished rivet head gave the appearance of a ground surface and proved highly satisfactory.

An Automobile Oiler

The sketch shows an oiling device for use in lubricating general machine bearings which is far superior to any methods generally employed. The oiler cannot fail through any of the common causes, and dirt only gives a better seating for the ball valve. It is readily adjusted, by turning the cup in or out of the pillow block, to flow any desired quantity of oil.

In construction, the bushing is recessed, as shown, the recess size depending on the shaft size. About 1/8

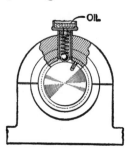

in. square will be suitable for shafts up to 4 in. in diameter. Traveling in this recess is a slotted headless screw turned tightly into to a tapped hole in the shaft.

The ball in the cup stem does not quite touch the shaft and is held firmly in its seat by means of a coil spring, as shown. In operation, the revolving shaft carries the screw around in the groove, the screw at each revolution coming in contact with the ball valve and raising it from its seat so that a quantity of oil flows onto the shaft. When the screw has passed the ball, the latter is then reseated by the spring. The spring is held in place by a bushing tapped into the stem of the oil cup and through a hole in which the oil flows. As the oil reaches the shaft, it is carried lengthways by means of a longitudinal groove.

When it becomes necessary to remove the shaft, or its bushing, the oil cup is removed first; then the shaft is turned until the screw comes directly under the oil hole, where it is easily removed with a screwdriver.—Contributed by J. B. Murphy, Plainfield, New Jersey.

¶Pulleys should be placed far enough apart on a shaft so that the belts will drop between them.

To Preserve Linoleum

When oilcloth or linoleum is first laid, apply a coating of varnish or shellac, and it will last much longer. In scrubbing the surface of these materials the color and design are worn away, as well as by the usual wear of walking on them, but the coat of varnish forms a protection and preserves the colors. It is only necessary to apply a coat of varnish from time to time to keep them in good condition. —Contributed by Leslie E. Turner, New York, N. Y.

Makeshift Lamp Standard

The ability to improvise necessary apparatus at a moment's notice is no small asset to the practical mechanic. I recently observed a mechanic working under difficulties, who was suddenly confronted by the necessity for an additional light. He immediately attached the extension cord to the head

An Electric Lamp Standard Made of a Hammer and a Large Clamp

of a hammer, fastened the hammer in a large screw clamp, and supported the light as shown, all with complete satisfaction.—Contributed by John D. Adams, Phoenix, Ariz.

Centering Long Bars in a Lathe

The illustration shows a very simple form of tool for centering long bars in a lathe. The tool is set in the tool post of the lathe so that the bottom of the V-shaped part is on the same plane as the center of the lathe. In centering both ends of a bar, say, 2 ft. long, one end is gripped in the chuck while the

other is set in the V-shaped notch of the tool. When the lathe is started, it only requires a slight adjustment of the tool, in or out, to make the end of

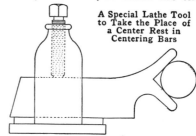

A Special Lathe Tool to Take the Place of a Center Rest in Centering Bars

the bar run perfectly true. The center drill is held in the tailstock and is fed toward the end of the work. If there is a number of bars of the same size to be centered, it is only necessary to leave the tool set, and the bars can be centered in a great deal less time than if a center rest were used.—Contributed by Charles Homewood, Waterloo, Iowa.

Marking Guide Lines for Letters on Drawings

A very simple and handy tool for the draftsman is shown in the sketch. Its use is for laying out guide lines for dimension figures, notes, etc., on drawings. The construction and use of this tool is self-evident. The pointed end is pressed on the paper and the imprint makes the guide points, correctly spaced for the three lines. In general practice these lines are drawn by guess, but it is just as easy to set them off right and have all

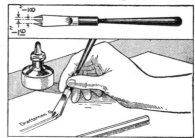

Marker for Laying Out Guide Lines to Make Letters and Dimension Figures Uniform on Drawings

letters uniform on all drawings. It is especially useful for making tables or notes where several lines are required.

A Universal Emery-Wheel Dresser

The tool shown in the illustration is designed for the shaping, dressing, and duplicating of forms in the various

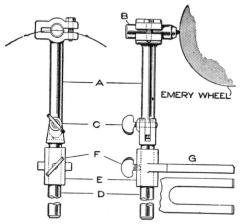

Dresser Adaptable for the Tool Room in Shaping Emery Wheels to Special Forms

shapes and sizes on grinding wheels used in a tool room. A wheel having been formed to a special shape or angle, may be dressed as often as necessary, and the form accurately preserved.

The main arm A carries the black-diamond holder B at its upper extremity, the lower end being fitted into a hinge joint, C, on the vertical adjusting rod D. A wing screw is used on the hinge joint so that it can be clamped in any position desired. The bracket E holds the vertical rod D with the wing screw F, and has a clamping arm, G, for attaching it to any part of the table, or grinder head.

The wing screw F holds the diamond at the desired height; the arm A and the vertical adjusting rod D, of course, are free to turn in the main bracket E, and when turned to the desired position the screw is set to hold it. The diamond is then set, and the arm A moved in the direction of the curved line by hand, the rear of the diamond holder being used as a handle.

When the diamond has been passed back and forth across the face of the wheel a sufficient number of times, the

dresser is removed without changing the screw F, and if the position is marked on the dresser, it can be replaced and the wheel redressed any number of times without changing its form in the least.

Driving a Motorcycle without a Carburetor

While out riding over a rough mountain road I took a tumble in a deep rut with my single-cylinder motorcycle. After righting myself and the machine, I discovered that the carburetor was a wreck, having come in contact with a rock in the roadway. To push a motorcycle is a hard and thankless job at the best, and on a very hot day it is doubly so, therefore I proceeded to get out of my predicament in the best way possible.

What was left of the carburetor was removed, also the hood covering the intake valve. Then I bent the gasoline-feed pipe until the end projected slightly over the end of the valve housing. Opening the needle valve in the tank, a small stream of gasoline was allowed to trickle over the intake valve, and when the motor was turned over, it started up quickly. By adjusting the needle valve in the fuel-supply line I managed to get a fairly good mixture. The engine ran about the same as if the carburetor had been intact and the throttle wide open. The 12-mile trip home was made without trouble, although I was forced to use the magnet cut-out occasionally to slow the machine down around corners.—Contributed by J. Walter Briggs, Stanfordville, N. Y.

An Alloy for Pattern Letters and Figures

A good alloy for casting pattern letters and figures, and similar small parts, in brass, iron, or plaster molds, is made of lead, 70 parts, and 15 parts each of antimony and bismuth. To make perfect work the molds should be quite hot.

Shop Notes

Substitute for Dynamo Oil

One night I found that I had so little dynamo oil left that a burned-out bearing would be the result if the machine were run much longer. A diligent search was of no avail, and nothing but some kerosene could be found. In the medicine chest there was a large bottle of vaseline. Taking quite a bit of this, I placed it in a tin cup and heated it till it melted, then poured some of the kerosene in it and allowed it to cool. In cooling it hardened, and by adding more kerosene, I made it the consistency of thick cream. The oil cups were filled with this grease, and it gave good results.—Contributed by E. A. Gardener, Rochester, N. Y.

A Swamp Shoe

The frame is made of narrow strips of wood, the center piece being somewhat wider than the others, or a trifle wider than a shoe sole, to which a toe strap is attached. The frame is then covered on the under side with sheet metal. Such a device is a boon to duck hunters

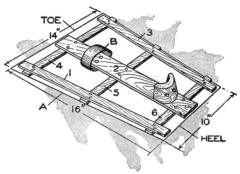

The Shoe Is Similar to a Snowshoe, and is Used to Walk in Swamps

and others that may need to travel over swamp land.—Contributed by J. C. Noble, Toronto, Can.

A Counterfeit-Coin Detector

Genuine coins will not break and are exceedingly hard to bend. Owing to this characteristic composition it is

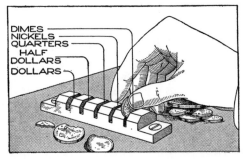

A Genuine Coin will Not Break, and It Is Exceedingly Hard to Bend

easy to provide a detector to test out the coins that appear to be counterfeit. Such a detector can be made of a piece of brass, 4 in. long and ⅝ in. square. Cut off at each end a piece, ½ in. long by ⅜ in., as shown, and drill holes for screws to fasten it to a desk or other convenient place. Cut five slots about ½ in. apart, ⅜ in. deep and a trifle wider than the coins, for a nickel, dime, quarter, half, and a dollar. To use, insert the coin in the proper slot and press forward. If the coin is a counterfeit it will easily bend or snap in two.—Contributed by Maurice Baudier, New Orleans, La.

To Open Ignition Circuit Automatically When Gas Engine Stops

Considerable difficulty is experienced in the operation of gas engines with a make-and-break ignition circuit in having a run-down or discharged battery caused by the engine stopping where the sparking contacts are touching and the attendant failing to open the battery circuit. It is the object of the automatic device described to prevent such a thing happening, and its operation, in brief, is as follows: The wiring

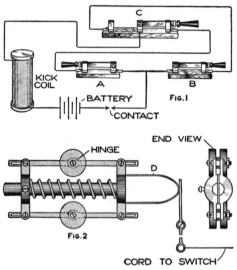

A Governor to Operate Switches in an Ignition Circuit When a Gas Engine Stops

of the ignition circuit is shown diagrammatically in Fig. 1. The two switches A and B are single-pole pull switches; that is, they are operated by pulling a small chain or cord, alternate pulls opening and closing the circuit. The switch C is a single-blade, double-throw type.

A special governor, similar to the one shown in Fig. 2, serves to operate the two switches A and B, Fig. 1. When the governor is revolving, the V-shaped piece D moves to the left and thus loosens the tension on the cord connected to the switches. When the engine stops the switches are both operated, so that if one was originally closed and the other open, the switch C will need be changed in order to close the ignition circuit again. The construction of the governor is not given in detail on account of the wide variation in requirements, but the one illustrated will work quite satisfactorily if properly constructed.

⟨The flanges, or washers, used on an emery-wheel arbor should have a slight concave to their face.

Running Motorcycle with Acetylene Gas

Gas in tanks used for lighting purposes on motorcycles can be used to advantage, in cases of emergency, to run the motor when the gasoline gives out. A piece of ¼-in. rubber hose, such as is used for connecting up gas lamps, should be carried in the tool kit, a piece about 3 ft. long being sufficient. When it is necessary to use the gas from the tank for running the engine, disconnect the gasoline-feed pipe from the carburetor and attach the rubber hose from the lighting tank. Remove the small needle valve which is attached to the float to give the gas a free passage. It will be necessary to alter the air adjustment slightly.—Contributed by A. Dane, Pottstown, Pennsylvania.

Depth Gauge to Measure Pits in Boiler Plates

In the inspection of boilers for conditions of sheets, the discovery of pitted portions is not uncommon. In reports of boiler conditions, the depths of such pits must be exactly recorded. In making many of these report sketches, one inspector makes use of a very handy pocket depth gauge with which it is possible to ascertain quickly the depth of the sheet to which the metal has been corroded. The body of the gauge is simply a piece of ½-in. round steel, about ¾ in. long. The thumbscrew and needle attachment are easily fitted in drilled holes. The il-

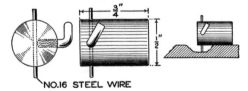

Depth Gauge Made of a Small Rod and Wire to Measure Pits in Boiler Plates

lustration of the gauge shows its application clearly.

Such measurements can be taken with a scale and a piece of wire, but wire is not always easy to find, and a long scale cannot be used as a straightedge in many places. The gauge is something easily carried in the pocket, and can be used in almost any place on a boiler where a sheet pit is liable to occur.—Contributed by F. W. Bentley, Missouri Valley, Iowa.

To Empty a Barrel Gradually

The sketch shows a labor-saving method of emptying a barrel of powdered, or granular, material where the emptying is to be done slowly. Instead of taking out the material by scoopfuls in order to fill it gradually into a machine hopper, for instance, the workman quickly upends the headless barrel and works it over toward the edge of the platform and the material flows to the hopper. As the barrel settles down it must be rocked

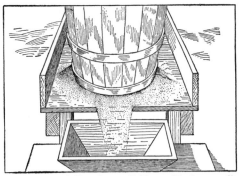

An Overturned Barrel on a Table, or Platform, will Permit Its Contents to Run Out Slowly

slightly so as to keep the material flowing. When empty, there is a small amount on the platform to be scooped into the hopper.—Contributed by J. J. O'Brien, Buffalo, N. Y.

Lawn Cleaner and Sprinkler

Caretakers of a large acreage surrounding a capitol building found it difficult to keep the lawn clear of leaves that fall from the large elm trees in autumn with the use of the ordinary hand rake. One of the men devised a special apparatus to serve as a rake and sprinkler combined. This is shown in the illustration and consists of an iron-pipe nozzle bent to direct the stream of

water parallel with the ground. The jet of water drives the leaves ahead of it and clears an acre in a short time,

The Hoze Nozzle Serves a Double Purpose, That of Sprinkling and Removing the Leaves

leaving the lawn clean and well sprinkled.—Contributed by B. O. Darrow, Sacramento, Cal.

Razor Strop Made of an Old Leather Belt

Owing to the continual stretching and smoothing over the pulley face, a section of an old leather belt makes an excellent razor strop. Soak it in oil for a time and remove the grit, then equip it with a metal tip, fastened with small rivets and drilled with a hole for slipping on a swivel snap. This snap

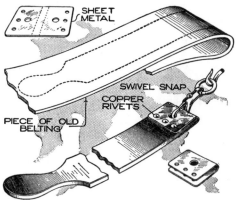

A Piece of Old Leather Belt Fitted Up for Use as a Razor Strop

makes it reversible. Rub polishing rouge on the rough side for putting on the edge, and leave the smooth side as it is for finishing.

Fitting Keys to Non-Take-Apart Cylinder Locks

With a hacksaw, cut the metal on the line A down to the rim, and bend the small strip back, as shown by the dotted lines. This will expose the plunger-pin holes. Remove the springs and plunger pins, then the cylinder plug can be easily removed. A key can be fitted by using the same pins and springs. In assembling, be sure that the strip of metal, which holds the pins and springs in place, is bent back in its original position and soldered. A tumbler-pin cylinder lock is burglar-proof and cannot be picked or operated by a skeleton key.—Contributed by William J. Tolson, Lyons, Iowa.

Tire Economy

Many old tire shoes are sold for old rubber while they still have much service in them, and some owners, who are not economical, buy protectors when an old tire could be used for the same purpose. Tires generally blow out or wear out on the tread, or road surface, long before the sides show the slightest abrasion.

If the old tire, about to be sold for junk, is cut all around, as shown in the sketch, to remove the bead, it forms an outer protector, or cover, that will protect some tire already on the car which is showing signs of failure in the near future. By placing a bad spot of the cover on a good section of the tire two weak places will not be in line. Two such old tires put together will last a considerable length of time.

To apply the cover, deflate the tire or remove it from the rim altogether. The latter is the easiest way, even though two persons are required and a couple of tire tools. Anyone who has applied such a cover will have no doubt of its staying on when inflated.

Distributing Oil to Wide Milling Cutters

When using a wide cutter on a milling machine, the ordinary single spout from the oil bucket directs the oil to only one place on the cutter, frequently leaving the other parts without sufficient lubrication. To overcome this, an oil distributor can be made from a piece of small tubing, with holes drilled for the desired number of spouts. One hole should be provided in the center to admit the spout of the oil receptacle. The ends of the tube are plugged up with corks, or wood, and the device is held in place by a wire fastened to each of its ends, and suspended from the nozzle.—Contributed by G. Jaques, Chicago, Ill.

How to Mix Lime Mortar

In mixing mortar a stronger batter will be had by adding some lime to the water used for making the mixture. A mixture consisting of 3 parts of fine sand, 4 parts of coarse sand, 1 part of old slaked lime, and some water, will make a good mortar. The very best, however, is made when the lime has been slaked and buried in the ground for some weeks, or even months. The mixed mortar can be buried, and it will prove fully as strong as cement, besides being like butter in applying it on the surface. Freshly made mortar is short and hard to apply.—Contributed by A. Kelly, Malvern, Pa.

Pattern and Core Box for a Small Air Chamber

Small air chambers of a form similar to the one illustrated in Fig. 1 are quickly and easily made if the half pieces are glued up solid. Two pieces of 2-in. stock are used for each half pattern.

The stock is prepared for the lathe in the usual way by jointing the halves and inserting the dowels. Enough extra stock is allowed at each end for the screws that are to hold the halves together. In Fig. 2 is shown the piece for the body of the chamber, all prepared for turning. It will be noticed that the ends have been cut on the band saw to the radii. These should be about ⅛ in., full, of the finished size on each end.

The largest diameter is first turned to size, then the neck, or smaller diame-

crown end is then finished to templet. This templet is made to just clear the end spud, and the lines for the fillet and

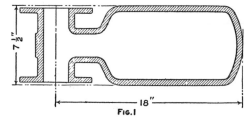

Drawing of an Air Chamber from Which a Pattern-maker Forms a Pattern and a Core Box

the neck end should be laid out on it, as it is used for finishing both ends.

The cross branch on the end is made with the flanges gained or checked into the prints. In Fig. 3 is shown the method of connecting or fastening the two parts with a lap joint. The lap is cut into the neck about ¾ in. in thick-

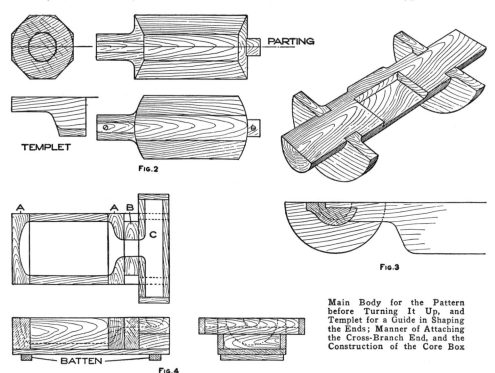

Main Body for the Pattern before Turning It Up, and Templet for a Guide in Shaping the Ends; Manner of Attaching the Cross-Branch End, and the Construction of the Core Box

ter, is finished. The rest is then moved to the top, or crown, end, and the spud on the end with the screw in it is turned to, say, 2 in. in diameter. The

ness, and a recess is routed out of the cross branch to receive it. This makes a very strong joint, and when fastened with glue and screws, it is not apt to become loose with the rapping in the mold.

The core box, Fig. 4, is made up of five pieces, fastened to a bottom board. The pieces marked A are turned in halves on a faceplate, B and C are worked out with the core-box plane. The piece B is fastened with glue and screws to one of the pieces marked A, and the large round corner is worked off to a templet. Two pieces of stock are fastened to the bottom board to raise the piece C to the same level as the other pieces.—Contributed by J. A. Shelly, Brooklyn, N. Y.

Guide for Longitudinal Lathe Feed

An ordinary 12-in. flexible-steel scale fastened to the bed of a lathe makes a good guide for the longitudinal feed.

Steel Scale Fastened to a Lathe Bed, to Provide a Guide for the Longitudinal Feed

This is a very handy device for roughing out work and is easily applied. In my case, I have placed the scale on the front of the bed, and the carriage passes over it, but it can be placed on top of the bed if desired.—Contributed by A. E. Holiday, Union City, Conn.

Metallic Effect on Clockface Decorations

In repainting the ornaments on an old clockface, I found that the metallic luster shining through the color had been secured by first laying a piece of metal leaf, silver or gold, on the surface and in the exact shape of the ornament. In the case mentioned it was a sea shell. The desired effect was secured by glazing it lightly or heavily with the proper colors.

To Determine the Coloring Matter of a Typewriter Ribbon

There are two kinds of typewriter ribbon, one that gives an indelible record and one that does not. The color used for the former has a true carbon base, while the latter is made with aniline colors. To distinguish the two, soak a corner, or piece, of the ribbon in very hot alcohol, scrape off a little of the coloring matter and smear it on a piece of white blotting paper. The smear will widen on the blotting paper as the alcohol is soaked up by it, and if this spot is colored all the way to the edge, the color used is aniline, that is, the ribbon is of the cheaper grade that does not produce an indelible record, while, if the size of the original smear is simply surrounded by an uncolored edge of wet, it is a sure sign that the ribbon is made with genuine carbon color. The reason is that aniline black is dissolved by the alcohol, while true carbon black is not.

Lubricating Tappets on an Automobile Engine

The existence of friction in a gasoline engine, or, in fact, any machine, necessarily means a loss of power, particularly at such an important point as the valve tappet. In order to minimize the friction at this point it is well to drill four reasonably large holes in the tappet guide, as shown in the

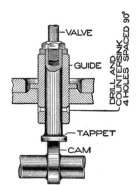

sketch. This will allow the lubricating oil in the crank case to find its way more readily to the tappets. It is well to slightly countersink these holes for the purpose of allowing the oil to reach the inside of the guide readily.

Making a Special-Shaped Gas Flame

Anyone who has attempted to temper small tools, or bend pieces of steel, knows how difficult it is to get a uniform heat without overheating. The most satisfactory solution is to make a special gas stove in the manner illustrated, which will not require much time in the construction. Cut out a small block of wood, 1 in. thick, and hollow out a small channel of the desired shape with a knife. Bore a ¼-in. hole in one end and connect the channel by means of a second hole drilled in a vertical direction. Force a short piece of brass tubing into the end hole for the gas connection, and then cut out a piece of tin or sheet metal large enough to cover the top. Lay out the desired curve on this in a position directly over the curved channel in the block. Prick, or drill, a series of pin-

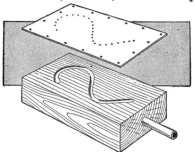

A Gas Stove That Produces a Special-Shaped Flame to Temper Pieces of Bent Steel

holes in the metal along the curved line, making the holes about ¼ in. apart, and then tack it firmly to the block. If the gas can be arranged to pick up a little air as it passes into the stove, in the same manner as this is done in the ordinary gas range, the flame will be free from carbon.—Contributed by John D. Adams, Phoenix, Arizona.

Adjustable Fastener for Celluloid Eye Shade

The head strap of a celluloid eye shade is usually held with a brass paper fastener which often breaks when no fasteners are at hand. A much better way is to use a very small bone or com-

position collar button secured with an elastic rubber washer slipped over the

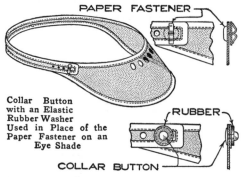

Collar Button with an Elastic Rubber Washer Used in Place of the Paper Fastener on an Eye Shade

head. This method admits quick adjustment of the shade and is not at all clumsy.

Tool Holder for Machining Blanking Dies

The illustration shows a holder and tools especially designed for use in machining blanking dies. The holder can be adjusted to accommodate the return stroke of the shaper and can be used to get any desired shape by forging the proper tools.

The holder A is held firmly to the swivel block B by means of a clamping screw, C. The cutting tool D passes through the hole E where it is clamped with the screw F. Various tools, like those shown at G, can be forged to meet requirements. The tools are forged from ⅜-in. drill rod, and the screw C

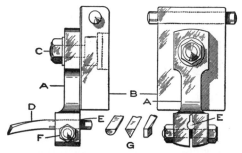

Adjustable Tool Holder Attached to the Shaper Head Block for Shaping Blanking Dies

and holder A made of machine steel. The screw F is a stock-size, ⅜-16, cap screw with a nut.—Contributed by George F. Kuhne, E. Rutherford, N. J.

Lifting Springs for Tool-Clamp Plates

The tool holder, or clamp plates, on heavy lathes cause considerable trouble by dropping down when the heavy tool

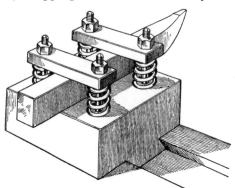

The Coil Springs Placed on the Bolts under the Plates Keep Them Up

is drawn out for sharpening or change of cutting edge. The sketch shows how a number of comparatively heavy steel-wire springs can be utilized to raise the strips free of the tool and hold them up out of the way as soon as the nuts are loosened. Much loss of time and injury to fingers will be avoided by the springs on any tool-holding arrangement of this kind.

Preventing Flywheel from Breaking Fastening Bolts

It happens quite frequently that the bolts connecting the flywheel to the crankshaft flange shear off, due to their carrying an excessive strain. To prevent trouble of this nature, I inserted 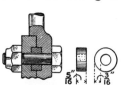 a small drive collar on each alternate bolt of the six which were used. The flywheel and crankshaft were counterbored, and the three collars were securely pressed into them when the bolt nuts were tightened up. In this manner the three collars did the greatest part of the work, and therefore the bolts were relieved to a great extent.—Contributed by Adolph Kline, New York City.

An Electric Remote-Control Switch

The remote-control switch described will be found very serviceable when it is desired to control electrical circuits from one or more points that may be quite a distance apart, or that may be in different buildings, or on different floors of the same building. The switch mechanism consists of two electromagnets, each operating a separate armature, and so connected that they may be energized independently by merely pressing one of two push buttons located at the points from which it is desired to control the switch. One of these magnets is called a closing magnet, because its armature, when drawn up, closes the main electrical circuit, and the other is called the opening magnet, because the electrical switch is opened when its armature is drawn up. A sketch from which the electrical and mechanical operation of the switch may be understood is shown in Fig. 1. The armatures of both magnets are pivoted at one end, and a spring is attached to each at the hinge which tends to hold them away from their respective cores. A V-shaped piece of metal, A, is attached to the free end of the armature of the closing magnet, which serves to connect the two springs B and C when the armature is drawn up against the core of the magnet. The two springs B and C form the terminals of the electric circuit which the switch is to control. A specially shaped piece of metal, D, is fastened to the free end of the armature of the opening magnet, which serves as a double latch for the armature of the closing magnet. If the armature of the opening magnet is drawn up, the armature of the closing magnet will move under the action of the spring away from its core until the free end strikes the end of the piece D, and the connection between the springs B and C will be broken. When the armature of the closing magnet is drawn over against its core, its free end moves beyond the bend in the piece D, the armature of the opening magnet moves by the spring away from its core, and the armature of the closing magnet is held in its energizing position even though there is no current through the winding of the magnet. The springs B and C then remain in electrical connection until the armature of the opening magnet is drawn up by sending a current through the winding of the magnet.

The current operating the magnets may be furnished by several dry cells connected in a common wire so that the same cells serve for both magnets. The connections of the pairs of push buttons are as shown, and there may be as many combinations as desired. One of the great advantages of the switch is the ease with which the control circuits may be installed, no greater precautions being required than in the ordinary bell circuit. The pair of push buttons located at any point may be painted, one white and the other black, which will serve as an indication for the control of the magnets, the dark one representing an open circuit and the light one the closed circuit.

The construction of the switch is as follows: Two spools are made with iron cores, and heads, or ends, of thin fiber insulation, similar in form and dimensions to the one shown in Fig. 2. One end of each of these spools is tapped to accommodate a ⅛-in. machine screw. Wind each of these spools full of No. 26 gauge cotton-covered copper wire, and bring the ends out through the small holes drilled in the fiber ends. A layer of suitable insulating material

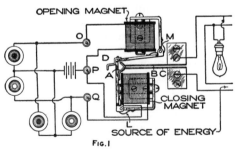

OPENING MAGNET

CLOSING MAGNET

SOURCE OF ENERGY

FIG. 1

Diagrammatic Arrangement of the Opening and Closing Magnets to Control a Current at a Distance

should be placed outside of each of these spools so as to provide a good mechanical protection. Cut from sheet iron, 1/16

in. thick, two pieces, as shown in Fig. 3. These pieces are to form the support for the coils and the armatures, and at the same time serve to complete the

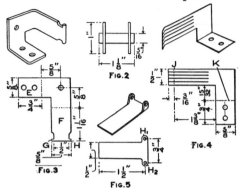

FIG. 2

FIG. 4

FIG. 3

FIG. 5

Details of the Parts for Constructing the Switch to be Operated on a Battery Circuit

magnetic circuits of the coils and thus increase their pulling force on the armatures. In each of these pieces three ⅛-in. holes are drilled, as shown, and the projections E and F bent up along the dotted lines until they are at right angles to the main part of the piece. The two small projections G and H are to form part of the hinge for the armature, and they should be filed round to make pins 1/16 in. in diameter.

The two springs indicated by B and C, in Fig. 1, are made from sheet brass, about 1/64 in. in thickness and cut to the shape shown in Fig. 4. Drill two holes in each piece, ⅛ in. in diameter, for use in mounting them on a base. There are four slots cut in each piece to form five narrow springs. The ends of these springs to the left of the dotted line J are bent up on one piece, and those on the other piece are bent down, until they are at an angle of 45 deg. to the main part of each piece. The extension below the dotted line K is bent up and down, respectively, for the two pieces.

The armatures should be cut from sheet iron, about 1/32 in. thick, to the form shown in Fig. 5. The projections are drilled with a 1/16-in. drill. Before completing the armatures the coils and springs B and C must be mounted on a suitable base, such as a piece of slate. The location of the parts is shown in

Fig. 1. A thin piece of brass, ⅝ in. long and ¼ in. wide, is cut and bent to the shape shown at A. This piece is attached to the end of the armature of the closing magnet, but is insulated from it. A very light spring should be attached to the ends of each of the supports for the armatures, as shown at L and M. The strength and shape of these springs should be such that they will hold the armature away from the core of the magnets, regardless of the position in which the switch may be placed. The armature is then mounted in position by bending the two extensions over at right angles to the main part so that they will fit on the two projections G and H shown in Fig. 3.

Rivet a thin piece of sheet brass to the free end of the armature of the opening magnet. This piece is about ¾ in. long and ⅛ in. wide. The armature of the opening magnet is fastened in place by bending the two extensions over as in the case of the armature of the closing magnet. The opening magnet is mounted in place on the base so that its armature and the piece of brass attached connect as previously described.

The three small terminals O, P, and Q are mounted on the base and the windings connected to them as indicated. The small bolts used in mounting the springs B and C may serve as terminals for the circuit which the switch is to control. A suitable covering, preferably of metal, should be made and fastened in position over the switch in such a manner that it may be easily removed. Holes are drilled through the base near the connecting terminals of the switch, through which the wire may pass and thus not interfere with the cover in any way. Two additional holes are drilled through the base, in a suitable place, through which the mounting screws, or bolts, for the switch may pass.

Tool to Remove Stock between Drilled Holes in Dies

In making a die it is often necessary to remove a part of the metal by drilling holes close together on the line of separation, then chiseling out the metal between the holes. The tool illustrated is quite convenient for removing this metal. It is made of tool steel with the body a sliding fit in the holes drilled; then a side cutter is formed to extend into the next hole with a cutting edge on one end. It is only necessary to drive the tool through the holes.—Contributed by Chas. C. Davies, Washington, D. C.

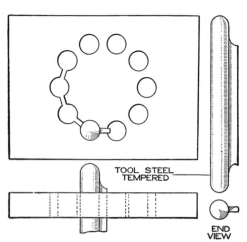

TOOL STEEL TEMPERED

END VIEW

The Extending Part on the Side of the Tool Removes the Metal between the Holes

The Lost Art of Hardening Copper

The hardening of copper by the ancients has never been proven, although many statements have been made to that effect. The supposedly hardened copper implements are made merely of alloys of copper and tin. Often the lost art of hardening copper is bewailed as a real loss to the people of today, but the uses to which hardened copper could be put are not many. Its use for tools is only a myth, for with the price of copper many times that of steel no one would buy the former even if it were as durable. Copper and brass are made much harder, or stiffer, by drawing, pressing, and hammering. Rods, bars, and wire are regularly listed as "soft" and "hard." The term hard, for copper, does not imply a quality to be compared with similarly designated products of the iron and steel trade.

Quite frequently copper may be found that is really hard, so hard that it cannot be filed. In overhauling the canopy switches of trolley-car switches of the jackknife type the contact members have been found to be as hard as glass, sometimes for a length of 1 in. These switches are located over the motorman's head and in conjunction with fuses were, and are still, used on the older-type cars, and smaller ones for the same combined purposes as the circuit breakers with which all modern trolley cars are equipped. Seemingly, the only way to account for the hardened area of the contacts is that the cars had been run with the switches barely closed and that continued arcing had set up a fusion that had produced this result. In all of the cases noted, the blades had not gone so far as to interfere with the working of the switches. In no case had the switches been taken out solely for repairs to them.

Repairing a Torque Rod on an Automobile

A tubular torque rod on an automobile was broken as shown in the sketch. It was repaired as follows: Both sections of the broken rod were removed, and a piece of round drill rod was forced part way into the large portion A, after which an additional piece of tubing, B, was forced over the torque rod on the outside. The other portion

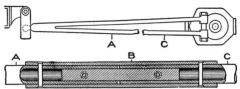

Torque Rod of an Automobile Repaired with a Rod and Tube Riveted in Place

of the torque rod C was then forced into position, and the joint made permanent with four rivets.

The Care of Lettering Brushes

Lettering brushes after being used should be cleaned out and wrapped with paper to keep the hairs straight. Many

Wrapping a Paintbrush without the Use of a String, to Keep the Hairs Straight

painters, when out of a job, wrap the brushes in paper and put them in a pail of oil, the paper keeping the hair straight, and the oil preventing them from hardening. The manner of wrapping the brushes without the use of a string or rubber band is shown in the illustration.—Contributed by Wm. A. Temple, Fort Dodge, Iowa.

Sealing a Box Cover Fastened with Screws

Recently I received a shotgun packed in a pine-wood box, the cover being secured with wood screws and the screw heads set in a counterbore, whereupon the depressions had been filled with sealing wax to prevent tampering with the contents. I have received a great many valuable guns for repairs, and this was the first one placed in a package secured in this manner.—Contributed by M. E. Duggan, Kenosha, Wis.

To Store a Lead Storage Battery When Not in Use

One of two methods is usually employed in putting a storage battery away for the winter, one known as "dry storage," and the other as "wet storage." The condition of the battery and the length of time it is to be out of service are the principal factors governing the selection of the method to be used. If the battery is in good condition and there is no real necessity for dismantling it on account of needed repairs, the wet storage is the preferable method, provided the battery is not to be out of service for more than about twelve months. On the other hand, if the battery is in such condition that repairs are, or soon will be, required, or if it is necessary to store it for more than a year, the dry method is the better.

The battery should be carefully examined, paying particular attention to the condition of the plates, separators, and the amount of sediment in the bottom of the containing jars. If the plates are found in good condition, and there is very little sediment in the bottom of the jars, the battery may be given an equalizing charge, and then placed in storage where it will be free from dust and dirt. The equalizing charge is a low-rate overcharge, continued until there is no increase in specific gravity of the electrolyte in any of the cells. Should the gravity in any of the cells exceed 1,300 during this charge, some of the electrolyte should be drawn off and distilled water added to reduce the gravity. After the electrolyte in all the cells has reached a constant gravity, and no change has been noted for three or four hours, proper corrections being made in the gravity readings for any change in temperature, the charge may be considered complete. The gravity in all the cells should then be adjusted to a value between 1,270 and 1,280 by removing some of the electrolyte and adding water, or 1,300-acid, as may be required. It often happens that only one or two cells may require a prolonged charge, in which case it is always best to disconnect them from the others and charge them separately.

While the battery is in storage, the loss through evaporation should be replaced periodically by adding pure water so that the plates are covered to a depth of at least ½ in. About every three or four months, the battery should be given a charge, using half the normal finishing rate recommended by the makers, until the cells have gassed continuously for at least three hours. If any of the cells fail to gas, they should be examined and the trouble corrected. If the examination of the battery indicates a poor condition of the plates and a large amount of sediment in the bottom of the jars—it should be at least ⅜ in. from the lower edge of the plates—it must be dismantled and placed in dry storage as follows: First make a sketch of all the connections and mark all terminals and their polarity. Next remove all connections between cells, and by means of a putty knife, take off the covers. The covers must be thoroughly cleaned by placing them in hot water, which will melt any of the sealing compound adhering to them, and clean off the acid. The hot water will soften the covers, and these, to be kept straight, should be placed in a pile and a weight put on top of them.

The plates are then carefully removed from the jars, and the separators between them taken out by parting the lower ends slightly. The separators are then washed, dried, and tied in bundles.

The positive and negative groups of plates are then separated, which will permit of a more careful examination. When the positive plates show a great deal of wear, they must be scrapped. If not thrown away, all loose particles adhering to them are removed with a smooth paddle. If the active material of the negative plates is swollen beyond the surface of the grid, it should be pressed back into position before the plates dry. This can be done by placing boards of suitable thickness between the plates and clamping them in a vise. The acid is then carefully poured out of the jars to keep it as clean as possible; then the sediment in the bottom is removed, and the jars are thoroughly washed. The acid is kept, to treat the negative plates. The positive groups of plates are combined in pairs and placed in the jars, and are then ready for the storage.

The negative groups of plates are also placed together in pairs, put in the remaining jars, covered with the acid and allowed to remain about six hours. The acid is then removed and the jars with the plates stored.

When it is desired to put the battery back in service, the positive and negative groups of plates are reassembled and the separators placed between them. Place the elements in the jars and fill with acid of a specific gravity of 1,250 so that the plates are covered ½ in. Connect the cells in series, and put the battery on charge at the regular finishing rate. After charging for a few minutes, note the voltage of each cell and make a record of these readings. Each cell should record about two volts, and those not showing this voltage are more than likely to be connected backward, which should be remedied. The cells are then closed and the connections made permanent.

When the cells begin to gas freely, the charging rate should be reduced to half the normal finishing rate, or less, if the temperature of the electrolyte exceeds 110 deg. F. Continue the charge until the gravity of all cells has become constant for a continuous period of 10 hours, but do not allow it to exceed 1,300. After the charge is complete, adjust the acid in the cells to a value of 1,270 to 1,280.

A Dual Pencil for Draftsmen

For the draftsman who desires to save time in drawing uniform parallel lines, for lettering and other purposes, the dual pencil shown in the illustration will be found exceedingly useful. It is made by cutting away the sides of two pencils until the lead is just exposed and joining them face to face by means of a ferrule from an old pen-

holder. This ferrule should be short so as to allow the necessary degree of flexibility. If one is not available a tight wrapping of string, or wire, at

Two Pencils Joined Together with Ferrule on Upper Ends, and Sliding Wedge to Draw Parallel Lines

the top answers the purpose almost as well. A small wood or cardboard wedge inserted between the pencils permits the easy adjustment of the points by sliding it up and down.— Contributed by Morris G. Miller, New Rochelle, N. Y.

To Shorten the Legs of a Chair

Usually when the legs of a chair or stool are sawn off carelessly one, or all of them, will rest on the floor like that shown at A. The cut should always be made parallel with the floor and not with the seat. To insure correctness, place the chair on a level surface and mark each leg all the way around with a pencil resting on a block which is slid around the leg, as shown at B. In this

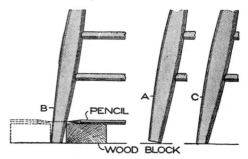

Marking a Chair Leg so That It can be Cut Off to Rest Level on the Floor

manner a proper guide line is made for the saw, and when cut, the leg will rest on the floor, as shown at C.

An Electric Foot Warmer

The hot brick, or slate slab, can be easily supplanted by an electric stove where electrical energy is available. It is only necessary to procure a large

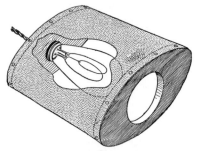

A Large Incandescent Electric Globe Constitutes the Heating Element in the Tin-Can Body

fruit can, about 1-gal. size, and remove both ends, being careful not to disturb the seam where the ends of the body are joined. This part of the can is then pressed into an oval shape and crosspieces of wood are fastened into the open ends. A large-size incandescent electric globe is then introduced in this covering and fastened so it will be in the center. This is connected to a lamp cord with a plug at the opposite end, the cord being long enough to reach and connect with a lamp socket.

Hook for Lifting Metal Plates

Steel plates are usually stored in a horizontal position, and when worked in a press, punch, or shear, they are carried in this position. The illustra-

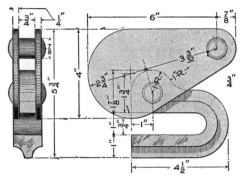

Hook to Grip the Edge of a Plate for Lifting It with a Crane

tion shows a hook, of which three are used, for lifting each plate with the crane. The opening in the hook part will admit plates up to ¾ in. in thickness. A link is attached to the end of the eccentric piece for attaching the chain of the crane. These hooks will grip the metal tightly and there is no danger of dropping the plate.—Contributed by Joseph K. Long, Renovo, Pennsylvania.

Reflecting Stage Scenes on Orchestra Music Racks

Orchestra leaders and players for moving-picture shows will find it worth while to rig up a set of mirrors to reflect the play on the stage so that it is not necessary to look up. If a large mirror is placed just back of the orchestra, and a smaller mirror set close to the music rack, they will reflect the scene close to where the music is read. The mirrors can be easily set to reflect at the proper angle.—Contributed by Roy Douglas, Terre Haute, Indiana.

An Automobile-License Holder

Almost all states require the driver of an automobile to have a license and to carry it at all times while driving. If this paper is carried in the pocket loosely it will soon become worn or possibly lost. The best way to carry the license is in the small holder used for pencils. Remove the pencil, make the license into a small roll and put it in the holder. Fasten the chain to the key ring, and the license will be ever ready and clean.

Waterproofing a Waxed Finish

A waxed finish may be effectually protected against water, or other form of moisture, by applying the following coating: Zanzibar copal varnish, boiled linseed oil, and spirits of turpentine; six parts of each, by weight. Mix these well together. This protective coating will not affect the appearance of the wax finish or change it in any way.

The Private Garage

By JAMES STANTON

SINCE private garages are usually built as ground-floor or one-story structures, with practically no space under the floor, a convenience like a pit appears a luxury, for the expense of digging and properly lining and protecting the walls is out of proportion to the benefits derived from it. But such buildings, if set on sloping ground, offer all the possibilities of a pit with but few shortcomings, as will be detailed.

When, as is often the case in suburban localities, the lot on which the garage is to be built slopes from 4 to 10 ft. in the length of a building, substantial supports must be provided for the elevated side. It may be that a basement, or cellar, is excavated to the lower level and a floor put down, or the ground may be left in its natural slope, but in any case the expense of inclosing the space below the main floor is not large, and the future will prove it worth while. A garage so built may have a trapdoor in the floor, and a man standing below can work at the under side of a motor without stooping. An inspection lamp will only supplement the natural light that will come from below, and a dropped object can be located with ease.

Such a pit does away with crawling on the floor, lying on a creeper and holding a light in one hand while assembling two or three pieces with the other; with the grease and litter of the average floor, and the discomfort of having to work in a strained position. Moreover, inspections and adjustments of hard-to-get-at parts are often neglected when there is no pit.

An excellent example of a private garage embodying some of the features mentioned was found in a barn built on a hillside, which was converted into a garage. It was a single-story affair and had at one side of the large room a stairway leading to the cellar, or basement. It was decided to utilize

A Stairway in the Corner of a Large Barn Floor Makes an Excellent Place to Get at the Under Side of an Automobile for Adjustment or Making Repairs

the stairs for work under the car. To that end two windows were cut through the wall near them, which gave an abundance of light, and a platform was built that formed a floor at a convenient level. This platform was strongly constructed, one end resting upon the stairs, and made wide enough to prevent articles from falling off. It did not require any fastening and could be easily moved out of the way when not wanted.

The trapdoor over the stairs was removed, and a substantial railing built around the opening. A hinged bar, lifted to permit a car to run over the hole and dropped back into place when the car is moved away, made the opening perfectly safe. A construction such as this is feasible also for a public garage wherever state regulations permit any floor opening at all. It is cleaner and lighter than a pit, and more comfortable for the workmen. The addition of a trapdoor, working auto-matically with the removal of the car, would overcome the only objection.

Experience with automobiles has taught that rainwater is the best to use in radiators. Yet few use it, although it is as easy to get as to attach a hose to the faucet. Provide a gutter on one side of the garage roof and a short length of pipe leading from it, together with a substantial barrel, or half barrel. That is all the initial investment and there is no upkeep cost, for no meter need be applied. A spill-way, or drain, will naturally be laid to carry off the water from the roof, and the barrel will stand on this and over-flow into it. A more elaborate arrange-ment would be to set the barrel with the top at the height of the eaves, in which case the water may be piped to suit the requirements. A few drops of kerosene on the water every 10 days will prevent the breeding of insects. This will provide a good supply of the softest water obtainable.

Road Roller Made of an Old Boiler

One of the old-style boilers without an attached fire box, or an upright one, makes a fine road roller. In building

An Old Boiler with Frame Attachment for Use in Rolling Soil for a Roadway

roads in a southern state, one of these boilers was used. A hole was drilled through the center of each head, and a shaft run through them, the ends being used for hauling it over the roadway by means of a special-built frame and tongue for a team of horses. The heft of the boiler was sufficient to pack very loose soil to make a solid roadbed.

Makeshift Tightener for a Guy Line

One day while working for a mining company, I was sent alone up an in-cline to tighten the guy line on a sheave-pulley frame. The only tool I had was a small monkey wrench, and when I arrived on the job I had to think of some easy way to do a hard thing. I thought of a way and re-turned to the shop for some cable clamps and two long bolts with nuts and washers. I run more threads on the bolts to make them 8 in. long. On my way back along the railroad track I found four fishplates and bolts, used to join the ends of rails. With these parts assembled, I soon had a tightener ready to work as shown in the illus-tration.

The fishplates are shown at A, with

the bolts in place, drawn just close enough so that the bolts B move freely. Four wood blocks were fitted and placed in at C, to keep the bolts B close up to the center bolts of the fish-plates and to keep them in line with the cable. The cable clamp was placed on the loose end of the cable, at D; then the fishplates were spread apart as far as possible, and another clamp fastened to the cable, at E. It was only necessary to turn the nuts on the bolts B to take up the slack in the guy line. When the end of the threads was reached, the line was still slack and needed more tightening. A clamp was then placed on both lines just ahead of

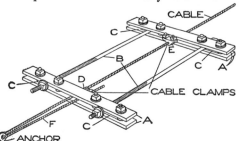

A Homemade Tightener Used in Taking Up the Slack in Cable Guy Lines

the anchor bolt, at F, to hold the slack taken up. The tightener was then re-set and used as before.—Contributed by E. C. Lane, El Paso, Texas.

A Method of Applying Gold Leaf Economically

Recently I had quite a lot of gold leaf to apply and was assisted very materially by a stunt I found in an old English sign painter's manual. The directions called for a paper prepared in a certain way, but I used ordinary paraffin wrapping paper as a substitute.

Taking the pieces of paraffin paper, I placed them carefully over the gold leaf in the book and rubbed them with my fingers. The gold adhered to the paper and could be handled without danger of its blowing away. When placed against the sized surface and rubbed with a piece of cotton, the paraffin paper allowed just enough gold to be released to cover the sized sur-

face. The illustration shows the gold leaf on a sheet of the paper and how it appears when the gold has been re-

Handling Gold Leaf with Paraffin Paper to Prevent Waste and for Covering Only Necessary Surface

moved to cover the surface of a letter. —Contributed by James M. Kane, Doylestown, Pa.

Holding Spring for a Gear-Box Filler Cover

The small cover closing a hole through which the grease was poured into a gear-box case was held in position by means of two studs with ordinary wing nuts. The nuts would become loose and drop out, and the studs, being made of very soft material, wore badly. It was finally decided to discard the stud-and-nut method of holding the cover, and the arrangement shown was substituted in its place. The studs were first removed from the case and the holes left by them filled with lead. A piece of flat spring steel was bent into the proper shape and

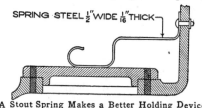

A Stout Spring Makes a Better Holding Device for a Gear-Box Cover than Bolts

bolted in such a position that its end pressed at the center of the cap. In this manner the troublesome nuts were eliminated, and the advantage of having a cover device that could be quickly operated was gained.

Ice Creepers

In crossing a pond in winter where the ice would carry my weight, I found it difficult to travel when a very light snow or frost had fallen. To save time in traveling and to prevent slipping, I purchased two skate straps and made creepers of them. They were cut to a length to reach over the ball of the foot, as shown. The portion of the strap under the shoe sole was filled with tacks so that their points would enter the ice. I can now walk over the ice without fear of falling—Contributed by W. A. Potter, Lexington, Mass.

Guard Holder for Flat Drills

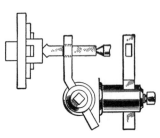

The common flat drill, used for drilling preliminary boring holes in chucked work on the lathe, is held in various ways to suit the convenience of the lathe operator It is, of course, not only necessary to hold the drill rigidly so that it will not turn, but the center of the tailstock, holding the end of the flat drill, must be operated so as to act as a feed for the drill. It being impossible to do two things at once, an accident is often the result of trying to perform such an operation, as a wrench cannot be relied upon to keep the drill from turning.

The sketch shows a jig, held by the tool post and provided with a slot, through which the flat drill passes. The only attention required of the operator is to feed the drill by the center of the tailstock. The jig can be easily and quickly centered for the drill. It is also an excellent safety device, for it is impossible for anything to get caught, or fly around and injure the operator of the machine, since the common flat drill, when ground correctly, will not dig or drag into the work in the chuck, cutting only when it is forced by the pressure applied to the center of the tailstock.—Contributed by F. W. Bentley, Missouri Valley, Ia.

Calibrating Thumbscrew on a Ruling Pen

It is quite difficult for the beginner in a drafting room to set the nibs of the pen each time to draw uniform lines. This can be done accurately if the thumbscrew is calibrated and a mark made on the nib of the pen as shown. It is an easy matter to turn the screw a certain number of times to a mark that will set the nibs the same distance apart each setting.—Contributed by A. Jaminet, Denver, Col.

Softening the Harsh Tone of a Violin

All violins of the inexpensive kind, and many high-priced ones, have a loud, harsh, and unmusical tone. A good remedy for this is to purchase a new bridge, and instead of cutting it down, drill holes just large enough for the strings as shown. If the sound is too much muffled, trim a little off from the top of the bridge until the proper tone is secured.—Contributed by C. E. Wurth, New York Mills.

Stenciled Initials or Monograms on Automobiles

By JAMES M. KANE

THE practice of placing the owner's initials, or monogram, on some portion—usually the doors or side panels—of the automobile is becoming more common, and with a good reason. Possibly it was unnecessary some years ago when cars were few and not many alike, but with the rapid increase in the output of cars, especially of the lower-grade cars, there are considerably more cars alike, and since the majority of car owners probably could not remember their license numbers if put to it, there is need for some identifying mark that can be distinguished at a glance.

I find that the use of a carefully cut stencil insures clear, quick work, as it can be placed on the exact spot without resorting to the preliminary outlining, trial marks, and spacing lines necessary when working in the usual way. As the high gloss on the varnished surface of an automobile will show the least scratch, the fewer preliminary marks the better, hence the stencil for safety. In addition to this, it can be put away for future use, insuring the car owner of an exact duplicate of the letters when the car is repainted, or when another car is purchased.

Ordinary stencil paper is not so

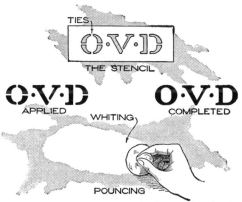

The Stencil as It is Cut; after Applying; Completed Letters; Sized and Pounced

good for the work as heavy, smooth-surfaced writing paper, or bond paper thinly coated with shellac. As the

blank spaces left by the ties in the stencil are afterward filled in so as to form a complete letter, these ties can

Applying and Holding the Stencil in Position, and Removing It after Painting the Surface

be left at portions of the letters that are most likely to curl up. Ordinary stencil work requires that the ties be placed with due regard for the general appearance of the finished work, as the

Applying Metal Leaf with a Camel's-Hair Brush and Removing the Surplus Leaf

tie spaces are not filled in. The stencil described must lie flat at all points, and the ties are designed with this object in view. The ties should not be too heavy.

As the stencil will lie closely to the varnished surface, the finger nail would seem to be the most natural thing to use in removing it, but as this would be likely to result in a scratch as well as in smudging the letters, the best plan is to turn up two corners of the stencil, either of which can be easily grasped and the stencil lifted off without trouble. The color used should be almost dry so that it will not slip beyond the outlines of the letters. After the stencil has been removed, the color can be used more freely in going over the letters and filling in the spaces left blank by the ties.

While color gives very satisfactory

results, metal leaf is much better, as it insures an even surface, wears better, and shows no brush marks. Gold or silver leaf may be difficult for the amateur letterer to handle, but aluminum leaf is stout enough to be applied by the inexperienced person. Gold

leaf is now put up on prepared paper that can be laid over the work and gently rubbed, causing only the gold that comes in contact with the

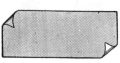

painted or sized surface to adhere, the balance of the leaf remaining on the paper.

The work should be pounced if metal leaf is applied, as the least tackiness of the varnish will cause the leaf to stick where it is not wanted. The pounce is merely a small bag made of fine cheesecloth, filled loosely with whiting. This is dabbed on the surface and forms a resist against the leaf. It does not prevent the paint or size from adhering,

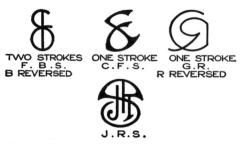

Original Monograms, Showing How Three Letters may be Combined to Make an Individual Mark

however. A wet sponge removes the whiting after the letters are dry.

While letters are sufficiently distinctive, the use of a monogram adds an air of exclusiveness and individuality to the job and removes it from the commonplace.

¶In taking pipe apart when the joints are stuck so that they will not turn, heat the coupling or fitting; or hammer it, not the pipe, and the pipe can be easily unscrewed.

Making Use of Broken Concrete-Sidewalk Material

Through a mistake there was delivered to my house a load of defective concrete-sidewalk material that had been torn up by the contractor for replacement. Not caring to pay for hauling it away, I sought some use for it, and found such a satisfactory one that I am going to get another load, which can be had for the hauling, as usually the contractor must haul it a long distance to dispose of it.

I squared up the concrete into flags with a cold chisel, and with the various sizes matched up on the edges, it made an excellent 2-ft. walk through the poultry yard. The ground was excavated about 5 in. deep, and filled in 1 in. with heavy soil. Then water was turned into the trench, making a slush, and while in this condition, the flags were set in and forced into the slush, which ran up between them. The soil, when dried out and hardened, made a firm base conforming to the uneven bottom surface of the flags.

With the odd broken pieces and chips, I constructed four drains directly under the drain spouts from the house, carrying the water well into the soil and into the garden bed, where it can be used to better advantage than on the lawn. This also avoided the gullies on the lawn that heavy flows from the drain pipes are apt to create.—Contributed by Victor Labadie, Dallas, Texas.

Repairing Pedal Crank on a Motorcycle

The weakest point on the crank hanger of a motorcycle is the

threaded projection on the end, and this usually is broken in case of a spill. The usual remedy is a new crank, but this expense can be avoided by the simple repair shown. The end of the broken part is filed, or ground down, level with the shoulder, and a hole drilled and tapped for a machine screw. This will not only hold as well as before, but it will make possible a quick repair on the road in case it is damaged in a like manner.—Contributed by E. K. Marshall, Oak Park, Ill.

A Disappearing Desk Light

On high desks, such as bookkeepers use, the ordinary standing lamp is in the way, not only during the day, but also when in use among large books. This condition led me to contrive a light which could be pushed into one of the pigeonholes when not in use. A thin board was cut as long as the pigeonholes are deep and just wide enough to slide freely in and out. The front piece was then nailed on, and a small brass knob placed in the center. A lamp receptacle was then screwed on, and a piece of bright tin bent into a semicircular shape to serve as a reflector. Tack this to the board and then fasten in a thin strip of wood on each side of the pigeonhole near the top for the board to slide on. Screw in the lamp and connect up with a flexible cord, which should be run out through a hole in the back of the desk, leaving the cord sufficiently loose to permit the lamp to be drawn out.

A light arranged in this manner leaves the bed of the desk perfectly free,

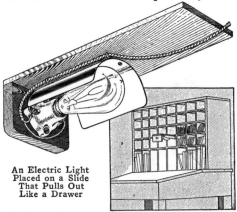

An Electric Light Placed on a Slide That Pulls Out Like a Drawer

shades the eyes, and illuminates the work in a very satisfactory manner.—Contributed by John D. Adams, Phoenix, Ariz.

One-Man Control for a Double-Deck Boat

In my seagoing yacht I installed a one-man control after building an upper deck so that the boat could be

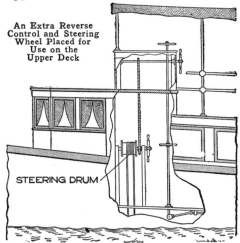

An Extra Reverse Control and Steering Wheel Placed for Use on the Upper Deck

STEERING DRUM

handled from either deck. The added control and steering device was practically the same as used in the wheelhouse. The rod controlling the reverse was simply extended to the deck above, and a handwheel attached to it. The wheel used was one purchased from an automobile dealer, taken from a steering post of an automobile. A sort of countershaft was installed, carrying the extra steering wheel on the rear end and a sprocket from which a chain was run to the steering-drum shaft.—Contributed by W. F. Quackenbush, New York City.

The Appearance of Casehardening Given to Steel

A solution of 1 part nitric acid to 20 parts of water will produce a surface on polished or ground steel to give it the appearance of casehardening. Immerse the object about 20 seconds, then rinse in cold water.

❡Most drills are broken by unfair usage, such as crowding too hard before the drill has entered its full cut, or after the point has come through the work.

Base for a Motor Drill

A decided improvement on motor drills, as shown in the illustration, is to replace the handle on the head with

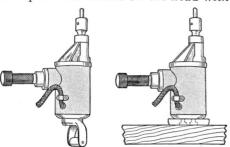

The Attached Base to the Motor Drill Makes a Flat Surface for Setting It on a Bench

a flat, round wood base, about 1¼ in. thick, with a diameter equal to the body of the motor. This will allow the motor to stand on end, which makes it most convenient for the insertion of drills.

It is also a safety attachment, as in taking hold of the motor by the chuck end, it can be placed almost anywhere on a machine with safety and without danger of rolling off. It makes a better breast pressing surface, and once used, will never be discarded. It also makes it possible to use the motor as a speed lathe for dressing up the ends of taper pins, and the like.—Contributed by Russell Hollis, Chicago.

❴Do not put up cleats on electric wiring with nails.

A Compound Rest for a Wood Lathe

Metal turning is rarely done on a wood lathe, and, if attempted at all, the hand tools used give poor results. By adding a compound rest to a wood-lathe equipment, its scope is broadened, and even steel and cast iron can be turned if the diameter is not too large. It is also very useful in wood turning, especially so on accurate taper work and patterns.

The base is made of oak, or maple, wood, as shown, the lower piece being slotted to admit a clamping bolt. The shears and carriage body are made of cold-rolled steel, 3¼ in. long by ¼ in. thick, and the shear for the cross slide, 2 in. long and ¼ in. thick. The general dimensions given in the sketch are for a rest to fit on a lathe of 9½-in. swing. In fitting the angle pieces, care should be taken in drilling the screw holes and in fitting the screws. The main, flat shear is fastened to the base wood member by means of six large wood screws. The two wood pieces are clamped together on a glued joint with four ¼-in. carriage bolts.

The cross slide is fastened to the carriage plate with four ¼-in. flat-head machine screws, and is supported by four pieces of ¼-in. pipe of equal lengths. The cross-slide tool block has a ¼-in. tapped hole in the rear, and this is counterbored to ⁵⁄₁₆ in. in front, to provide clearance for the feed screw. This block has a ¾-in. tapped hole in

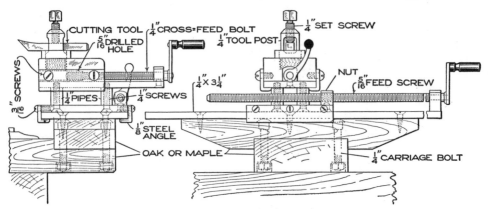

A Compound Rest Adds Greatly to the Equipment of a Wood Lathe, Which Makes It Possible to Turn Accurate Tapers as Well as to Turn Small Diameters in Metals

its upper surface for the tool post. Tools made of ⅜-in. steel are ideal for all purposes. Small boring bars can be made of the same material and a hole drilled in one end to hold 3/16-in. round steel tools. The end of the bar is then split, and a 3/16-in. setscrew used to clamp the tool tightly.—Contributed by Joe V. Romig, Allentown, Pa.

Buggy-Spindle Straightener

Any blacksmith can add, by using a little spare time, a very useful tool to his shop, to straighten buggy axles quickly. The one shown is made up as follows: The arm A is made of a 1-in. square steel bar, bent as shown, and the shorter end grooved to fit the axle, a ring, B, being used to hold them together while in use. The other end of the bar is slotted to receive the threaded end of a ½-in. rod, C, that is 2 ft. long. A piece, D, is forged to fit over the other spindle, close to the

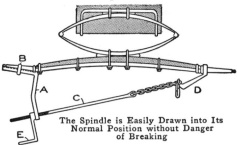

The Spindle is Easily Drawn into Its Normal Position without Danger of Breaking

back, or larger, end, with a hook on the opposite end for attaching a chain that connects the two pieces. A crank, E, threaded to fit the ½-in. rod, is used to draw the bent spindle straight.—Contributed by D. C. Goff, Knoxville, Tennessee.

An Alarm Signal for Repair Tracks

In freight-car repair yards men are subjected to a great deal of danger, and many accidents have resulted in pulling cars from the running repair tracks. In order to prevent accidents and give men warning that the switch leading to such a track is open, and to keep from under the cars, the device illustrated was put into service. Air is always piped along

these tracks for use in testing out air brakes, and the air pipe from the device is coupled to the air line. When the switch on the repair track is opened it opens up the cut-out cock, allowing the

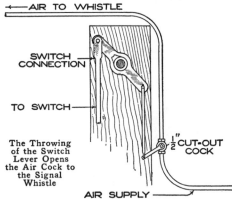

AIR TO WHISTLE

SWITCH CONNECTION

TO SWITCH

The Throwing of the Switch Lever Opens the Air Cock to the Signal Whistle

½" CUT-OUT COCK

AIR SUPPLY

air to pass through a whistle until the switch is again closed. When the whistle stops blowing, this indicates that it is safe to go under the cars. The air pipe is ½ in. and fitted with a ½-in. cut-out cock. The length of the arm that works the cock lever is optional and is made to suit the conditions.—Contributed by J. R. Minter, Washington, Ind.

Keeping Cable Tube Clean on Automobile Engines

In overhauling an automobile engine recently we noticed that the tube carrying the spark-plug cables was so clogged with grit and dust that it was impossible to remove the cables. This trouble can be easily avoided if both ends of the tube are plugged in some manner, preferably with a piece of hard, red fiber, as this forms a very good insulator between the copper tube

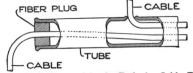

FIBER PLUG

CABLE

CABLE

TUBE

A Fiber Plug Inserted in the End of a Cable Tube to Keep Out Dirt

and the wire cable. The illustration shows the end of one of these tubes with a fiber plug inserted.—Contributed by Adolph Kline, New York City.

Number-Plate Bracket for a Motor Truck

A quickly made bracket for a truck number plate can be constructed from two pieces of ⅜-in. by 1½-in. cold-rolled steel, hammered in the

form of the letter "C" and riveted in the position shown. It is best to rivet the bracket to the vehicle frame, but it can be fastened by means of small machine screws. To give the plate a neat appearance, flat-head screws should be used with the heads facing the plate.

Blower for a Small Forge

Having constructed a light forge, I had no way to furnish the blast unless a fan was made, and not wanting to take the time for making one, I used our vacuum cleaner as follows: The hose attachment to the cleaner was fitted to the discharge pipe and run to the forge tuyère; thus obtaining as good a blast as could be desired for the forge fire.—Contributed by Luther Turner, Beardstown, Ill.

An Emergency Torch

Procure a piece of pipe of any metal, about 6 in. long and ¾ in. in diameter, with both ends open, and fill it with

absorbent cotton, or if this is not at hand, ordinary cotton, or even common waste, will answer the purpose, but it is not so good as the absorbent cotton. A very small part of the cotton is allowed to project at one end. Pour several tablespoonfuls of gasoline or benzine on the cotton to saturate it, but not enough to make it drip. This torch will burn with an even, steady light for about 30 minutes on one filling. It will burn lying or standing, and is absolutely safe.

An ordinary case, such as used for putting up shaving sticks, makes a good torch to carry around, as it will not let the gasoline evaporate when the top is screwed in place. To extinguish such a torch place the lighted end against any flat surface.—Contributed by James E. Noble, Toronto, Can.

Covering Engine-Case Breather to Prevent Dust from Entering

The breather on a gasoline engine of an automobile serves the purpose of allowing any excess pressure in the

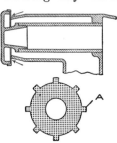

crank case to escape, and also provides an opening to pour in the lubricating oil. The breather construction, as shown in the illustration, will allow considerable grit and dust to enter and cause havoc with all the bearings. While it is necessary to have some opening at the top, it also is a problem to keep out the dirt and dust. A piece of very fine mesh and comparatively thin brass-wire screen, cut to the shape and necessary dimensions to fit the breather cap, will eliminate the trouble. The projections A are bent over the side of the cap for the purpose of holding it in place.

An Eyeglass Cleaner

The most common cleaner for eyeglasses is a silk pocket handkerchief which is rubbed for a considerable length of time over the glass surface before they are clear. Tissue paper is an excellent cleaner but is not always on hand, and instead an old dollar bill can be used. It cleans the glasses as clear as crystal without "breathing on them." An old, worn bill is preferable to a new one.

A Convenient Demountable-Rim Tire Tool

The motorist living in a large city is not troubled with tire changes, as the service man takes care of the work. In smaller places the person who drives must make his own tire changes. The introduction of the demountable rim enabled the driver to carry an extra tire and make emergency changes on the road.

Although the demountable rim is split transversely, and at first glance, the tire would seem to be easily removed, such is not the case. In fact, it is about as difficult to get the tire off the rim as it is to remove it from the old-style clincher-rim wheel. If the ends of the rim where it is transversely split could be lapped and the rim contracted, the tire would fall off of its own accord.

The removing may be easily accomplished by means of a turnbuckle, as shown in the illustration. Two holes must be drilled in the rim, one close to the split and the other about 10 in. from it. A turnbuckle, 12 in. long, can be purchased from any hardware dealer. The ends should be heated and turned at an angle, to hold securely in the holes drilled in the rim. It will be found that the stiffest rim may be contracted and the old casing removed

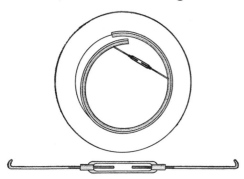

Rim-Contracting Tool for Demountable Rims, for Quickly Removing Tires in Making Repairs

with little effort, and replaced while the rim is contracted. New tires may be put on the rim in a like manner.—Contributed by James F. Gwinner, Memphis, Tenn.

Carrying T-Square on a Drawing Board

Most drawing boards have battens on the back to keep them straight. To provide a place for the T-square it is

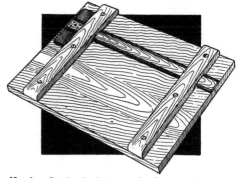

Notches Cut in the Battens of a Drawing Board to Admit the Blade of the T-Square

only necessary to cut out a notch in each batten on a line with each other and of a size to admit the blade. This makes a convenient way to safely carry the T-square.

Uses for Beeswax

Beeswax has been used to advantage to take the impression of a door key, but there are several other places where it comes in handy as well. When filing a key and using another key for a pattern a very small amount of the wax placed between the two and squeezed in a vise will keep them together until finished. The wax also makes a first-class fillet in pattern work, by putting it on in little pieces and then going over it with an iron just a little hotter than is necessary to melt it. It makes an excellent composition for filling holes and little imperfections in wood, where it is superior to putty, as it does not shrink and leave a depression. A small leak in a pan, or other receptacle for liquids, may be made tight for the time being by pressing a very small piece over the holes, or melt a few drops with a hot iron and let them fall on the place to be plugged.—Contributed by A. Dane, Pottstown, Pa.

Removing Milled Work from a Mandrel

Often in turning up milled edges, or fancy hand nuts, of medium thickness, it is necessary to tap the nut to the required size and screw it on a mandrel,

A Wrench Made of a Stick and a Piece of Leather to Remove Finished Parts from Arbors

or arbor, previously turned down and threaded and held in a lathe chuck, while finishing one side of the nut, then take it off and replace it to get at the other, or opposite, side. In turning, the lathe tool tightens the nut on the arbor so that it is necessary to use a vise and wrench to remove it, thus damaging the finished part.

To prevent marring the partly finished piece, I simply screw the arbor in the vise, then remove the piece with a wrench made as follows: A piece of leather belting, any convenient width, is nailed on a strip of wood to form a loop, which is placed around the finished part and used in the same manner as a chain pipe wrench.—Contributed by W. E. Day, Pittsfield, Mass.

Live-Wire Detector

It is not generally known that if one terminal only of the ordinary telephone receiver 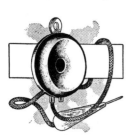 is placed in contact with a wire carrying the usual 110-volt commercial lighting current, a faint buzzing sound will be heard. This static effect not only shows the extreme sensitivity of the telephone receiver, but affords a convenient and absolutely safe means of identifying live wires without endangering the fuses or disconnecting. For work among covered wires, the end of the single conductor from the receiver may be connected with a darning needle firmly set in a small awl handle, which will readily penetrate the insulation.

Greasing Crosshead Pins

Considerable trouble was experienced in lubricating crosshead pins with oil, which resulted in adopting other means of lubrication. Pin grease was used successfully on the side and main rods of the locomotives for lubricating the brass and crank pin, and the idea embodied in the sketch was worked out, which clearly illustrates the method. The grease is put into the cavity, and

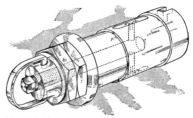

A Method of Lubricating Crosshead Pins with Grease, and a Substitute for Taper Pins

the plug forces the grease into the slots cut in the bearing surface of the pin.

In order to overcome delays in removing bent taper pins, which were used to prevent the nuts from working off the crosshead pin, a spring ring was devised. The sketch shows the method of its application. To remove the device, insert a chisel and pry the ends out of the holes.—Contributed by J. R. Minter, Washington, Ind.

Holding Tools in Their Handles

A good adhesive for holding tools in their handles is rosin and a small quantity of rottenstone. The hole in the handle is filled with the powdered rosin to which has been added a little rottenstone. The tang of the tool is heated and pushed into place. When cold, it will stick firmly in the handle.

Combined Bench Hook, Shoot Board, and Miter Box

This handy accessory to the workbench should be made of hard wood, preferably maple, and all parts accurately finished before assembling. The amount of stock required is as follows, the dimensions being in finished sizes: One piece, 12 in. long, 8 in. wide, and ¾ in. thick; one piece, 8½ in. long, 5¾ in. wide, and ⅝ in. thick; two pieces, 5¾ in. long, 1⅞ in. wide, and ¾ in. thick; one piece, 5¾ in. long, 2 in. wide, and ⅞ in. thick, and one piece, 8 in. long, 1 in. wide, and ¾ in. thick.

The various parts are assembled by gluing and screwing them to the larger piece that forms the base. The screws are put in from the bottom so that no heads will show when the box is in place on the bench. Care should be taken to keep the screws away from the places where the miter cuts are made.

As a shoot board, it is used with a 14-in. iron plane. The plane lies on its side and is pushed back and forth on the 2¼-in. ledge. For planing miters, a piece with one end cut to a 45° angle is placed against the forward

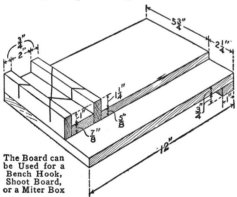

The Board can be Used for a Bench Hook, Shoot Board, or a Miter Box

stop. This holds the piece to be planed at the correct angle, and perfect joints will be the result.—Contributed by J. A. Shelly, Brooklyn, N. Y.

❡In raising a shaper knee do not loosen the screws too much, as this will allow chips to drop behind it.

Reflecting Light into Boiler Tubes for Inspection

An inspector finds it very difficult to detect any flaw, or other imperfection, in boiler tubes, superheater tubes, and

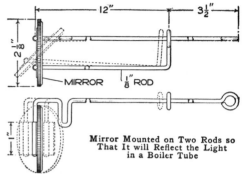

Mirror Mounted on Two Rods so That It will Reflect the Light in a Boiler Tube

arch pipes at the front, or near where they are kneaded or welded to the flue sheet. This is due to the small amount of light to be had in these places. The illustration shows a very simple device that will reflect the rays of light on the parts that require the most attention.

The device is very simple. The mirror used is similar to those given out for advertising purposes, on the back of which is soldered a strip of tin bent around the two rods, the ends of the rods being slightly riveted to hold the glass in place. Either of the rods may be pulled to turn the mirror at an angle in directing the light rays. The small bend in one rod is to prevent the glass from being pulled too far over the proper angle.—Contributed by Joseph K. Long, Renovo, Pa.

To Prevent Squeaking Noises on an Automobile

One frequently hears a series of squeaking noises when driving a car, and upon careful examination the trouble cannot be found. Nearly always the squeaks are caused by the body bolts and nuts loosening up a little. The body, being an extremely heavy part of the car, has a natural tendency to work loose from the chassis frame, and for this reason, secure locking means should always be provided on the various nuts.

Preventing the Loss of a Hub Cap

Quite frequently one of the hub caps of an automobile is lost, especially where no locking means is provided. Such a loss can be prevented by using a locking device as illustrated. A comparatively stiff helical spring is inserted in the cap and over the nut, as shown in the sketch, so that the cap is screwed down against the action of the spring. This spring being constantly compressed, it has a tendency to push the cap outward against the sides of the threads, and in this manner a secure locking means is obtained.

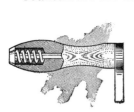

To Prevent the Rattle of an Automobile Crank Handle

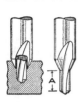

Counterbore the handle end so that a short piece of coil spring can be inserted over the handle pin. This will keep the handle tightly against the crank and prevent it from rattling, yet allow sufficient free action to turn in cranking.—Contributed by Thomas M. Ritchie, Waterloo, Iowa.

Removing a Broken Drill

In using center drills it happens quite often that the part A breaks off and remains firmly imbedded in the work being centered. In such cases grind the body, or more properly, the countersink part remaining as shown. The center drill is then rechucked and run down in the hole. This cuts a clearance around the drill and allows it to be removed with a pair of pliers. The only result in bad cases is that it makes the center a little deeper than intended. This idea, of course, cannot be applied to standard twist drills or to taps, but is thoroughly efficient for the work mentioned.

Water Guide for an Eave Trough

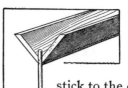

Having trouble in setting a barrel beneath the eave trough to catch the water during rainstorms on account of the varying volumes of water, one owner nailed a stick to the end of the trough, as shown in the illustration, and his troubles were over. The water would follow down the stick and into the barrel, no matter how much or little water was running. The stick should project above the bottom of the trough to catch the water.—Contributed by H. V. Olson, Hibbing, Minn.

Remedy for Loose Eyeglass Lens

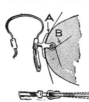

Eyeglasses generally have an annoying way of becoming loose at the screws which hold the lenses in place. This can sometimes be remedied by the insertion of a piece of cotton thread in one of the two places indicated in the sketch. If there is a space between the inner edge of the glass and the shoulder of the clip, or if the hole in the lens is too near the edge, the glass will swing slightly about the screw every time the glasses are cleaned, and this naturally loosens the screw. By removing the lens and placing a piece of thread at A, this movement is prevented, or at least greatly minimized. In addition, this makes the inside of the hole in the lens bear on the side of the screw, thus keeping it in place tightly. If the jaws of the clip are slightly open at the edge of the lens, as shown in the lower sketch, thus making the lens wobble as indicated, it can be remedied by inserting a piece of thread, B, around the screw, crossing the ends while tightening the screw, then cutting them off, and the job is finished. The "give" in the cotton provides a sort of spring-washer effect.—Contributed by Morris G. Miller, New Rochelle, N. Y.

Puller for Concrete-Form Bolts

The action of the puller is the same as that of the lever jack. The holding device is made of a steel plate, 3 in. square and ½ in. thick. A hole is drilled near the center on an angle of 60° to the surface. It is only for use with headless bolts such as are com-

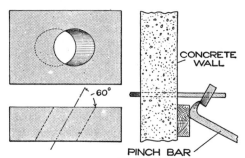

The Oblique Hole in the Steel Block Forms a Grip Like a Lever Jack

monly used for concrete-wall forms. With this style of bolt a collar and setscrew takes the place of the head. A pinch bar is used in connection with the piece of steel, as shown.—Contributed by J. J. O'Brien, Buffalo, N. Y.

Renewing Dowel Holes in Old Wood Patterns

This is usually a job disliked by the patternmaker, as the holes must be plugged and new holes bored. In boring the holes the bits will be damaged by striking nails or old molding sand. It is much more satisfactory to make a cut with a ½-in. chisel, or the size suitable for the dowel, on each side of the dowel hole, running with the

grain of the wood, then drive in wedges until the wood is forced to reduce the

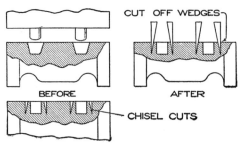

Wedges are Driven in Chisel Cuts on Each Side to Reduce the Dowel-Hole Size

dowel hole to the proper size.—Contributed by J. C. Hansen, Maywood, Illinois.

Reinforcing a Loose Steering Post

A loose steering post on an old automobile truck was reinforced in the following manner: A piece of flat steel stock, 1½ in. by ⅜ in. in cross section, was annealed and then forged into the proper shape and dimensions, as shown. This was slipped over the steering post and clamped to it by means of a ⅜-in. screw and nut. The base in turn was fastened to the steel dash with suitable

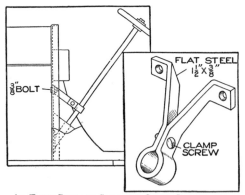

An Extra Brace to Support a Loose Steering Post of Very Old Construction

screws. This supported the steering post at two points and consequently made it very rigid.

❡A forge shop should never be made too light, as the workman cannot see the heats well in a brightly illuminated shop.

A Lining and Tool-Setting Bar

The sketch shows a simple gauge for lining up various machine tools and for setting them to cut different depths. As the indicator consists al-

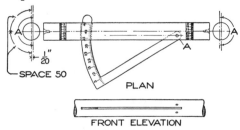

PLAN

FRONT ELEVATION

A = LENGTH OF GRADUATION
A Lathe-Lining and Tool-Setting Bar for Making Accurate Adjustment of the Tailstock

most of one solid piece, it is practically accident-proof and there is nothing to get out of order. The bar, or body, of the tool is first turned true, the slot for the protractor arm is cut, and the hole for the pin A drilled. The bar is then chucked, and both centers are faced off almost entirely, leaving just enough of the original centers for a marker. From this marker lay off new centers, each toward the same side of the bar and $\frac{1}{20}$ in. from the original centers, as shown. On the full side of the bar mark off the graduations, spacing them for one-quarter of the circumference with 50 graduations in each space, each graduation representing .001 in. The shaping and fitting of the protractor arm and its hub require no explanation, save to state that no locking screw is provided, the protractor arm being merely a tight fit. Caseharden the bar and grind-finish all over.

To use the instrument, set it freely on the lathe centers, move a square-point tool to almost touching the "low" side of the bar, and carefully turn it. Supposing the bar touches the tool at $20 + 3$, or 23 thousandths of an inch, without changing the tool, let the bar swing clear, and run the carriage up to the other end, and carefully turn the test bar again. If it touches the tool indicating $15 + 1$, then the lathe is out of line .007 in., and since the greater number was found at the tail-

stock end, the tailstock must be moved forward .007 in. The use of the protractor needs no further explanation. —Contributed by J. B. Murphy, Plainfield, N. J.

Care of Tires Using Skid Chains

The cutting of tires with skid chains can be eliminated to great extent by using just a little care in applying the brakes, thereby increasing the mileage considerably. When the brakes are jammed on hard and quickly, instead of easily and slowly, one or both rear wheels will cease to revolve, and the section of the skid chain that happens to be between the tire and the road heats up quickly, at times becoming almost red-hot, and burns into the rubber tread. Dirt and water then get between the rubber and fabric, and loosen the tread, which wears off quickly.

The chain burning is many times called a chain cut. Although chain burning and chain cutting amount to the same thing, they are actually two very distinct damages, and by bearing in mind that rubber will burn under the conditions mentioned, much expense can be saved.—Contributed by L. E. Turner, New York City.

Shock Produces Greater Strain than Pressure

Why does a hammer blow start a "stuck" shaft when a screw pressure will not? Assuming, for example, that the pressure applied is 1,000 lb. in each case. It is a law in mechanics, known and observed by all machine designers, that a force suddenly applied produces twice the stress of one gradually applied. A blow is twice as powerful as a static pressure. In designing machine parts this must always be kept in mind, for a part built to carry a ton weight would fail under a ton blow from a power hammer.

⟪Use plenty of good lard oil when cutting threads on steel.

Shop Notes

Washing Unopenable Windows

While using a special preparation for washing windows, apply the inside coat crosswise and the outside coat lengthwise; then, after the preparation has dried, the streaks will determine which side is not wiped clean. This is especially handy when washing windows that cannot be opened, as it will save many trips around to the outside when the streak is on the inside.

Portable Fan Outfit for Cooling Furnaces

In a large plant where there are many boilers having automatic-stoker furnaces, great delay was experienced in waiting for the hot brickwork to cool sufficiently to allow a workman to enter for the purpose of making repairs. The illustration shows how the delay was lessened. The fan cools

A Motor and Fan Placed on a Truck for Use in Cooling a Furnace for Making Repairs

the furnace to a workable temperature in a very small part of the time formerly required.—Contributed by J. J. O'Brien, Buffalo, N. Y.

Cover for a Drinking-Fountain Pipe

The drinking fountain in the playground in our city, when first erected, was merely a section of pipe with the cup attachment screwed into it. Recently a concrete base has been added, and a terra-cotta chimney top bedded

Terra-Cotta Chimney Top Used as a Protection and Ornament about a Drinking-Fountain Pipe

into it as shown. The concrete base is convenient for the youngsters to stand on, and the chimney top serves the double purpose of protecting the pipe and carrying the waste water down into a drain pipe running from the bottom of the chimney out into the gutter.—Contributed by James M. Kane, Doylestown, Pa.

Cutting Long Square Holes in Wood

It is often necessary to cut square holes through blocks of wood, and if the holes are of considerable length it is difficult to make them square and smooth. The tool illustrated is quite an aid for such work, and is simple enough for anyone to make.

An ordinary corner chisel is represented at A, into the angle of which is soldered a small block, B. To this block is fastened, by a small screw, a spring, C, of sufficient size to reach the opposite corner of the hole to be cut. The hole should be roughed out

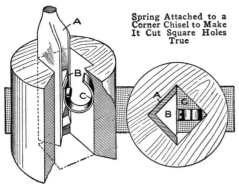

Spring Attached to a Corner Chisel to Make It Cut Square Holes True

first, after which it is easily finished with the corner chisel arranged as shown, since the spring C always forces the chisel down flat and holds it firmly in the corner as it is pushed through.—Contributed by J. A. Brearley, Washington, D. C.

A Portable Drawing Outfit

The illustration shows the construction of a self-contained drawing outfit, which is of value to engineers and students who find it necessary to carry drafting instruments to and from work. The size of the board is such

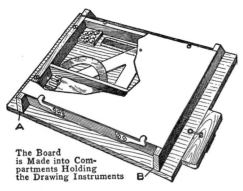

The Board is Made into Compartments Holding the Drawing Instruments

that it can be easily carried in a suitcase, and fair-sized drawings can be made upon it.

The drawing board is made of soft pine, or poplar, $\frac{3}{8}$ in. thick by 14 in. long, and 12 in. wide. Three strips, with the grain of the wood running lengthwise of the board, are used for the board. The edges are made perfectly square and straight, for the use of the T-square.

The compartments for the instruments on the back of the board are made between two hardwood cleats, A and B, placed 1 in. from each end, and two similar cleats lengthwise, 1 in. from the sides. The cleats should be fastened to the board with wood screws.

The compartment formed within the cleats is divided in the center with another small cleat. A cover is made from a piece of sheet metal, aluminum preferred, and fastened in place by slots on one side which slip under round-head screws, and by two spring clips on the other side. The screws are driven almost down and filed flat.

In one compartment there is fitted a small chamois pouch, having pockets to receive the instruments, while in the other side there is room for a scale, protractor, triangles, pencils, etc. In one corner of one side, glue a small block of soft wood, to hold the thumb tacks. A T-square may be made to fasten across the face of the board by using small brass screw eyes and hooks. The blade of such a square should be about $1\frac{1}{2}$ in. wide, and just as long as the board.—Contributed by C. H. Van Fossen, Fayette, Ohio.

A Place for the Automobile Switch Key

If the key for the switch lock of an automobile is made of steel, it can be safely and conveniently kept in the car when not in use by attaching it to a small permanent magnet, concealed under the false dash, or elsewhere. Should the key be of brass, a steel duplicate can easily be made, or one may be made of tool steel, then hardened and magnetized so that it will adhere to any steel, or iron, part of the automobile. — Contributed by Carl F. Woodbury, Halifax, Nova Scotia.

Economy in Making Templates

A piece of work, shown at A, required holes drilled accurately, and quite a number of them were needed from time to time, making it necessary to have a template, as shown at B. The template was first made of machine steel and casehardened. The holes wore rapidly, and the template had to be discarded, and a new one made quite often.

To make a template that would stand the wear and not require a large amount of tool steel, one was turned up of machine steel, and the places for the holes were located and drilled for tapping with a 3/8-in. machine tap. Then the holes were tapped, and a piece of 3/8-in. tool steel was threaded and turned into each hole, and slightly peened over. The piece was then faced off, the places for the holes accurately marked on the tool-steel inserts, and drilled. The whole piece was heated, and the tool-steel pieces tempered. This formed a template as good as if

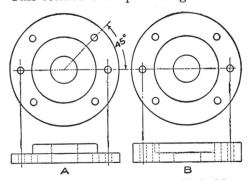

A Template Made of Machine Steel with Tool-Steel
Inserts for the Holes

it had been made entirely of tool steel.—Contributed by Clarence H. Anderson, Worcester, Mass.

Cutting Threads on Foundation Bolts

In placing an engine on a foundation in a stone quarry, I found that some of the bolts had to be shortened about 3 in., and as these bolts were split on the lower end and an iron wedge inserted in the split it was impossible to remove them. The threads varied in size owing to the bolt sizes, and by cutting off the necessary length from each bolt the threaded portion would

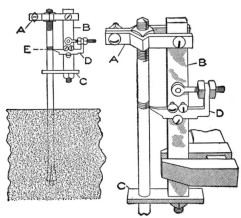

The Threaded End of the Bolt Provided a Means
of Feed for Cutting Other Threads

be removed, thus making it necessary to cut new threads on the bolt ends. The bolts being located so close together, it was impossible to use ordinary stock and dies. It required a special threading tool, which was made as follows:

The nut was placed on the end of the bolt and turned to catch one thread. A clamp, A, was made of flat iron and screwed fast to the nut with screwhead bolts, as shown. A piece of flat iron, B, was drilled to fit the clamp A, the other end being provided with a thread and nut. An arm, C, was made of a piece of iron and bolted fast to the flat iron B. A thread-cutting tool, D, was made of flat tool steel, ground to the proper cutting point, and then clamped to the flat iron B with three screws. The device was placed on the bolt and the nut given a turn on one thread, then a wrench was applied to the bar B and by turning the nut, the tool cut the thread, the nut being used as a means for the feed. After cutting the thread the bolts were cut off at E. —Contributed by A. L. Kerbaugh, Allentown, Pa.

⸢Turn the tailstock center of a lathe sufficient to take up the slack, and no more.

To Remove Burrs from Holes

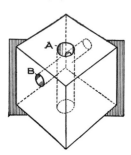

The block shown is typical of many drilling jobs. Two holes, A and B, are to be drilled and one runs into the other. It makes no difference which hole is drilled first, the second hole throws up a burr in the first. The softer the metal the larger the burr, especially on brass. If one of the holes cuts only part way through, a small, thin shell of metal is left rather than a burr.

To take out the shell or burr, grind an ordinary twist drill flat on the end, and give the usual clearance to the flat edges. A drill so ground will do better and quicker work than one having a taper point. It will cut fast enough, and remove the proper amount of metal to please the most exacting production manager.

Another way in which this can be done is to insert a plug in the hole first drilled. If one or two pieces are to be drilled, this is a good way, but is too slow for quantity work. For a hole that only comes half through, a half round may be filed in the plug and it can be used over and over again.

Covering Paint in Pots Overnight

Paint in pots left overnight will harden on the surface sufficiently to make a scum that must be removed before starting work the next day. I avoid this by covering the surface of the paint in the pot with a disk of wax or paraffin. The disk is about ¼ in. thick, and should be of a size to fit snugly in the pot so that it will float on the surface of the paint. This covering prevents any scum from forming and keeps the paint free from small bits of hard paint. When molding the disk a piece of wire should be put in so that a part of it will project from one surface, to make a handle for lifting the disk out of the pot.—James A. Hart, Philadelphia, Pa.

Dial to Locate Swing of Oil-Cock Control

The oil cock on the engine of an automobile was of the combination filling and drain type; that is, it could be opened one way to receive oil into the crank case, and the other way, to drain the lower half of the crank case of oil. The lever controlling the cock was made, as shown, without any provision for guiding it. The case was frequently drained by mistake when it was desired to open it

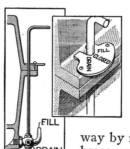

for filling, causing the sod pan to drip continually from waste oil. A plan was finally devised to prevent the turning of the control the wrong way by making a piece of brass on which the words "fill," "closed," and "drain" were stamped, and then fastening it to the flange of the upper case by means of screws.

Making a Reamer Cut Oversize

When a smooth, round hole of small diameter is required, a hand reamer is used to produce it, and many times the reamer is from .001 to .004 under size. The reamer may be made to work effectively in the following manner: With a scraper made of a medium-size, half-round file, burnish the face of each flute with the oval side. This will raise an edge and cause the reamer to cut larger, the size depending on how long and hard the faces are burnished. This, of course, does not make a permanent edge, but it does very nicely in an emergency.

A Small-Farm Workshop

By FRANK L. RUSSELL

IT makes little difference whether a person owns a large farm or a truck garden, a place for small tools is not only convenient but almost a necessity. The house can be of a size proportionate to the requirements. The one illustrated is suitable for a small farm, and makes a place for the small hand tools, as well as provides a place where one can occupy spare time in making repairs and keeping the implements in proper shape.

The size of the house is 7 by 12 ft. and 7 ft. high at the eave. Lay out the ground selected for the size of the house and make a level place, digging into the earth from 4 to 6 in., on which to place a solid floor. A box or inclosure should be made of boards so that its inside dimensions are 7 ft. by 12 ft.

A Place for Small Tools Is Not Only a Convenience but Is Almost a Necessity for the Farm, and a Workshop for Leisure Hours is Provided at the Same Time

The height of this box may be from 6 to 8 in., depending on how high the floor is to be raised from the surface of the earth. The upper edge of these boards should be well leveled in all directions so that in making the filling of concrete the surface will be level.

Tamp in a solid bed of cinders so as to make the surface a trifle lower than the surrounding ground. Make a mixture of concrete, using 1 part cement, 2½ parts sand, and 5 parts of broken stone or gravel, and fill into the space to within about 1 in. of the top, tamping it down firmly while putting in the mixture.

The space left at the top is filled in with what is called a neat mixture, 1 part cement and from 1 to 2 parts sand.

This is struck off level with the upper edges of the boards and troweled to make it smooth.

As this forms a perfectly level surface there is no way to fasten the wood structure on top of it. The fastening, however, may be made in one of two ways: by setting bolts in the concrete while it is soft, or by drilling holes in it after it has hardened and leading bolts in the concrete. In setting the bolts, be sure to have them about 1¾ in. from the edge, and that about 2 in. of the threaded end projects above the surface of the concrete. Two or three ½-in. bolts are required for each end of the building, and four or five should be used on each side.

A plate made of studs, 2 by 4-in. material, is fastened with the bolts so that its outer edge will be flush with the cement base. After these are securely fastened with the bolts, construct the ends and side wall studs in the same way as building a house, cutting the studs to square the ends and making them with both top and bottom plates just 7 ft. over all. It will require four studs for each end and seven for each side. It is built up square on the ends as well as the sides, using two studs together at the corners. The upper plates are mitered at the corners so that the frame will be securely held together in a rectangle.

The rafters are cut to the pitch desired and fastened in position with a narrow board between their upper ends for a ridge. Ordinary siding can

2593

be used, but since this is just a tool house and workshop, rough sheathing boards are put on, using halved joints

tle pressure is sufficient to prevent the glass from turning. The tube was chucked and centered by running the

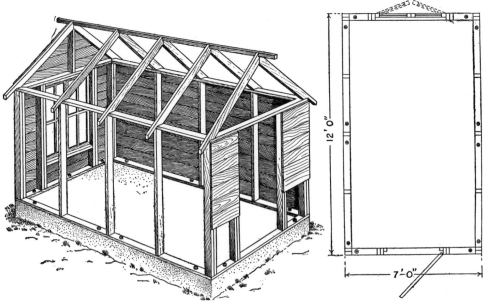

Ground Plan Showing the Location of the Studs and the Openings for the Door and Window, the Former a Regular Batten Door and the Latter Made Up of Two Casement Sash to Swing Outward

at the corners and allowing door and window spaces in the ends. Sheathing boards are put on the rafters and shingles laid.

The arrangement of the bench and hooks, or clips, for holding the tools can be made as desired and in the manner suiting the builder best.

Working Glass in Machines

At one time we had an order for a lot of glass tubes, inside diameter ½ in., outside diameter ¾ in., and 10 in. long, to be threaded on each end with eight threads to the inch. The lathe was geared up for this thread, and a three-jaw universal chuck put on the spindle. The tubes were chucked with a piece of leather placed between the jaws and the glass. Near the other end of the glass tube the center rest was set, and a piece of leather was folded over each end of the center-rest jaws and wired in place.

This leather idea was to prevent scratching the glass surface. Very lit-

tail center up and setting the jaws of the center rest.

A 4-in. drum pulley was taken from the small tool grinder and put up over the lathe, and a tool-post grinder, carrying a beveled emery wheel, was set in the tool post instead of the threading tool. The tool-post grinder was belted to the 4-in. drum pulley, and the emery wheel set with a center gauge, whereupon the thread was cut as usual.

We found that by using hard wheels, dressed to suit the work, or by using a combination of wheels, glass can be worked as easily as cold-rolled steel. This would apply to planer work as well. Glass should be worked at high speeds, and a dull surface will be the result. The emery wheel must be kept wet, either by using a centrifugal pump or by means of the tin can with a hole punched in the bottom.—Contributed by J. B. Murphy, Plainfield, N. J.

⁅A little salt put in a forge fire will sometimes help wonderfully.

Homemade Magneto Coupling

In overhauling an automobile it was desired to change the ignition system from low to high tension. The high-tension system necessitated the installing of a magneto generator, and in addition a special type of adjustable coupling between the generator and the engine. The adjustment is necessary in order that the spark may be advanced or retarded at will. The magneto installed was a secondhand one, but to install a new coupling meant an expenditure of nearly twice that of the magneto. This being the case, it was decided to make one, with the result shown in the illustration.

A search of the junk heap in a near-by garage produced an old transmission spur gear and an old clutch ball-bearing housing. The gear was carefully cleaned up in a lathe and rebored to fit the magneto shaft, after which it was riveted in place, a piece of 3/16-in.

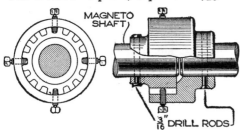

A Spur Gear Used as an Adjustment in the Coupling Driving a Magneto

drill rod being used as a rivet. The old ball-bearing housing was then rebored to fit the water-pump shaft, while the other inside diameter just happened to fit the outside diameter of the gear. Four holes were drilled, evenly spaced as shown, and tapped for four setscrews. The housing was then riveted to the shaft, the same as the spur gear. The setscrews serve as a connection between the two members of the coupling. The relative position of the two parts is varied by merely unscrewing the setscrews and turning the gear as desired. A small leather cover was provided for the complete coupling, to protect it from the grit and dust.—Contributed by Adolph Kline, New York City.

Stretching Window Screens on Frames

The screen wire is first fastened along one side with tacks, then this edge of the frame is placed against

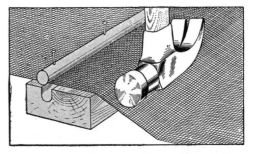

Stretching Window-Screen Wire on Frames with the Use of the Hammer Head

some support while it lies on the bench top or table. The screen is then stretched with the hammer head placed on the extending end of the screen and pressed down in the successive positions as shown. The screen will stay taut after removing the hammer, as the bend will hold it while the tacks are driven.—Contributed by E. K. Marshall, Oak Park, Ill.

A Faucet Lever

Upon a self-closing faucet I attached a piece of band iron, A, bent as shown and hooked over the faucet lever B and under the spout. The shape of the angle was such that if the lever was raised by taking hold of it at the end, it would pull down the faucet lever B, allowing the water to

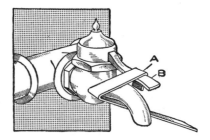

An Extra Lever Attachment for a Self-Closing Faucet to Hold It Open

run as long as desired. Pushing the iron back closed the faucet.—Contributed by R. F. Pohle, Lynn, Mass.

Buzzers without Contacts

How often a person sees the inscription "60 cycles" on alternating-current motors without stopping to think what it means. Nine people out of ten will underestimate the duration of time designated as a second, so that it is safe to presume that very few have any adequate conception of 60 cycles per second. The buzzers about to be

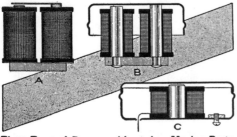

Three Types of Buzzers without Any Moving Parts for Use on Alternating-Current Lines

described will furnish direct and positive evidence to the ears, and will demonstrate, where an alternating current is available, that make-and-break contacts, with their liability to get out of adjustment and become corroded, are quite unnecessary. The small bell-ringing transformer, operating directly on the commercial lighting circuit, is largely replacing batteries as a source of power for bell and annunciator systems, and it is very natural that such should be the case, because the results are more positive, and the expense in the end less than that occasioned by the constant replacing of exhausted cells. While the small transformer greatly reduces the voltage, it does not, of course, affect the alternations or their frequency; hence, all that would appear necessary in order to make a buzzer, would be to provide a suitable armature and a coil with an iron core.

Simple though this may appear, in carrying out the idea in actual practice one is apt to learn several things about the subject of vibration. As a simple initial experiment, provide a coil with an iron core, and if the resistance is not 50 ohms or more, so that it may be connected directly across the 110-volt

circuit, connect it up in series with a small water rheostat. Clamp a strip of steel—an old hack-saw blade will do—in a vise and bring the coil near, having previously arranged a piece of board on which to place it. Vary the length of the spring projecting from the vise and note that there is just one length, about 2 in., for which the vibration will reach a maximum. It may also be noted that by shortening up the spring beyond this point, it may again be brought into phase by adding a small weight near the end. As 60 cycles means 60 reversals of the current per second it will cause 120 distinct magnetizations of the iron core, and when the spring is freely vibrating it is doing so at that rate. To furnish a comparison it may be stated that the middle "C" on the piano vibrates about 256 times per second.

This immediately suggests the simple form of buzzer indicated by the diagram A. Lay a piece of spring steel, or even tin, across the poles of a magnet and solder one end to one of the poles, which may be more easily done if a small hole is drilled in the spring at that point. With the edge of a knife slightly raise the other end barely the thickness of a sheet of paper, and the buzzer is complete. If the distance of the spring away from the pole is small enough, so as to cause it to hit the pole at each vibration, the tuning will be perfect.

In the buzzer B, the sound is considerably increased by replacing the spring with a small tin box, from 1½ to 2 in. in diameter. After the solder sets, be sure to do no more than just pry the tin loose from the other pole.

In the diagram C is shown a buzzer that has a decidedly commercial appearance, as it is completely self-contained within a small tin box, such as used for shoe polish. The soft-iron core in the center should be just long enough to reach from the bottom to the cover. File it off squarely and solder it to the bottom. Slip the coil on, and if it fits loosely, fasten it with shellac and paper packing. Ground one wire to the tin, and solder a small battery nut on the inside so that a connection can be readily made. The other wire may be let out through a hole. Put on the top and adjust it until a good loud buzz is secured, and then fasten it with a drop of solder. Test it again, and add a second drop of solder, about one-third of the way around. If the buzz still remains loud and clear, the addition of a drop of solder at a third point will settle the matter. It will be evident that as the buzzer is dust-proof and has no moving parts to get out of order, it should last indefinitely.—Contributed by John D. Adams, Phoenix, Ariz.

Homemade Belts for a Cyclecar

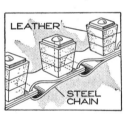

The V-chains, or belts, on my cyclecar wore out, and I constructed two chains that gave good satisfaction, in the following manner: I procured enough galvanized-steel chain to extend around the pulleys, then from the nearest cobbler I procured enough scrap leather to make V-blocks for the links. The leather was put to soak, then cut into small pieces, and a hole was punched in the center of each piece for a rivet. The pieces were built up on a rivet to the desired thickness, and then they were cut to form a V-shape to fit the groove of the pulleys. For every link in the chain, a leather block was made and riveted to the link, as shown in the illustration.—Contributed by B. O. Bates, Campbellton, Can.

A Center to Face and Polish in a Lathe

It often happens that amateurs, and sometimes even skilled workmen, have the troubles shown in the illustration when facing the ends of shafts in a lathe. In taking a roughing cut, more metal is removed than the depth of the center hole in the work, as shown at

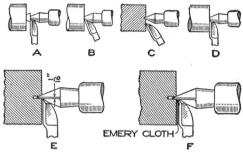

Center with a Cut-Out for the Tool in Facing and Polishing Work in a Lathe

A. At B is shown a tool set over at such an angle that it leaves tool marks, as exaggeratedly illustrated at

C. If the tool is set as shown at D, the angle on the tool is too blunt at the point to fit into the space between the work and the lathe center, so that a burr is left similar to the one shown at A.

A good way to overcome or avoid these troubles is to use a center, as shown at E and F. A regular center is ground, or milled, to within about $\frac{1}{16}$ in. of the center point. This will allow the point of the tool to enter the center, and it will face the work smooth; besides, the work may be very easily polished by folding a piece of emery cloth, holding it between the tool and the work, and pressing it against the tooled face by means of the lathe carriage while the work is revolving.—Contributed by Geo. M. Jager, Irvington, N. J.

Repairing an Automobile Brake

The internal expanding brake on a certain automobile gave trouble, and finally the car had to be laid up while repairs were made. In action the brake did not respond as quickly as it should, and when it did take hold it was so suddenly and so hard that the wheels slipped. An examination revealed nothing very wrong except that two

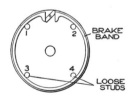

of the four studs, or posts, that spaced the brake band were loose. When new ones were made, driven in tightly, and riveted, the trouble ceased. These two loose studs let the band rise to the top when the cam was turned, and after considerable travel of the brake rod, the slack was taken up suddenly and so hard that it resulted in the slipping of the wheels.

An Aid in Drawing Fillet Lines

One of the most tedious operations in layout or detail work in a drawing room is the filling in of the lines of

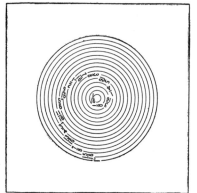

Any Circle Set on Two Intersecting Lines Locates the Center for Drawing Fillet Lines

fillets, or arcs, tangent to two or more lines. The usual way of measuring the distance between points of the compass and then trying to strike the right center is slow and tedious. A simple contrivance for finding this center can be made as follows:

Procure a piece of transparent celluloid, about 3 in. square. Set the points of a pair of dividers $\frac{1}{16}$ in. apart, and with one point as a center, set it as near the center of the celluloid as possible and strike a circle, scratching the celluloid so that the circle can be plainly seen. Then with a $\frac{1}{8}$-in. radius and the same center strike another circle. Make similar circles, increasing the radius by $\frac{1}{16}$ in., up to 1 in., or larger, if required. Prick a hole through the celluloid with the divider point at the common center. Scratch the radius length in figures on each circle, as shown.

If, for instance, it is necessary to draw a full-size $\frac{7}{16}$-in. arc between two intersecting lines, lay the celluloid on the drawing, placing the circle marked $\frac{7}{16}$ in. tangent to the two lines for the arc. Run the marker through the center hole until it pricks the paper sufficiently to be seen when the celluloid is removed. This point will be the exact center of the arc, and a compass, spaced to $\frac{7}{16}$ in., will draw the arc correctly. It is not necessary, however, to space the compass on the rule, as the center is found and the spacing can be done directly from the drawing.—Contributed by W. A. Scranton, Detroit, Mich.

How to Mix the Electrolyte for Lead Storage Batteries

The electrolyte used in the various types of lead batteries consists of a mixture of pure sulphuric acid and pure rain, or distilled, water. Sulphuric acid, when concentrated, is a liquid having a specific gravity of about 1.835; that is, it is about 1.835 times as heavy as water. It is customary to carry all gravity readings out to three decimal places, and the gravity of water, which is 1, is written 1,000 and read 1,000 rather than 1. Then, by this reading, pure sulphuric acid has a specific gravity of 1,835. A lead storage battery will not operate with acid of this strength, and it is necessary to dilute it with water. The electrolyte should be mixed, preferably, in a large jar, or lead-lined tank, and the acid must always be poured into the water while stirring the solution vigorously. In the operation of the storage battery the specific gravity of the electrolyte reaches a maximum of 1,250 to 1,300 when the cells are fully charged, and drops from 100 to 150 points when the cells are discharged. The lower and upper working limits of the gravity of the acid may then be assumed as 1,100 and 1,300, respectively. The following table may be used in determining the parts of water both by weight and volume, and the percentage of acid to water to produce the different gravities. The results in this table are based on the sulphuric acid having a specific gravity of 1,835 at 70° Fahrenheit.

The electrolyte used in the storage battery expands when heated, and its specific gravity will change, although the actual strength of the solution will remain the same as before heating. The gravity of the electrolyte will change approximately one point for each 3° change in the temperature on the Fahrenheit scale. For example, if the electrolyte has a specific gravity of 1,250 at 70° F. and its temperature has changed to 85° F., the increase in temperature will cause the electrolyte to expand and its gravity will decrease one point for each 3° rise in temperature, or the total decrease in this case will be five points and the gravity at 85° will be 1,245. Similarly, a decrease in temperature will result in an increase in gravity. As a matter of convenience 70° F. is considered the normal temperature and all corrections in gravity due to a change in temperature are made so as to give the value of the gravity at 70° Fahrenheit.

Specific Gravity of Solution 70° F.	Parts of Water to One Part Acid		Percentage of Sulphuric Acid in Solution
	By Volume	By Weight	
1100	9.80	5.40	14.65
1110	8.80	4.84	16.00
1120	8.00	4.40	17.40
1130	7.28	3.98	18.80
1140	6.68	3.63	20.10
1150	6.15	3.35	21.40
1160	5.70	3.11	22.70
1170	5.30	2.90	24.00
1180	4.95	2.70	25.20
1190	4.62	2.52	26.50
1200	4.33	2.36	27.70
1210	4.07	2.22	29.00
1220	3.84	2.09	30.20
1230	3.60	1.97	31.40
1240	3.40	1.86	32.50
1250	3.22	1.76	33.70
1260	3.05	1.66	35.00
1270	2.90	1.57	36.10
1280	2.75	1.49	37.30
1290	2.60	1.41	38.50
1300	2.47	1.34	39.65

Parts of Water by Weight and Volume and the Percentage of Acid to Produce the Different Gravities

The temperature at which the electrolyte in the lead storage battery will freeze depends upon the specific gravity of the solution. The curve given in the sketch shows the approximate relation between specific gravity and freezing temperature. This curve, as well as the other relations given, is used by one of the leading battery

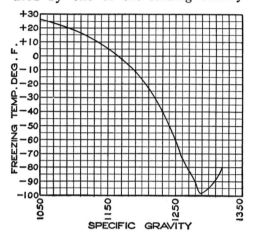

Curve Showing the Approximate Relation between Specific Gravity and Freezing Temperatures of the Electrolyte

manufacturers and may be considered, for practical purposes, fairly correct.

Attaching Casters to Angle-Iron Posts

The illustration shows a method of attaching casters to porch cots, or any equipment constructed of angle iron, that must be moved from time to time. Many persons use cots of this construction on their sun, or sleeping, porches, and have had finely

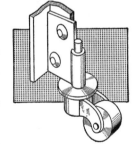

finished floors scratched and marred by the moving of the bed. The complete equipment is made up of two loose pin butts, using only the side with the double lugs, and is sawed in halves and riveted to the angle iron with the caster in place.—Contributed by W. D. Smith, San Francisco, Cal.

⁋Use turpentine instead of oil when drilling hard steel, saw plate, and the like.

Automatic Draft Deflector for a Window

An office clerk working at a desk to the right of which was a large window, on many occasions found it impractical, or uncomfortable, to raise the lower section of the window on account of the cold draft and for the sake of the

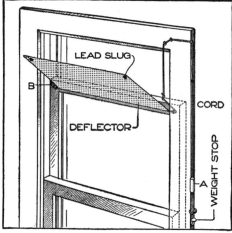

LEAD SLUG

B

CORD

DEFLECTOR

WEIGHT STOP

A

Deflector Attached to Upper Crosspiece of Top Sash and Operated by the Sash Movements

safety of the papers on the desk. It was also impractical to lower the upper section of the window, as the current of air was directed downward with almost the same results.

The sketch is descriptive of an automatic deflector applied to the upper crosspiece in the top sash, in such a manner that when the section is lowered, the deflector automatically rises to an angle of 45°, and the air rushing through the opening is deflected upward, ventilating the room perfectly without any inconvenience to the occupants.

The deflector is made of a piece of canvas, stretched over a wire frame. As the window section is lowered, the weight A pulls the deflector up to a point where it is held at 45° by a small lug, or stop, B. As the window is lowered farther, the weight A is only pulled a trifle more in serving its purpose. When the top section is again raised, the weight A falls until it rests on the small stop or shelf, and

the loose string then lets the deflector drop flat against the window. Two small lead billets in the corners of the deflector aid it in dropping when the raising weight is lowered to its shelf. The weight A is a small piece of lead, which is not conspicuous, since it runs along the thin side of the casing. The canvas deflector can be painted the same color as that of the casing and sash, and does not give any unsightly appearance to the room.—Contributed by F. W. Bentley, Missouri Valley, Iowa.

A Threading Tool for Taper Work

The sketch illustrates a very handy tool for cutting threads on short tapers, shoulders, and the like. While the tool was designed for work similar to that shown at A, it is also good for straight work.

The casing, or body, is a steel block, drilled and tapped for a plug at one end, the plug having a bearing for the tool-holder end. In boring the casing, a small shoulder is left at the end opposite the plug, to afford a seat for a ring on the tool holder. This ring also provides a seat for a helical spring,

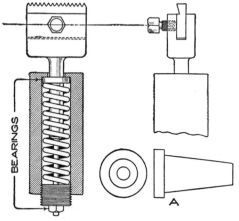

BEARINGS

A

Tool for Use on a Lathe Not Provided with a Compound Rest, for Cutting Taper Threads

used to hold the cutting tool to the work, yet allows it to be forced away from the work when the pressure becomes too great, which occurs when the tool begins to remove more metal than is necessary to produce the thread. The cutting tool is simply a standard "chaser," used in every shop of any size.

The pitch of the chaser, of course, must agree with the pitch of the thread to be cut, and the line of the teeth points must coincide with the taper of the work to be threaded, and, having been so set, it is only necessary to tighten the setscrew, set the tool for depth, and start the lathe just as in cutting any thread. The lathe, of course, must be geared for the same thread that the chaser is to cut, so that the feed of the lathe carriage may not conflict with the thread the chaser is cutting.

The work may be either chucked or carried on the centers, and the tool is clamped on the carriage, as it is too wide for the tool post. At the end of the cut, the feed is thrown off, and the tool quickly backed out by hand as usual. The spring arrangement takes the place of the compound rest in this class of thread-cutting.

Cutting Key Seats in Taper Holes

To cut key seats in magneto gears, or couplings on automobiles, which

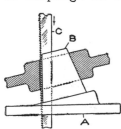

have a taper bore, is quite a task if not properly equipped for cutting them. The illustration shows a simple jig to use with a tool similar to a broach. The jig consists of a casting, A, with a steel plug, B, tapered to fit the work. One edge of B is set so that it will be perpendicular to the base, and a key seat is cut in it. A toothed drift, C, is made of tool steel to fit the key seat, and tapered along the teeth so that the upper ones extend far enough to give the proper depth to the keyway to be cut. It is only necessary to set the work on the plug B and drive the drift in the same as a broach. —Contributed by Allan J. Monahan.

Two-Way Switch for a Hall Light

A very handy contrivance for those using gas to illuminate a house is a small electric lamp to run on a battery, the lamp being operated with two switches, one placed just inside of the door and the other under the nearest gas light. This will allow a person to see the way clearly until the gas is lighted, when the electric lamp can be

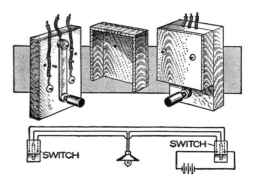

Operating an Electric Light in a Battery Circuit by Switches Located in Different Places

turned off without the trouble of returning to the door. For this purpose two-way switches must be used. They can be purchased cheaply, but are easily made by anyone at all handy with tools. The illustration shows the construction and scarcely needs a description. A small wood base, a piece of spring brass, a fiber, or wood, handle, and three screws are all that is necessary for one switch. The cover is in the form of a small box with one side removed, which can be fixed to the base with two screws. The wiring is shown in the diagram. The wires pass from the outside terminals of one switch to the outside terminals of the other. The center terminals connect directly to the lamp. The battery is connected to the two outside terminals of either switch. By this system of wiring, the lamp can be turned on or off at any time from either switch. The system is applicable to large rooms and basements where the gas light is some distance from the door.—Contributed by Morris G. Miller, New Rochelle, N. Y.

Reinforcing Hammer Handles

The illustration shows a method of bushing handles to prevent them from breaking at the eye of the hammer. The idea is one that will be appreciated by all machinists, toolmakers, and engineers that prefer tools of good ap-

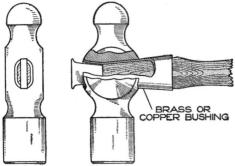

Bushing a Hammer Handle near the Head Where It Is Apt to Break Off

pearance and efficiency. Remove the handle from the head, and file the eye to the general shape shown, so that the bushing may be peened back to hold it in place. The front part of the eye is tapered uniform with the flat wedge, so that in driving the wedge into the end of the handle it also expands the bushing to the taper, and its sides force the wood of the handle and the soft bushing to the taper. This makes a neat and durable job, and adds much to the appearance of the hammer.

Hatrack for a Clothes Closet

Most clothes closets are built with a low ceiling, and do not provide sufficient space for hat hangers, so that the hats are apt to fall when taking out the clothes. In such a closet I made racks of a single piece of wire,

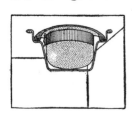

bent as shown and nailed to the ceiling of the closet. Hats placed on these racks are more secure from falling, while within as easy reach.—Contributed by J. V. Loeffler, Evansville, Ind.

Cleaning Steel of Burnt Oil

The oil, coming in contact with the surface of steel when hardening, will burn in places, and is hard to remove. The cleaning can be accomplished easily by immersing the hardened tool in gasoline, and when exposed to the air, it will dry immediately. This will leave the part to be polished without the marks of burnt oil.

Shifting Continuous Flow of Liquid without Loss

It is practically impossible to change cans under a flow of liquid without spilling some of it or at least having it run down the sides of one or both cans. The sketch shows an arrangement of fittings which will positively eliminate this trouble. The flow of liquid from the vat, or tank, is through a pipe leading to the place for filling the cans. On the end of this pipe a tee is fitted and nipples, A and B, turned into the tee openings. It is only necessary to

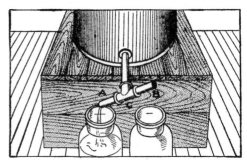

No Liquid can Escape in Turning the Tee from One Can to the Other

turn the tee, C, to change the flow from one can to the other, and there will not be a drop of waste.—Contributed by Ralph E. Frizzell, Cleveland, Ohio.

Lathe-Center Lubricant

White lead and sperm oil, mixed together with just enough graphite to give it a dark color, make a good lubricant for lathe centers. This grease can be kept in a tin box, and oil added when necessary, to keep it from becoming too thick.

To Keep a Long Stencil from Sagging

Doing stencil work alone on walls and ceilings is a tedious job, especially when the stencil is 10 in. or more long. In brushing one end, the other end hangs down in the way, and there is also danger of smearing the work. A remedy for this is to tack a thin strip of wood to one side of the stencil—a yardstick is about the right size. This will hold the stencil flat to the wall and avoid all danger of smears. In making lines on ceilings, I alone have in this way handled stencils that were 3 ft. in length, and made a good job of it.—Contributed by Claude O. Soots, N. Salem, Ind.

Removable Spurs on Ladder Ends

Working as a beltman in a large manufacturing plant, I had considera-

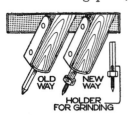

ble trouble in keeping the spurs on my ladder sharp. The floors were of wood, and a great many times the spurs would strike nails or pieces of metal on the floor, thus dulling the points. When dull, it was quite a task to remove and sharpen them. To overcome this difficulty I made the ends to hold a threaded spur, as shown. It is now very easy to remove the spur when it becomes dull, insert it in a holder, and grind a sharp point on it.—Contributed by William F. Gunn, Chicago, Ill.

Stiffening Thin Wall Board

If thin wall board, the cheap kind that is weak and flexible, is given a coat of filler and a coat of oil paint on each side, it will not only be preserved against warping, but will become decidedly stiffer and stronger. Painting on one side only does not prevent warping, and only slightly increases the strength.

To Make a Stovepipe Elbow

In a mining camp, far from a supply station, we received a lot of stovepipe, but there was not one elbow

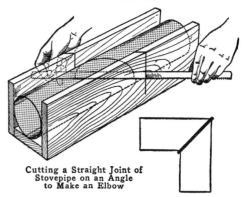

Cutting a Straight Joint of Stovepipe on an Angle to Make an Elbow

among them. To construct an elbow, which was badly needed, I made a box like a miter box, and cut a slot with a saw across the top, at a perfect 45-deg. angle. Then, with a hacksaw blade held in the hands, I sawed down through a straight length of pipe as shown. About ¼ in. of the stock on each slanting end was turned up like a flange. These flanged ends were set together to form the proper angle for the pipe, and then riveted, after which they were folded over to make the joint smoke-tight.—Contributed by W. A. Lane, El Paso, Tex.

Holding Threaded Studs in a Bolt Cutter

Short studs, or studs with only a small part left without threads, present a problem for the bolt cutter. In a certain machine - repair shop the usual scheme was to use a locknut, or to let a nut jam on the imperfect threads of the end first threaded. Both of these methods are crude and inefficient, as much time is lost in removing the stud. The following is an effective

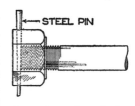

and simple solution of the difficulty. A hole, drilled through the base end of a nut as shown, is provided with a slightly tapered pin. The operation is evident. One end of the stud is threaded, the nut is placed in a vise, and the stud run up against the pin. After the threading, the pin is easily backed out by a slight rap and the stud removed with the fingers.

Flat Step for a Round-Rung Ladder

One who is not accustomed to painting, finds that the rungs of the ladder soon make the feet tired. This may

Flat Step to Fit on Ladder Rung, to Prevent the Feet from Becoming Tired

be prevented by procuring a plank, 1½ in. thick, 8 in. wide, and as long as the width of the ladder, and cutting notches in the ends to fit the sides of the ladder, for a step. Nail a small strip on the step, as shown, to keep the feet from slipping. The plank can be changed from rung to rung as desired.—Contributed by W. S. Drace, Richmond, Mo.

Heating Tips of Tools for Hardening

When it is necessary to heat the tips of tools to harden or anneal them, use a raw potato to prevent any other part of the tool from heating, as follows: Stick the tool through the potato, leaving only the portion to be worked projecting, and the heat will reach only the exposed part.

Using a Large Planer for a Press

Sometime ago we had several steel tubes, about 5 in. in diameter and 4 ft. long, which had to be a press fit over the piston rods they were to cover. Not having a press large enough to handle the job, we were stuck until the following idea was hit upon. There was about .003 in. left for a force fit. Both ends of each tube were capped and live steam turned into them, which enlarged them about the amount mentioned.

The rods were bolted upon the platen of a 36 by 36-in. planer, and a solid back stop was erected just far enough away to allow for starting the tube. When all was ready, the steam was turned off, the caps removed, and the tube lifted in position and shoved on by hand for about 8 in., when it began to go hard; then the planer was started very slowly, which pushed the tube home without further trouble. The whole scheme worked out very nicely and without much trouble or outlay.—Contributed by A. Dane, Pottstown, Pa.

A Carpenter's Clamp

The clamp illustrated is quite handy, as it can be made adjustable for almost any size of work. The bar is of cold-rolled steel, 6 ft. long, 2 in. wide, and ½ in. thick, with one end forged into a round shank and threaded. Two dogs are used on the bar, one adjustable for any position with the aid of holes through which a pin is inserted in the bar. The other dog travels only the

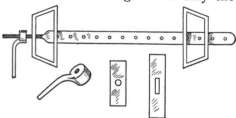

One Dog can be Set at Any Position within the Limits of the Bar, and the Other Used for Clamping

distance of the threads on the shank by the use of the handle.—Contributed by H. J. Olsen, Hibbing, Minn.

Shop Notes

Protecting the Surfaces of Enameled Road Signs

The use of enameled road signs is becoming very popular, but a great deal of trouble is caused by boys throwing stones at the signs, which chip the enamel from the iron surface. I have found a remedy that has ended the trouble in this locality and saved many dollars, for the signs are expensive. This simple remedy, while not hindering the reading of the signs, will effectively protect them from serious injury if they are hit with a hard object. On the back of the sign at the top and bottom, holes are drilled, and supporting brackets are attached to hold a thin mesh wire over the face of the sign. This will protect the sign, and answers the purpose better than anything that has been used.—Contributed by C. H. Thomas, Kennett Square, Pa.

Thawing Frozen Water Pipes

When the water freezes in the pipes of a house and the location of the frozen part is known, fill a water bag with hot water and place it on the frozen part, open the faucets to give vent, and before the water in the bag becomes cool the frozen part will be thawed out and the water running. This method has been used to advantage several times, and there is no danger of starting a fire as when using a gasoline torch.

Hose Drainer for Small Fire Stations

A great many laborious methods are sometimes employed to drain the hose of small fire stations before winding them on the reel for the next emergency. I have seen them pulled over rafters, shafting, and any projection which afforded a drop sufficient to drain the water out. The sketch illustrates a neat arrangement employed by

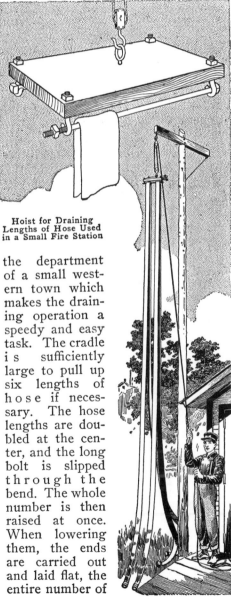

Hoist for Draining Lengths of Hose Used in a Small Fire Station

the department of a small western town which makes the draining operation a speedy and easy task. The cradle is sufficiently large to pull up six lengths of hose if necessary. The hose lengths are doubled at the center, and the long bolt is slipped through the bend. The whole number is then raised at once. When lowering them, the ends are carried out and laid flat, the entire number of lengths being prepared for winding on the reel. The arrangement is inexpensively erected, and it saves a great deal of work in the draining before the hose is wound on the reel.—Contributed by F. W. Bentley, Jr., Missouri Valley, Iowa.

Preventing the Loss of Spring-Bolt Caps

A most troublesome accident on one's automobile is to lose the cap of a spring bolt. These bolts are usually of a special type and carry a reservoir of grease for the purpose of lubricating the shackle. A spring inserted in the head against which the cap is screwed will prevent the latter from coming loose.

Figuring Width of Slot to Cut in Piston Rings

When turning up a set of piston rings for a gas or steam engine, the "blank" is turned larger than the bore of the cylinder; then when the rings are cut off to the proper width a certain portion is cut out of each ring, and the ring is sprung, closing the gap, to fit in the cylinder. The spring thus created in the ring causes it at all times to fit the cylinder tightly and make the piston gas or steam-tight under all conditions.

To the novice, and to many experienced men, the amount to cut out of a ring is a matter of guesswork, although a simple calculation will reduce the uncertainty to a certainty. As a general rule, blanks are turned 1/4 in. larger in diameter than the cylinder for every foot, and proportional amounts for smaller cylinders; a blank for a 12-in. cylinder being 12 1/4 in. in diameter and a blank for a 6-in. cylinder,

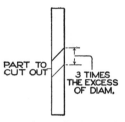

PART TO CUT OUT

3 TIMES THE EXCESS OF DIAM.

6 1/8 in. The amount to be cut out is three times the excess of size over the cylinder diameter, measuring on the circumference. For a 6-in. cylinder the amount would be 3x1/8 in., or 3/8 in. The exact amount would be 3.1416 x1/8 in., or .392, or fully 1/64 more than stated, but it is better to cut just three times, and leave the excess for filing off the rough edges left by the saw cut, and allowing sufficient metal to make a nice, close fit of the ends.

Recesses for Coiled Springs

In a certain hardware article a pawl was made to engage a rack, and was held by a coil spring set in a hole in the back of the pawl. The hole was drilled 1/4 in. in diameter, or .01 in. larger than the spring. So much trouble was experienced by the spring working out that the sale of the article was seriously affected, and yet, for

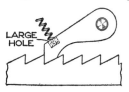

LARGE HOLE

certain reasons, the construction could not be changed. A tighter fit for the hole was tried, but each degree of tightness, while it lessened the trouble, reduced the resiliency of the spring. Purely by accident a gross of the pawls were put in with a hole 3/32 in. larger, and strange to say, no spring came out. As the adopted construction it proved a success.

To Keep Hot Water Constantly at the Faucet

Some hot-water tanks are installed in the basement where they are connected either with the furnace or with a gas heater. When the water is drawn, it is necessary to let it run for a time until the hot water comes. To overcome this, I continued the pipe from the faucet back to the tank, making the connection at the lower part. This will keep the water in the pipe in motion and thus keep the hot water at the faucet and prevent the waste every time hot water is wanted. I also put the hot-water pipe alongside the cold-water pipe to keep the latter from freezing. Where the pipe ran under the house, I cased it with boards to keep the heat in from the hot-water pipe.—Contributed by F. J. Schellhase, Mount Healthy, Ohio.

A Lettering Instrument for Draftsmen

The illustration shows a device to take the place of the lettering triangles and templates. The tool is constructed entirely of wood, cherry preferred—excepting, of course, the screw A—and is so simple that very little description is required. Its method of operation is also apparent. The tool is designed for plain Gothic letters, although the head may be graduated for any style of letter, or for two or more styles.

The tool reads right and left, as shown, and possesses a far greater range than any triangle, or lettering template, in sizes of letters, since the blade can be made to telescope, so that by extending it, large sign letters can be formed with it. From the small size shown it is possible to make all letters on drawings from the large to the small, ⅛ in. high, used on drawings. The tool is very much neater in appearance than the standard lettering

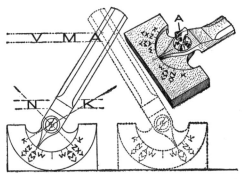

An Instrument to Take the Place of the Lettering Triangles and Templates Used by Draftsmen

triangles or templates, and occupies less space than the several triangles it replaces.—Contributed by J. B. Murphy, Plainfield, N. J.

An Emergency Fireplace Grate

As usually constructed, fireplaces are built for wood only, and cannot be used for coal unless especially provided with

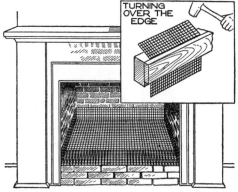

Grate Made of Coarse-Mesh Screen, to be Used for Coal in a Wood-Burning Fireplace

a suitable set of grates, which for the particular size and style of a fireplace might not be available. A removable grate for such an emergency can be made of woven wire screening, of about ¼-in. mesh and of ⅛-in. wire. Most any piece of screen, such as is scrapped from a gravel screen, will answer the purpose, providing it has no hole that would allow the coal to drop through.

In laying out the screen preparatory to bending up the edges, as shown in the illustration, it is best to make a wood template which easily fits the fireplace. This shape can be marked off on the wire, leaving about 2 or 3 in. for bending up at the sides and ends. This border strip is cut at the corners to allow for the turning up of the edge. To turn the edges, fasten the screen to a beam, or the workbench edge, with a board on the outside, then beat the projecting edge over with a hammer.

The screen grate, when finished, can be supported with brick laid around the outer edges and on the floor of the fireplace, with one brick in the center, to prevent sagging under the heavy weight. The ashes can be removed in the usual manner from underneath the grate by means of a shovel. For appearance, and to prevent ashes from falling out, a temporary row of brick can be set up in front of the grate.—Contributed by F. W. Buerstatte, Pullman, Wash.

A Washing-Machine Water Heater

The illustration shows a simple homemade attachment for a washing machine, to keep the water hot. As

The Water is Heated and Kept Hot in the Machine All the Time While Washing

may be seen, the heating unit consists of two ¾-in. pipes, one return bend, two unions, and two close nipples, which are screwed into the sides of the machine. The stove is a single-burner hot plate. The unions permit the ready dismantling of the pipes in case they become clogged with dirt. This attachment, fitted to a power machine, lightens the work considerably.

Flexible Holding Means for an Automobile-Engine Bed

It happens quite frequently that a supporting arm of a truck engine becomes fractured, due to sudden twists to which the frame is exposed on rough roads. A good method of fastening the engine of an automobile is shown in the s k e t c h. The device consists of a rather stiff helical spring, placed between the bottom of the bolt head and the top of the boss on the supporting arm. The spring takes up the twists and strains given to the frame as the car passes over rough roads.

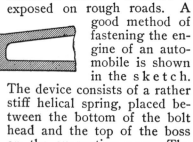

How to Make an Aluminum Screen for Moving Pictures

In making an aluminum screen for moving-picture theaters, the amateur will find it a difficult job if he tries to apply the aluminum paint with a brush, as it dries too quickly for the inexperienced to put it on without making laps, and laps mean that veil effect that must be avoided if clear pictures are desired.

A simple way in which an amateur can make a first-class screen is as follows; the description being for a screen 8 by 10 ft., but the size can be varied to suit conditions. First make a light frame of wood to hold the cloth, then shrink the goods by washing it in alum water. A handful of alum to a 2-gal. pail of water makes the solution. When the cloth is dry, tack it on the frame, making sure that it is stretched tightly and without wrinkles. To make a neat job tack about every 4 in. The filler consists of 1 gal. linseed oil; 1 pt. japan drier, and 6 lb. of white lead. Stir until well mixed and apply with a brush, giving the cloth a second coat after letting the first dry 12 hours. When the second coat is dry, which requires about 16 hours if the room is moderately warm, it is ready for the aluminum, or bronzing, liquid. This is the proper condition of the cloth for either method. This size curtain will require ½ gal. of bronzing liquid, and if it cannot be readily obtained, use varnish slightly thinned with turpentine. Place the screen face up on horses, or on four chairs, and pour the liquid on it. Tilt the screen first one way and then the other so that the liquid will cover every part of the face, or smooth side. Sprinkle on aluminum bronze all over the screen before the liquid dries. Tilt the screen as before, and it is well to shake it also so that the bronze will be distributed over the surface. Place the screen on the horses, as level as possible, and let it lie until dry, which will require about two hours. Then stand the screen up on edge and tap it lightly on the back to jar off any loose bronzing powder. This will produce a screen without a lap or any veil effect. It is the only method by which anyone not familiar with the different kinds of paints can handle a screen with the desired effect, leaving out the streaks and laps.—Contributed by Claude O. Soots, North Salem, Ind.

Removing Locomotive Crank Arm Easily

When a main rod of an engine equipped with a valve gear has been taken off, the side rod cannot be removed until the crank arm is taken from its place. A great many locomotives with such valve gears have the crank arms, which fit in a bored-out portion of the crank pins, a drive fit and kept tightly in place with a long bolt through the crank pin. These crank arms are very difficult to remove, and for this reason the device illustrated was designed to make the work easy, and it gives entire satisfaction. The device is placed on the pin, and the wedges are driven in to remove the

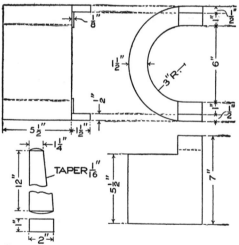

Eccentric-Crank Arms Made to a Drive Fit on Pins are Easily Removed

crank arms. The lugs are provided to keep the wedges from working out and away from where they are most effective.—Contributed by Joseph K. Long, Renovo, Pa.

ℭ Do not screw pipe together for either steam, water, or gas without putting white or red lead on the threads.

Spraying Pipe for Washing Windows

A local merchant in a small town had some difficulty in washing the plate-

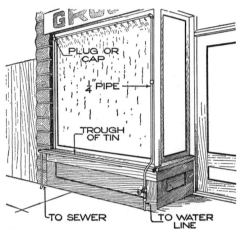

The Spray Pipe Flushes the Glass with Water, and the Drain Runs It to the Sewer

glass windows. One or two pedestrians accidentally stumbled into the bucket of water which the clerk was using to flush the window glass. The difficulty was overcome very nicely, by him and by many other merchants, in the following manner: A pipe perforated with small holes was run along the top of the window, and one end of the pipe was connected with a valve to the city water main inside of the store. At the bottom of the window a small tin trough or eave was run, one end of which emptied into the sewer drain. The water was turned on from the inside and a small valve was put in on the outside, to control the flow. The window was at once flushed with clean water, but at the same time without the necessity of handling a heavy pail and a splattering swab. All the work necessary was to dry the pane with the thin rubber blade for that purpose. The convenience of the arrangement was well worth the time and expense.

ℭ The minute specks sometimes seen on mahogany piano cases are caused by oil that exudes from the wood. Shellac varnish will not hold it back. The only cure is to rub it down and revarnish.

Hand Rest for Bookkeepers

The one disadvantage of the ordinary arm rest for bookkeepers is that its surface is too low for comfort.

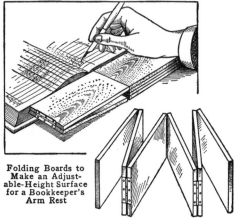

Folding Boards to Make an Adjustable-Height Surface for a Bookkeeper's Arm Rest

When its end is placed between the book pages the rest part is not level with the page on which the entry is to be made. This difficulty is entirely overcome by making a series of thin boards, the width desired for the rest and as long as the book page is wide. These are hinged together at the ends so that they will spread out similar to a hearth screen. It is easy to stack them for the proper height.

Curb Blocks for Road Pavements

In making paved roadways in the country, and especially in sandy soil, there is no necessity for having a curb

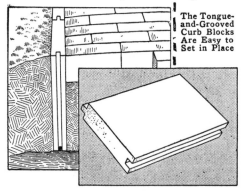

The Tongue-and-Grooved Curb Blocks Are Easy to Set in Place

with a gutter. The curb should be merely a support for the paving edges or blocks and a protection against damage by the vehicle wheels. One municipality, where it was necessary to build a paved roadway in sandy soil, used an interlocking curb block that was tongued and grooved, the blocks being about 24 in. long, 18 in. deep, and 4 in. wide, made of concrete. These blocks were set in the soil on the curb line so that their upper edges were level with the tops of the paving blocks. The shape of the block and the manner in which it is placed in the earth are clearly shown in the illustration.

Making Teeth for Gear Patterns Quickly

The making of teeth for gear patterns is always a tedious job, and when they are worked out one at a time, no matter how carefully they are laid out or how skillful the workman, the results are seldom satisfactory. With the use of the jig shown in the sketch and a correctly made sanding cylinder, hundreds of teeth may be made which will all be duplicates, and if the directions given here are carefully followed, it will be impossible to detect the slightest variation in size or contour between the first and the last tooth taken from the jig.

The jig is made the exact shape of the tooth required, but 3 or 4 in. longer, and with more than 1 in. of stock below what would be the root circle of the gear. It should be made of a piece of hard wood. This is planed up straight, with parallel sides and edges, and with the ends smoothed up for laying out the teeth. The laying out and working to the lines must be done very carefully. After the block is finished, the space for the tooth blank is cut away, and two screw holes are drilled to hold the blank in place during the finishing process. The projecting piece on the end of the jig is securely fastened with glue and a couple of brads. It should project about ¼ inch.

For the sanding cylinder, turn up a piece of hard wood, 2½ or 3 in. in diameter, and 1 in. or more longer than the jig. It should be the same diameter and perfectly straight from end to end. In the center a groove is then turned, about ¼ or ⅜ in. longer than the tooth blank, and of a depth slightly greater than the thickness of a piece of No. 2 sandpaper. The object is to fill the turned-out portion with sandpaper and still have a cylinder that will be perfectly straight from end to end. The sandpaper is cut in narrow strips and wound around the cylinder like a helix, fastening it with glue as the winding proceeds.

A groove is then turned to take the raised, or projecting, piece on the jig, and it should be so located that the tooth-blank space will come directly over the sandpaper-covered part of the cylinder, with the sandpaper projecting ⅛ in. or more beyond the space at each end.

The tooth-blank stock is cut the exact length of the tooth, and should fit snugly in the space in the jig. The bottom of each tooth is first planed with a round plane to fit the root circle of the wheel, and the flanks are roughly shaped to the tooth outline.

The operation of this device is as follows: The sanding cylinder is put on the lathe centers and the belt thrown on; the jig with a blank in place is taken in both hands and held on the revolving cylinder with the projecting piece running in the groove turned for it. This brings the blank

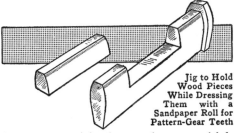

Jig to Hold Wood Pieces While Dressing Them with a Sandpaper Roll for Pattern-Gear Teeth

in contact with the sandpaper, which rapidly grinds it flush with that part of the jig that is in contact with the smooth ends of the cylinder. The jig is rocked back and forth while grinding, and the groove and projecting

piece keep it perfectly parallel with the axis of the cylinder.

Teeth for bevel wheels are made just as easily as for spur gears, and the same idea may be applied to many articles of woodwork that are to be duplicated many times.—Contributed by J. A. Shelly, Brooklyn, N. Y.

A Folding Shaving-Material Shelf

A simple and useful shelf upon which to place a mirror, and other

Shelf Attached to the Facing under a Window to Hold Toilet Articles While Shaving

toilet articles, while shaving, can be made as follows: Procure a board, ½ in. thick, and of the same length and width as the facing under the sill of the bathroom window, and fasten it to the lower edge of this piece with two small hinges, as shown. Support the ends with two pieces of small chain to hold the shelf at the right level. The position of the shelf affords a fine light, and if it is given the same finish as the woodwork of the bathroom, it will not be noticed when it is folded up.—Contributed by Frank L. Matter, Portland, Ore.

Antirust and Fireproof Paint

A good antirust paint for structural work is made of red lead, 60 lb., zinc white, 30 lb., and graphite, 10 lb.; all ground in raw linseed oil. The addition of some china clay will prevent too rapid drying. To make a good fireproof paint use the preceding formula and add to it ½ lb. of boracic acid or sal ammoniac.

Fishing Electric Wires into Walls

Having occasion to run an electric wire down between the plastering of a wall where the holes through the plate and the floor were not plumb, I tied a small iron screw to a line I let down through the ceiling-plate hole, and after feeling it hit the bottom I drew it back up about 1 ft. A small magnet was tied to a stiff wire and inserted through the floor hole, and I was able to attract quickly the hanging screw, which was easily drawn through the hole.—Contributed by Ed. Kresko, Port Jefferson, N. Y.

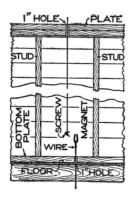

To Keep a Boot from Rubbing the Heel

To keep a boot that is rather loose from rubbing the heel and wearing the sock, take a piece of soft leather, about 15 in. long and 1½ in. wide, and prepare it as follows: Fasten a buckle on one end, and punch two or three holes in the other end for the buckle tongue. Cut a slit in the leather, beginning about 1 in. from the buckle and ending within 7 in. of the other end. Part the two pieces, slip the heel

Strap Split in the Center and Buckled over the Heel to Prevent Heel Movement

into the opening, pass the other end over the instep and buckle it on the outside. — Contributed by Maurice Fischer, Mokelumne Hill, Cal.

Care of Automobile Springs

Many motorists do not give the attention to the car-body springs necessary to keep them in good condition. These springs need oil the same as any bearing on the car. Many cheap devices are on the market for opening the springs so that oil or graphite can be inserted, and this attention should be given at least every six months if the car is used regularly. The springs should be taken apart and polished once every year, and thoroughly greased before being put together.

A Homemade Oil Indicator

An oil indicator placed on the dash of an automobile is a most desirable feature, since the driver can immediately

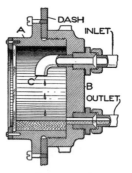

tell whether the lubricating system is operating properly, and thus many times burned-out bearings will be avoided. The car I owned had no indicator, and I decided to construct one, which resulted in the one illustrated made from parts picked up around the garage.

The body A of the indicator was made from an old hub cap, turned down on the inside and faced off on one edge, as shown. The cover B was made of an old adjusting nut of a clutch. Connections to and from the indicator were made by means of ordinary brass couplings, the upper, which is the inlet, being connected to a small pipe C for the purpose of leading the oil into the indicator. A glass cover is placed at the front of the instrument, as shown, which is held in place by means of a metal ring and small machine screws. The indicator is fastened to the dash in the manner shown, two machine screws being used to prevent it from turning and becoming loose.—Contributed by Adolph Kline.

Keeping an Oil Hone True

A simple way to keep an oil hone true and in good cutting condition is as follows. Wet a sheet of No. 1½ sandpaper and lay it, sand side up, on a flat surface, iron preferred. Rub the cutting face of the hone on the sand surface until it is true and flat. Next rub the face of the hone with another oil hone. This will remove the grit, or sand, imbedded in the surface, which is most important. Finish by holding the face of the hone on a revolving sand grindstone while plenty of water is applied. This will tone up the cutting qualities.

Marking Circles on a Clockface

In restoring an old clockface I used a mechanical aid to mark the circles bounding the hour numerals. It consisted of a wood arm pivoted on the post that holds the hands, and notched at two points to hold a ruling pen. For the sake of balance, the arm should extend for an equal distance on each side of the center. I found it much easier to make perfect circles in this way, as a ruling pen insures an even thickness of the lines and leaves no marks where they meet if the circles are drawn in sections. The old enamel

Drawing New Lines on an Old Clockface with the Aid of a Ruling Pen

surface took the drawing ink nicely after it had been washed with a weak solution of ammonia in water. The face was varnished after the marks were restored.—Contributed by James M. Kane, Doylestown, Pa.

A Bench Stop That Clamps the Work

The stop consists of two oak or maple blocks, about 6 in. long and ⅞ in. thick, cut in the shape shown and fastened to the bench top with screws through their centers. They are so set that the opening toward the work will be about

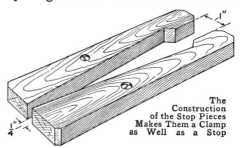

The Construction of the Stop Pieces Makes Them a Clamp as Well as a Stop

1 in. A board will be held firmly when it is pushed into the stop. The harder the work is pushed in, the tighter it will be held.—Contributed by T. S. Hastings, Detroit, Mich.

Beveling and Chamfering Tool for a Lathe

A simple little tool which is very efficient within its range is shown in the illustration. The tool is designed to be carried in the machinist's tool chest as a part of his equipment. This tool is to take the place of the compound rest on the various machine tools where such a rest is not provided; in fact it is a miniature compound rest.

While this tool may be set at any angle by means of a protractor, its chief work is short chamfers, such as lathe, and other, centers; valves, taps; the ends of reamer blades, etc., where it is especially convenient. The travel of the tool, operated by the feed screw A, is 1 in., and this will not cause enough overhang to make the tool chatter, if ordinary care is used in its operation.

The screw B is recessed into the tool holder C, and acts as a guide to prevent the tool from turning under the cut. The shank square D of the turning tool is a tight push fit in the tool holder C. The tool holder must be a firm running fit in the casing. The whole arrangement is set in the tool post just as an ordinary tool. If it is to be used on a very small lathe, or

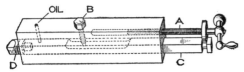

Screw-Feed Chamfering Tool to Fit in the Tool Post of a Lathe, Planer, or Shaper

other machine where the tool post is too small, it may be clamped to the tool-post block.

Clamp for Inaccessible Places

It often happens, when it becomes necessary to patch a piece of work, or

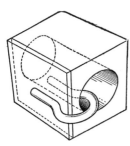

part of a machine, worn out or otherwise damaged, that the place to be repaired is quite inaccessible for a clamp to hold the patch while drilling the rivet-pin holes. A piece of steel rod bent as shown, close enough to give it a spring clamping tension, overcomes the difficulty admirably.—Contributed by R. Hollis, Chicago.

Reinforcing Flattened Pipe Ends

Ordinary wrought-iron pipe, used as structural material for railings, knee braces, etc., is

very desirable, because of its light weight and relatively great stiffness. It suffers from lack of strength at the flattened ends, however. These may be greatly improved by inserting a piece of pipe the next size smaller, or a flat bar of steel before flattening the metal.—J. J. O'Brien, Buffalo, N. Y.

Nozzle for a Fine Spray

For the purpose of coating a certain hardware specialty it was desired to pass the article before a fine spray, the spray to be forced by a power pump. It was also desired that the spray should come through a row of holes, about .003 in. in diameter, and extend in a straight line 1½ in. long directly across the path of the work. When it came to drilling the holes, it was found that a satisfactory spray could not be secured in this way. In the first place the holes were not close enough together, they would fill up, and some holes would blow more than others. The scheme finally hit upon was to run the pipe into the end of a piece of cold-rolled steel, 1½ in. in diameter, drilled and tapped to receive it. This hole was 2 in. deep, and at that depth four smaller holes were drilled crosswise, making eight outlets. The piece of steel ex-

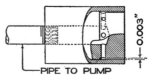

A Fine Spray, That will Not Clog, Obtained from an Annular Opening in the Nozzle

tending from the row of holes to the end was turned down, or reduced, .006 in. in diameter, and over the whole was pressed a piece of steel tubing having an inside diameter of 1½ in. This made an annular space .003 wide and covering the path of the work, 1½ in. wide, which gave a good spray.

Squaring a Planer Vise

Clamp a long straightedge in the vise, and then it is an easy matter to measure from the straightedge to the edge of the planer table with a 2-ft. rule and get it square quickly. In shops that are kept up, this method is not used much, on account of using the tongue-and-groove in the bottom of the vise to fit in the planer slots, mostly used in small repair shops.—Contributed by W. E. Butler, Wausaukee, Ill.

Measuring Wire without a Gauge

When a gauge is not at hand to determine the size of a wire, closely wind a sufficient length on a smooth nail to cover exactly ½ in. and then count the number of turns. Double this number and refer to the following table, which will immediately give the correct gauge.

Gauge	Turns per inch	Gauge	Turns per inch
10	10	24	50
11	11	25	56
12	12	26	63
13	14	27	70
14	16	28	79
15	18	29	89
16	20	30	100
17	22	31	112
18	25	32	126
19	28	33	141
20	31	34	159
21	35	35	178
22	39	36	200
23	44		

With smaller sizes it is only necessary to wrap about ¼ in. on the rod, or nail, to get the number of turns per inch.—Contributed by John D. Adams, Phoenix, Ariz.

Fire-Hose Attachment to a Switch Engine

An effective pressure, sufficient to throw a stream of water for fighting fires, was obtained by the use of an attachment on the injector of a switch engine used about the yards of a railroad. When used for a fire, the valve A on the boiler line is closed, and the valve B to the fire hose, which is normally kept closed, is opened. The hose is kept attached and the end

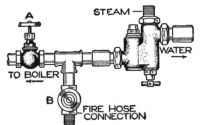

The Injector on the Engine Produces the Pressure for the Fire Hose

coiled on a reel at the side of the engine. As the tender carries 7,000 gal. of water, quite a supply is available for fire purposes before it runs too low for steaming.

A Lock for a Ladder

Being desirous of leaving a ladder standing against my barn for observation purposes and not wanting the boys

A Door Covering the Rungs of a Ladder is Locked in Place to Prevent Boys from Climbing

to be climbing it, I rigged up the ladder with a door which may be locked, as shown. The back of the ladder is also solidly boarded in.—Contributed by R. F. Pohle, Lynn, Mass.

An Extension for a Tire Pump

On automobiles having the valve-in-the-head motors, many owners find it next to impossible to use a spark-plug impulse tire pump, a type that has done much to relieve the work of inflating the tires. On these motors the valve rods interfere with the application of the pump when a spark plug is removed.

To overcome this difficulty a special connection may be made. It will not cost much and will be well worth the making. One end is threaded to fit the spark-plug threads in the cylinder, and the other to turn into the pump. Two plates should be put on the sides

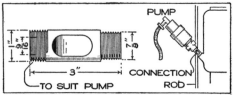

Connection to Attach a Tire Pump in a Spark-Plug Hole Where Valve Rods Interfere

so that a wrench can be used to tighten it. The illustration shows such a connection and how it is used.

Guard for a Punch Press

Where it is necessary to feed pieces by hand into a punch press for forming them, the possibility of injuring the operator's hands is very great, and to eliminate this danger there must be some kind of movable guard that will not be in the way of the feeding of the press, yet obstruct the way just before, and at the time of, making the stroke. The illustration shows a form of guard I have employed with success.

The lever A should be about 12 to 1, which will move the wood pieces about 5 in. across the die, this being sufficient for small dies. The vertical length of the pieces is limited to the height of the ram when it is down. The space

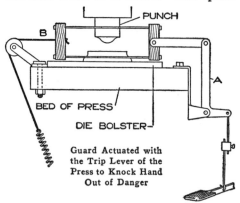

Guard Actuated with the Trip Lever of the Press to Knock Hand Out of Danger

will be from 4½ to 5 in. The pieces are held together with ⅛-in. wires. The guard is returned to its normal position with a small, round belt, or strong cord, attached and run over a

pulley to a long weak spring. The adjusting rod is hooked to the pedal near the footplate so that it will move farther than the part where the clutch rod is connected. In action, the wood piece B will be entirely across the die before the clutch is released, and will knock the hand away as it passes.— Contributed by S. C. Bunker, Brooklyn, N. Y.

Coverings for Marine-Motor Spark Plugs

Having no way to cover my boat engine I devised a way to protect the spark plugs in the following manner:

I purchased several hollow rubber balls, about 2 in. in diameter, and in each ball I cut a hole slightly larger than the base of the spark plug. About 1½ in. above this hole a smaller hole was cut for the wire connection to the plug. A slot was cut between the holes, and the ball slipped over the spark plug. The slit remains tightly closed when the ball is on the plug, thus forming a serviceable covering.— Contributed by L. H. Ritchie, Georgeville, Can.

The Use of Skid Chains

Never drive an automobile with a skid chain on one of the rear wheels only. When skid chains are necessary, it is far better to use two chains—one on each rear tire. When but one chain is used and the brake is applied, the wheel to which the chain is attached will stop readily, but the wheel without a chain will spin around many times, which tends to grind off the tread and causes it to wear much faster than if two chains were used. On an actual try-out it was found, at the end of a 1,500-mile run, that the tire having the chain was not at all damaged and the tire without a chain had the tread almost worn off.

To Fasten Runners in White-Metal Patterns

In making white-metal patterns, I have always found it difficult to fasten the runners securely to the pattern where they are to be used in bench molding. They can be firmly fastened, however, by casting them in the pattern when poured. The brass runners are first tinned, then a mold is made from the master pattern, and the brass runners are laid in their proper places. Then the runners are cut to cast the pattern so that the hot metal will flow around the brass pieces until the mold is full, which fastens them to the pattern. Two or more patterns are attached to the gate in the usual way.

I have two white-metal patterns that have been in use for some time, and they are still firmly attached to the gate, and are as satisfactory as brass patterns, while the cost is very much less. The patterns weigh 3½ lb.

Fastening Runners to White-Metal Patterns by Casting Them in the Piece When Poured

BRASS RUNNERS RUNNERS TO CAST PATTERN

each, and where the runners are attached the metal is only 3/16 in. thick, which would make it very difficult to fasten them in the ordinary way.—Contributed by W. E. Smisor, Waterloo, Iowa.

To Stop Planer Bed at Same Point Each Time

In planing out a keyway in a shaft, or up against a shoulder of any kind, it often happens that the planer will not stop at the same place every time, but goes farther, usually breaking the tool. Tighten up the reverse belt, and it will stop at the same place every stroke.—Contributed by W. E. Butler, Wausaukee, Wis.

To Stop the Chattering of a Large Lathe

A large lathe in one of our shops always gave trouble when it was used for finishing large shafts and bushings. No matter how tightly the head bearings and the tailstock might be,

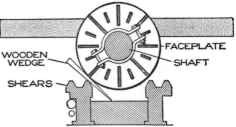

WOODEN WEDGE — FACEPLATE — SHAFT — SHEARS

The Wedge, Driven in Snugly between the Shears and Faceplate Edge, Stops the Chatter

it would chatter. One day a new man was set to work on the lathe to turn up several large shafts. When he came to the finishing part, he stopped the chatter by inserting a long, thin taper wedge between the shears and the faceplate edge. The wedge was set snugly with a hammer.—Contributed by Joe V. Romig, Allentown, Pennsylvania.

To Prevent Bookkeeper's Hand Rest from Slipping

The ordinary hand rest used by bookkeepers to slip in between the leaves of a large ledger gives considerable trouble by slipping out of place, if the book leaves are the least bit smooth. This can be easily remedied if two wide and thin rubber bands are

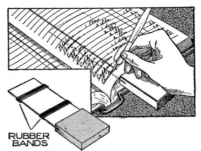

RUBBER BANDS

Rubber Bands on the Thin Portion of a Bookkeeper's Hand Rest to Prevent Its Slipping

placed over the thin portion that is inserted between the pages.

An Efficient Automobile Top

The style of automobile top illustrated is specially adapted for tank trucks where its rear projection causes

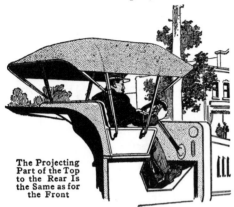

The Projecting Part of the Top to the Rear Is the Same as for the Front

no interference with the load. It will be noticed that the top differs from the ordinary single-seat top in that it projects to the rear as well as to the front, keeping the driver's back shaded without the use of a curtain, which hinders the view when glancing backward.

Doubling Capacity of Spring Scales

The ordinary variety of spring scales can be made to weigh double the amount given on the dial by the simple beam arrangement shown in the illustration. Suitable dimensions are given, although these may be varied to suit

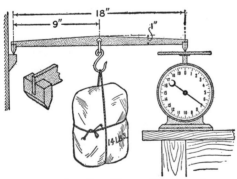

The Beam Provides a Means of Weighing Large Objects on a Small Spring Scale

the requirements. The only thing to remember is that the hook must be located exactly halfway along the beam

measuring between the two knife-edged pieces of wood fixed at the ends. The beam should be made of light but strong wood, ¼ in. thick, and the end pieces 1 in. long. In use, the beam should be approximately level, with one end placed on the center of the scale platform and the other end set on a support, which could be a piece of wood nailed to the wall, or any other support. The object hung on the hook will show only half its weight on the dial. Thus if the pointer indicates 15 lb. the object weighs 30 pounds.

A Convenient Test Gauge

A very convenient and easily made reference gauge for toolmakers and

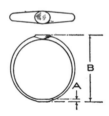

machinists is in the form of a finger ring. It is made of steel with three flat surfaces ground as shown in the illustration. The smaller dimension, A, should be about ⅟₃₂ in., and the larger one, B, in some common fraction. The ring may be made very artistic. It provides an accurate and always convenient reference gauge. A micrometer that is accurate at these two dimensions, that is one small and one large dimension, is usually safe for general work.

A Double-Capacity Clothesline

A clothesline of double capacity can be made of any-width net, or mesh wire, stretched between two supports to keep the wire taut. Clothes may be hung on both sides of the wire. Sheets can be thrown over the whole wire and easily kept off the ground.—Contributed by Autrey Monsey, Trickham, Texas.

❢Do not use a reamer in a pipe, as the flux, used in welding or brazing, is as hard as glass and will ruin the reamer.

A Hollow-Tile Ice House

By W. E. FRUDDEN

THERE is one kind of material that makes a good wall for an ice house and that is hollow tile. The plans shown are for a house to hold 25 tons, the amount consumed by the average family for one year. This size makes an excellent one for the farmer. Ice stored in a tile structure of this kind will keep during the hot summer months without much loss, and it makes a building of a permanent nature.

The floor and foundations are made of concrete, using a mixture of 1 part cement, 3 parts sand, and 5 parts gravel. A drain pipe is placed in the center of the floor, and the concrete made sloping from every direction toward it. The tile walls are 8 in. thick and are laid up 9½ ft. above the concrete work. A wood plate is bolted to the top course of tile, and the rafters are cut and spiked to it as in ordinary building construction. A crosstie is nailed to each pair of rafters on the plate for use in supporting the ice-carrier track. The gable ends are of frame with ordinary barn siding, and the roof is covered with shingles fastened with galvanized nails. A ventilator is placed in each gable to provide a means for letting the excess moisture pass out.

The door, or doors, is built up in three-ply thickness, using a tarred-felt insulator between each layer. The door is best made in two sections, and

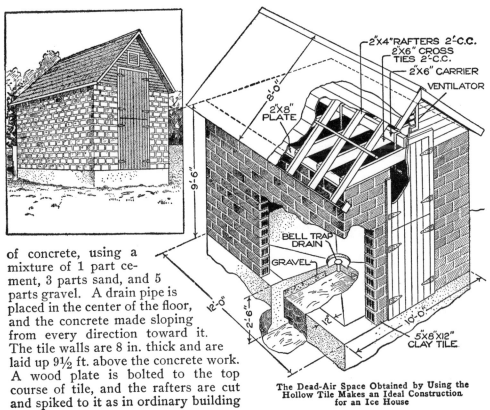

The Dead-Air Space Obtained by Using the Hollow Tile Makes an Ideal Construction for an Ice House

swung on heavy hinges. The frame for the door is constructed of 8-in. plank, and removable leaves are cut to fit the back of the frame, to hold the sawdust and ice away from the door.

To construct this building will require the following materials:

    5 bbl. cement.
    3 cu. yd. clean sharp sand.
    5 cu. yd. coarse gravel.
  840 hollow-clay building blocks, 5 by 8 by 12 in.
    9 anchor bolts.
    2 pieces 2 by 8-in. material, 10 ft. long, for plates.
    2 pieces 2 by 8-in. material, 12 ft. long.
    7 pieces 2 by 6-in. material, 10 ft. long, for cross-ties.
    1 piece 2 by 6-in. material, 12 ft. long, for carrier-track support.
   14 pieces 2 by 4-in. material, 8 ft. long, for rafters.
  140 ft. 6-in. flooring, for doors.
  225 ft. roof sheathing.
2,000 cedar shingles.

Wagon Racks for Hauling Pipe

Plumbers and steam fitters, or anyone having occasion to use a wagon for hauling pipe, will find two such

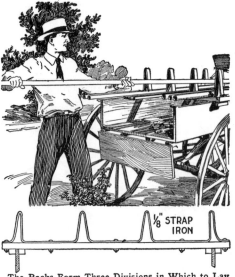

⅛" STRAP IRON

The Racks Form Three Divisions in Which to Lay the Pipe to Prevent Rolling

racks as illustrated very handy to prevent the pipe from rolling about. The racks, or frames, are made of 2 by 4-in. material with bent iron uprights forming three places to lay the pipe. The method of bending these is clearly shown, and such a contrivance will prove very handy to use, it being a simple matter to toss the frames across the wagon box.—Contributed by Patterson D. Merrill, Chicago.

Clearance of Milling Cutters

In grinding the clearance on the cutting edge of milling cutters, sufficient attention is usually not paid to the angle or exact amount of clearance the cutter will have on the work. This is a very important matter, as too much one way or the other will result in failure on the job.

If the clearance is too great, the cutter will have a tendency to chatter and make a rough finish, to say nothing of the disagreeable noise, and the loosening up of the bolts and clamps on the machine will cause the heel of the land to drag, making an uneven surface, and is liable to break the teeth.

The angle depends, to a great extent, on the diameter of the cutter and also on the material it is to cut, although, in general, milling cutters are used on almost anything that can be cut, from a piece of hard wood to high-carbon tool steel, making regular shapes, such as plain, slabbing, slanting, or angular, while in those that are made up for a special job and used for that purpose only, more attention must be given to the kind of material to be cut.

Generally soft materials will machine better with more clearance than tool steels, and the like, although conditions may cause the reverse to happen. Usually, for cutters up to 4 in. in diameter, from 6 to 7 deg. will be found ample on the outside diameter. Over and above this diameter, the angle may decrease, say, ¼ deg. for each 1 in. in diameter, until 4 deg. is reached, which is about the minimum amount for any cutter.

The clearance on the teeth of end mills should be from 2 to 3 deg., when the cutters are used for roughing and finishing. If used for roughing alone, a little more clearance will give better results.—Contributed by A. Dane, Pottstown, Pa.

❑A small piece of rosin stirred into melted babbitt will improve and make it run better. The rosin-treated babbitt will run into places where the plain will not enter.

Filling Pits in Varnish on Pianos

If the varnish on a piano has pitted, fill the pits with a wax made as follows: Melt together ½ oz. of carnauba wax, 2 oz. japan wax, or white beeswax, and 2 oz. of ceresin wax, in a suitable vessel. A good method is to place one vessel inside of another, place hot water in the outside one, and set them both on a stove. This is called a hot-water bath. When melted, add kerosene enough to form a mass like petroleum jelly, when cool. This may be tested by placing some of it on a piece of glass and letting it cool. If it seems too hard, add a little more kerosene. Rub in on the piano with a wool pad, giving two or more applications until the pits are filled.

Storing Paint without Waste

In shops where a great deal of painting is done it is difficult to store the paint in such a manner that it will not thicken nor a skin form on the surface. The illustration shows how the difficulty may be overcome. The paint is kept in kegs which are filled and emptied through a spout made of 1½-in. pipe, the end being covered with a pipe cap except when filling and emptying. The emptying is done by rolling the keg on skids to the proper position. By using small kegs, say 10-gal. size, the

Skids for a Paint Keg to Make the Pouring Easy and Prevent Waste

paint may be shaken up before it is poured.—Contributed by J. J. O'Brien, Buffalo, N. Y.

Connections for an Expansion Tank

In setting a radiator on the top, or attic, floor, make the connections to the expansion tank as shown, and there

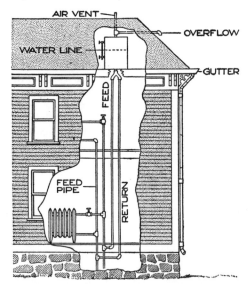

Pipe and Connections to the Attic Radiator and Expansion Tank to Keep the Latter from Freezing

will be no freezing of the water contained in it. A free circulation is obtained through the feed and return pipe to the radiator and it will always stay warm. The expansion tank will keep from freezing by installing a Y-connection, as shown.—Contributed by Geo. M. Crawley, Jr., Newark, N. J.

Heating Floor of a Small Shop

The brick floor in my shop is very cold in winter, and to make it more comfortable, I removed the brick and dug a hole, 36 in. long, 18 in. wide, and 18 in. deep, in front of the lathe where I stood most of the time. An old two-burner oil stove was procured and set in the hole. I then covered the hole with a board, made to fit tightly, and bored a number of ½-in. holes near the center. A large hole was also cut in at each side for draft. I was surprised at the results of this little heater. —Contributed by J. H. Priestly, Lawrence, Mass.

Operating Electric Switch in Hall from Outside

Switches controlling porch lights are usually placed on the inside of the house in the hall. To find the k e y h o l e at night it is desirable to have a light from the outside. To be able to do this without chang-

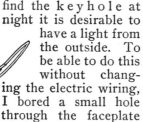

ing the electric wiring, I bored a small hole through the faceplate of the switch box just outside of the box, ran a brass wire through, and t u r n e d a ring on the outside end and a right-angled bend with a small ring on the inside end. I can now turn the wire until the inside arm is over the button and by pulling it turn the light on. By locating the hole the same distance from both buttons, the lights can be turned off in a like manner from the outside.—Contributed by J. Maynard, Cleveland, Ohio.

Guide for a Rubber Stamp Used on Tracings

When using a rubber stamp on trac-ings, a certain amount of time is

usually wasted in placing the s t a m p in the right position. A guide that will remedy this can be m a d e of a s t r i p of tin, or s h e e t b r a s s, a b o u t ½ in. wide, and long e n o u g h to go completely around the stamp block. When the ends are soldered together, it should be in the form of a loose-fit-ting frame. If this frame is laid accu-rately on the spot to be stamped, the impression will be in the correct posi-tion. — Contributed by Frank L. Matter, Portland, Ore.

How to Carry a Large Glazed Window Sash

Having occasion to convey a heavy glazed sash for a window that was 3 by 4 ft. about half a mile, and not wish-ing to call a dray, I carried it in the following manner: I ran the chain off the sprocket wheels of my bicycle and drew it up alongside of the rear fork and tied it to the saddle. Resting the sash on one of the pedals and leaning it against the frame of the bicycle, it was easily and quickly conveyed to the desired spot.—Contributed by Dr. F. G. Swartz, Croswell, Mich.

Reinforcing a Rubber Hose

The radiator, as well as the motor, on one of the automobiles in a garage heated very badly, and it was found that a flattened hose was choking the water circulation. The hose had a sharp bend, as shown, which accounted for its being distorted. It was neces-

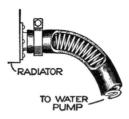

sary to reinforce the hose in such a manner that it would keep its shape. T o d o this, a helical coil was made of ¹⁄₁₆-in. steel wire of a pitch diameter slightly larger than the inside of the hose. The purpose of making it larger was to enable it to be sprung into the tube. A tube, if reinforced in this man-ner, can be bent into any shape de-sired, and the opening will remain the same.

Automatic Tap for High-Speed Work

The tap was designed for use by au-tomobile manufacturers, and others, using a thread of very fine pitch, such as 24 threads to the inch. The tap is readily set for tapping to any depth, and when the desired depth is reached it automatically collapses, thus en-abling a quick return. Upon being raised out of the tapped hole, the tap automatically expands to size.

As shown, the tap is set for cutting the thread. The cutting teeth are carried on the ends of the spring arms A, and on the under side of the spring arms is a lug fitting into B, causing the collapse, or release, of the cutting teeth from contact with the thread. The bracket C is secured to the main spindle bearing of the drill press, and in the slot D the pin E moves.

In use, the tap is set in a drill chuck, and the work is placed on the table of the drill press. The work is then raised as near the tap as possible, and the drill started. The tap is run down in the hole and upon reaching the depth for which the dogs have been set, the pin E comes in contact with the lower dog and is delayed, thus stopping the collapsing rod; and as the tap continues, the lugs spring into the groove B, col-

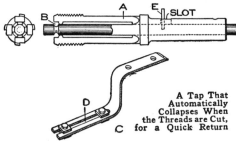

A Tap That Automatically Collapses When the Threads are Cut, for a Quick Return

lapsing the tap. The tap is then raised, and when clear of the hole, the pin E strikes the upper dog, delaying the collapsing rod again in its upward movement, and pulling the tap into the cutting position.

Holding Thin Disk or Ring in Chuck Jaws

When holding a thin disk, or ring, in the outer end of the jaws on a self-centering chuck, while boring or facing work, it is almost impossible to keep the surface true without something between the disk and the jaw. This may be accomplished by attaching a small ring, as shown in the illustration at A. It will be observed that the heavy ring is resting on the light one, which has an opening in it, to keep the ring a short distance away from the working surface and provide

clearance for the boring tool as it passes through. A similar chuck, holding a ring on the outside of the jaws,

A Ring Placed Back of a Disk being Worked in a Chuck to Keep the Surface True

is shown at B. In this case it is not necessary to reverse the jaws to turn the rings on the outside, which saves time and trouble.

Supply-Water Tank for an Automobile Radiator

To prevent the engine in my automobile from overheating and to do away with the necessity of stopping for water on long trips, I installed a separate water tank by which the radiator can be filled at any time without having to stop. The general construction of the device is as follows: A 5-gal. galvanized-iron tank was installed under the rear seat, an outlet was made at the bottom, and pipe connections were run to the top of the radiator.

Two holes were made in the tank top for pipe plugs, one of which was drilled and fitted with a tire valve. Pump-hose connections were made from the tire valve to an air pump conveniently located at the driver's seat. The other plug was used for filling the tank. A valve was placed where it could be easily reached, in the water line running from the tank. It is only

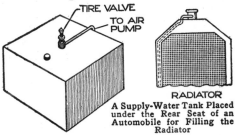

A Supply-Water Tank Placed under the Rear Seat of an Automobile for Filling the Radiator

necessary to pump a little air in the tank and open the water valve to fill the radiator.—Contributed by Harry Gahan, Victoria, B. C.

Making an Automobile-Engine Fan Bracket Rigid

The bracket supporting the cooling fan on an automobile engine became very loose, due to the insufficient base 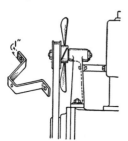 and holding power of the studs. This caused the fan to make a disagreeable noise when in operation, and a repair became necessary.

A piece of strap iron, $\frac{3}{16}$ in. thick and 1 in. wide, was bent to the proper shape and fastened with studs to the bracket and to the cylinder wall. The studs used in the cylinder wall were coated with white lead to prevent any leakage. Upon fastening the bent piece of metal between the bracket and cylinder a rigid support was obtained and the trouble eliminated. — Contributed by Adolph Kline, New York City.

Removing Small Bushings

Having occasion to remove a number of small brass bushings from certain parts of a pneumatic motor, I found them so placed that it was impossible to drive them out without damaging 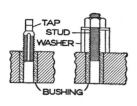 other parts. While they could have been chipped and broken down to remove them, it was not expedient, as that would occasion a loss of time on a hurry job.

The sketch makes clear a method used to get them out, which also can be applied in any case of a like nature. As the bushings were worn to a point of uselessness, a tap was run down into them deep enough to make three or four threads. A stud was then inserted, and by means of a large washer and nut of the same size as the stud, the bushing was easily drawn from the body of the device by turning the nut. This makes a safe and easy way for drawing bushings in a machine where it is impractical to force or draw them out by other means.—Contributed by F. W. Bentley, Missouri Valley, Iowa.

To Prevent Oil Sticking to Lubricator Glasses

To keep the inside of a lubricator glass free from oil, dissolve a very small piece of soap in the water. This will make the glass slippery and prevent the oil from adhering to the glass. A piece of soap put in the glass about once a week, will be sufficient to keep the glass always clean.—Contributed by Harry Piel, North Bergen, N. J.

Carrying Handle for Acetylene-Gas Tanks

Tanks containing compressed acetylene gas are not convenient to carry, 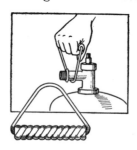 and for this reason I made a handle as follows: A piece of heavy wire, or leather thong, is run through a piece of pipe or flexible tubing, used for insulating electric-light wires, and is applied on the valve end of the tank. This makes it easy to carry the tank just the same as a pail.—Contributed by E. K. Marshall, Oak Park, Ill.

Glass as a Substitute for Tracing Cloth

Instead of using tracing cloth, or paper, in instances where the tracing is not to be kept as a record, a plain sheet of glass makes a good substitute, and one that possesses certain advantages. Take a plain piece of glass that is perfectly clean and dry, and it will take the drawing ink perfectly, and no sizing need be used. The ink dries as quickly as on paper, and when dry, the tracing may be dusted or wiped off without the slightest injury to the tracing.

When the tracing is no longer wanted, a damp cloth will quickly remove the ink, and the glass is then available for another tracing. The centers are located by means of a small piece of rubber, leather, or the like, moistened and placed on the glass. This gives a good rest for the point of the compass. This idea simplifies the blueprinting work, as it does away with tracing cloth, and a single glass will do for many tracings, besides which the glass always lies flat, without the use of thumb tacks, and the finest line is readily seen. It will not draw and wrinkle when the air is humid and cause a defective blueprint.

A Hot-Dinner Pail

This is simply an adaptation of the fireless-cooker idea, changed only in size and thickness of the insulating sides. It is not guaranteed to keep food as hot as liquid in a vacuum bottle, but will, if properly used, serve the dinner appetizingly hot.

The drawing is self-explanatory. Tin is the best material both for the inner and outer sides, as well as for the three food decks and a square tea or coffee bottle. The filling between the two shells may be the best nonconductor that can be had, but sheets of solid cork offer the lightest and easiest-worked filling. After the insulating material and the inner shell are in place, the upper edge of the box is covered with a ¾-in. strip of tin, soldered neatly. The lid, swinging on soldered hinges and fastened down by a catch, strap, or any other convenient method, is simply a ¾-in. deep tin box, 10 in. long by 4½ in. wide, filled with the nonconducting material.

The decks and bottle are made with round corners, excepting the angles of the sides with the bottom, which are left square. The upper edges of the sides being rolled inward any dish will stand firmly on top of any other one

inside of the box. In practice, the decks containing the hot food are first placed in position and pushed snugly

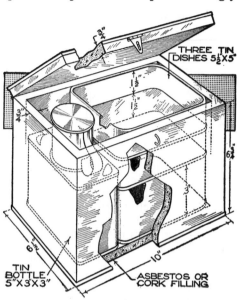

Pail Made Like a Fireless Cooker to Keep Edibles Hot until Lunch Time

against one end. The bottle is then set in, locking the decks in place. When lunch time comes, the bottle, of course, is first lifted out by the lugs soldered on its shoulders for that purpose, and the food decks are released. It may make the description of the decks a little more clear to state that they are just like large sardine boxes.

The dimensions given are intended to be merely suggestive and may be varied within reasonable limits. In fact, the idea lends itself to a number of variations from a simple individual two-deck kit to large boxes for automobile touring parties. Provision is easily made for carrying knives, forks, and spoons either inside or out.—Contributed by A. M. Parker, Edmonton, Canada.

❦To oxidize brass and copper objects, use the following solution: Nitrate of iron, 2 oz.; hyposulphite of soda, 2 oz., and water, 1 pt. Immerse the object in this solution and leave it until the desired depth of color is obtained.

Making Post Dig the Post Hole

In planting a piece of 1½-in. iron pipe for use as a hitching post, I tried to drive it into the frozen ground, but

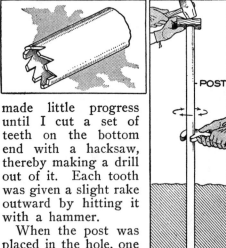

made little progress until I cut a set of teeth on the bottom end with a hacksaw, thereby making a drill out of it. Each tooth was given a slight rake outward by hitting it with a hammer.

When the post was placed in the hole, one man struck it on top with a sledge—a wood block being interposed to prevent battering—while I turned it with a pipe wrench. In this way I anchored the post quickly and firmly, as the teeth cut out the core of frozen earth just wide enough to receive the post. The core, of course, was forced up into the pipe.—Contributed by James M. Kane, Doylestown, Pa.

Protecting a Fish Line in the Ice

In fishing with lines through the ice the lines are often frozen during the

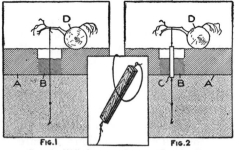

Boards Nailed over a Line to Protect It
When Cutting Out the Ice

night, and frequently, when chopping the ice from around them, the lines are

cut. The section A shows the ice, and B is the ice frozen in the hole during the night. A line holder is shown at D. To protect the line, I use two boards, C, nailed together over the line. If these freeze in the hole, it is an easy matter to chop them out without injury to the line. — Contributed by Geo. Goodwin, Jr., North Temiskaming, Quebec.

Weight, Power, and Speed, and the Light Automobile

The automobile-buying public takes in the various "arguments" put forth in favor of different cars as salesmen's talk and disregards some very important points in just this way, little guessing that a short period of use of the cars will prove many of the arguments to be truths backed up by indisputable principles of physics and engineering.

Consider, for instance, the arguments for and against the "light car." The light-car salesman claims more speed, more power, less fuel consumption, better hill-climbing qualities, and more carrying capacity, together with many other things that need not be mentioned. From an engineering standpoint the foregoing claims may be resolved into these factors: power, speed, and weight.

As an example, consider an engine of 30 h.p. It will move a light load farther than a heavy one, as with every increase of speed an increase of power in direct proportion is required; or to put it in another way, the power supplied remaining constant, the speed depends upon the load or weight that is moved. Naturally, it follows that a light car will go faster, uphill or on a level, than a heavier car of the same engine power carrying the same passenger weight. Also, the light car can go farther with one passenger than it can with five, the same being true of the heavy car as well. Hill climbing is merely raising a weight to a certain height, and the load it imposes upon the engine may simply be considered another weight. The engine has then three weights to move: weight of car, weight of the passengers, and the "weight" of moving both uphill. If any one is lessened, or removed, the engine can move the remainder at a higher speed. Or to get a higher speed is an impossibility without a decrease in weight.

As the weight of the car is a part of the load the engine must move, the light car can be run by a smaller engine, or by less overloading of the same engine; hence the lower fuel consumption of the light car carrying the same passengers.

First, the power required is directly proportional to the weight and the speed with which it is moved; second, the weight that can be moved is directly proportional to the power applied and the speed with which it is moved, and, third, the speed is directly proportional to the weight moved and the power applied. Other factors enter into car service, but the foregoing statements should be kept in mind. Measured by them alone, the light car has many advantages.—Contributed by Donald A. Hampson, Middletown, New York.

To Keep a Stovepipe Connected

The elbow is usually the first part of a stovepipe to pull loose where there is a long line. If, however, two loops of wire are twisted tightly around the pipe joints, at A and B, and also in the

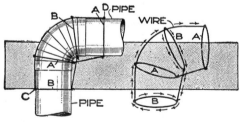

Tying the Elbow of a Stovepipe to Prevent Dislocation in a Long Line of Pipe

grooves of the elbow, then secured by the wire backbone from C to D, the danger of dislocation will be much lessened.

Turning Large Sheave Wheels without a Lathe

Having a number of V-groove, 7-ft. sheave wheels that required machining to receive a dovetail packing stamped from rubber belting, as shown in the sketch, but no lathe large

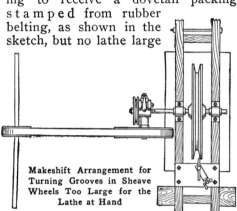

Makeshift Arrangement for Turning Grooves in Sheave Wheels Too Large for the Lathe at Hand

enough to swing them, I devised a temporary arrangement to do the work, as follows:

Two large timbers were placed over the motor pit, which lay parallel to the line shaft, and spreaders inserted between them and bolted together. They were braced sideways and the sheave wheel hung on an axle running in bearings attached to them.

The hand chain wheel was removed from a 2-ton chain block and a 14-in. pulley put in its place. The left chain wheel was removed and the square end of the shaft was inserted in the square socket previously cut in the end of the sheave-wheel axle. The chain blocks were fastened with a couple of large 7-in. bolts to a timber 12 in. square.

A heavy steel plate was then placed across the timbers in front of the sheave wheel, on which was mounted the extra tool-post head of the lathe. With this arrangement the speed was reduced and sufficient power obtained for practical work.—Contributed by H. V. Abeling, Burke, Idaho.

❡A lemon that has been squeezed for cooking purposes is still just the thing for cleaning the brass of lamp burners, etc. Add a little salt, and the black will come off easily.

Controlling the Inflation of a Gas Bag

What is known to mechanics as "bagging a pipe" is the insertion of a deflated rubber bag into a water or gas

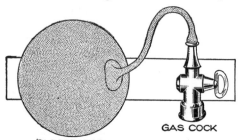

GAS COCK

RUBBER BAG

Gas Cock Used in Hose Connection for Controlling the Inflation of a Gas Bag in a Pipe

main. The bag is inflated through a rubber tube attached to it. This inflation effectually prevents the passage of gas or liquid through the pipe.

Some mechanics attach a gas cock to the tube. The air hose is screwed into this cock, and when the bag is sufficiently blown up, the key is closed. This does away with the necessity of doubling the hose and tying it, as would have to be done if the gas cock were not used. It also permits an easy renewal of inflation.

A Quickly Applied Lathe Dog

In roughing down a large number of shafts prior to grinding them, I found it took considerable time to adjust the

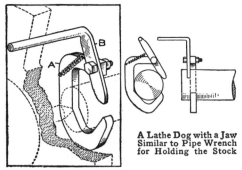

A Lathe Dog with a Jaw Similar to Pipe Wrench for Holding the Stock

dog and remove it. I set about making one as an improvement over the ordinary lathe dog and one that could be quickly applied, and the result was as illustrated. The body, or yoke, A, was

made of machine steel, 2¾ in. long, 2 in. wide, and ¾ in. thick, which was casehardened after it was forged into the shape shown. The tail B, on which a notched end was formed for holding the shaft, was made of tool steel and tempered. The tail swings on a pivot in the extending end of the yoke. A helical spring is placed in a drilled hole, as shown, to open the dog for removal. When driving the shaft it grips tightly the same as a pipe wrench.—Contributed by Jos. Pruell, Walpole, Mass.

A Homemade Oil Cup

The oil cup illustrated can be made from scraps of material found about most shops. The

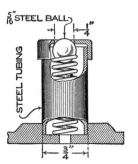

⁵⁄₁₆″ STEEL BALL

¼″

STEEL TUBING

¾″

body consists of a piece of steel tubing, threaded on both ends and turned into the thread of the bearing. The upper end is covered with an ordinary pipe cap, which is previously drilled with a ¼-in. drill. A steel ball, ⁵⁄₁₆ in. in diameter, and a helical spring, placed on the inside of the tube, complete the cup.

Marking Tools by Electricity

While trying to find some effective way of marking my tools, I tried the following method, which worked satisfactorily. I connected one side of a 110-volt circuit to one terminal of a toaster, joined the other terminal of the toaster to the metal of the tool to be marked, and fastened a piece of lead pencil to one end of a piece of wire and connected it to the other side of the line wire. By lightly tracing my initials on the tool with the lead pencil, an indelible and clearly legible identification mark was made.—Contributed by Henry Worthmann, Jr., Chicago.

Accuracy of Levels

It is really surprising how accurate one can be with a good level. With a first-class level, made of cast iron and having a graduated bubble glass, an erecting contractor would think twice before passing the job of installing a piece of machinery or lining a shaft if the bubble showed $\frac{1}{32}$ in. off center. Yet, in a level only 18 in. long, the bubble would indicate that one end was .001 in. higher than the other. Realizing this, it is little wonder that the ways of large planers and lathes are leveled up with an accurate level as recommended by the manufacturers.

Holding Large Doors Open

Large and heavy shop doors are, when caught by sudden gusts of wind, about as dangerous as anything around the establishment. A good many ways are employed to hold them open, but a strong wind readily tears a heavy door free from its anchor.

The illustration shows how a cheap, practical, and simple lock-open arrangement can be made from a piece of $\frac{7}{8}$ or 1-in. round iron. It is capable of holding a door of considerable size

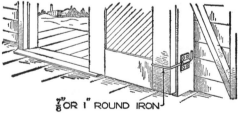

$\frac{7}{8}$" OR 1" ROUND IRON

Holder Made of a Rod to Keep a Large Door Open against a Strong Wind

open, no matter how strongly the wind blows, and on account of its shape it will not break loose.

Beaching a Motorboat

The device shown consists of a piece of 3-in. pipe, about 18 in. long, placed so that it will revolve on four inverted casters which are screwed to a board.

Inverted Truck Casters Placed on a Plank in Position to Hold a Length of Pipe

When the boat has been run aground, the device is placed under the keel, and the boat is pushed by hand until the entire length of the keel has traversed the roller. The device is again shifted forward and the process repeated until the boat is high and dry. If two sets of rollers are used the process is considerably easier. The outfit is small and can be readily carried in the boat for use wherever it is desired to beach it.—Contributed by J. J. O'Brien, Buffalo, N. Y.

¶To make a first-class oil for light machinery, take a bottle about half full of pure olive oil, place in it some thin strips of sheet lead, and expose it to the sun's rays for a month, then pour off the clear oil.

End-of-Page Marker for Typewritten Sheets

Many typists have often felt the need of a page-end indicator to enable them to see when the bottom of the page being

Indicator Made of Celluloid to Fasten on Page End of a Typewritten Sheet

typewritten is approached. Such an indicator can be made of thin celluloid, the celluloid cards given out as advertisements being suitable for the purpose. The celluloid is cut out, as shown, and bent back at the notches at the sides.

To operate, the page is started in the typewriter, and the edges of the indicator are pressed together between the fingers. If properly made, the indicator will give a click as the flap A bends through the opening B. The indicator is then slipped over the end of the page, with the flap A facing the typist. This sounds complex, but is in reality very simple. The edge C may be colored red to catch the eye as it appears.

To Hold a Loose Camshaft Bushing

The bushings within which the camshaft of a gasoline engine rotates are in quite a few cases merely pressed into

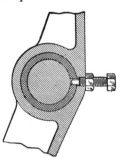

the aluminum crank case, and constant vibration, together with a difference in expansion of the bronze and aluminum, has in many instances caused the bushing to come loose. In such cases a new bushing would probably be the best solution. A similar case came to our shop, and it was decided to try holding the loose bushing by means of a setscrew. A $\frac{1}{4}$-in. screw was turned down on the end to make a projection $\frac{3}{16}$ in. in diameter and of such length that the end came $\frac{1}{64}$ in. under the inner surface of the bushing. The screw was held with a lock nut, as shown.—Contributed by Adolph Kline, New York City.

An Emergency Pulley Block

In an emergency, where I had to lower a large sheave wheel a distance of 50 ft. from its bearings, I used blocks made up as shown in the illustration. Clevises taken from a double-tree of a wagon were formed into pulley blocks by filling the pins between the yoke ends with washers. The rope was tied through the

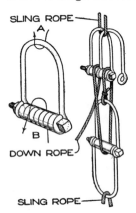

clevis, at A, as shown by the arrow, and the down rope, as at B, and to the sheave wheel, the opposite end being given a couple of turns around a cross timber. The washers revolved on the bolt like a small wheel. A double block can be made with four of the clevises, as shown.—Contributed by E. C. Lane, El Paso, Tex.

Receptacle for Motion-Picture Film Cement

Take an ordinary oil, or sewing-machine, can with an opening in the spout not over $\frac{1}{16}$ in., and put the cement in the can. When wanted, press the bottom as in oiling and draw the spout along on the edge of the film to be patched. The can not only saves time for those engaged in film rewinding, but also prevents evaporation of the cement.—Contributed by Geo. Yaste, Lonaconing, Md.

A Multiple Window Opener

In several states factory buildings are required by law to have fireproof stairways, or towers, in which the windows on all the landings can be opened simultaneously to clear them of smoke in case of a fire. The sketch shows one scheme which is used. The lower sash is fixed and the upper one is heavier than its sash weights. By pulling down on the cable, which extends through all

One of the Latches on a Window for Releasing the Upper Sash to Let It Drop

the floors, the latch A is withdrawn, and the heavy sash drops down, allowing the smoke to escape.

To Start a Cold Automobile Engine

Many older types of automobiles have carburetors of old design, and they are not suited to the low-test gasoline which is being marketed at present. It is almost impossible under these circumstances to start them in cold weather.

In order to make the starting easy, I tried various means and finally hit on an infallible cure. The manifold was wrapped with a thin layer of asbestos paper, on which was wound a number of turns of nichrome resistance ribbon, and the ends were fastened with asbestos cord. A length of lamp cord was spliced to the two ends of

the ribbon, and an attachment plug fitted to the lamp cord. When this was plugged into a lamp socket, and the current turned on, the pipe was made quite hot in one minute, and the motor readily started without priming. It formerly took about half an hour to warm up the motor with hot water. Of course, it is necessary to have current for this way of starting and a little experimenting will be required to determine the proper amount of resistance wire to use, according to the voltage.—Contributed by Chas. C. Heyder, Hansford, W. Va.

Extra Push Button for the Door Latch

In apartment houses fitted with an electric latch on the front door, the push button for working it is usually placed in the kitchen, which is obviously the place for it. If the apartment is long, it becomes tiresome when no one is in the kitchen to walk from the front to the back, every time the bell rings, to let a visitor in. This can be avoided very simply by fitting another push button in any convenient place in the front of the apartment and wiring it up in parallel with the kitchen button. No new battery is needed, just a length of double bell wire and the new push. The connections are shown in the sketch. The kitchen ends of the new wires are connected to the terminals of the old push without detaching the old wires, that is, they are put under the same terminals

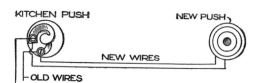

KITCHEN PUSH   NEW PUSH

NEW WIRES

OLD WIRES

Connections for an Extra Push Button at the Front of an Apartment for the Door Latch

and screwed up tightly. The front ends are connected to the new push button in the ordinary way. Pressing either button will open the latch.— Contributed by Morris G. Miller, New Rochelle, N. Y.

Modern Barn Construction

By W. E. FRUDDEN

THE framing of a barn has gone through an evolution in which the heavy timber barns of former years have passed out of existence, and trussing has taken the place of the large beams that have become exceedingly expensive. The first truss illustrated is for a standard-width barn of about 36 ft., and is, both in materials and labor, very economical. It gives a maximum of storage room in the mow; it is convenient, and will give the most space and best barn for the money.

The joists in this design are the heaviest pieces of timber in the whole frame, 16 ft. being the longest dimension required. Barns like these are stiff, safe, sound, and serviceable for a great number of years.

The scarcity and the poor quality of the long timbers that can be had now make this plan of construction very sensible, as it uses only short lengths of 2-in. planks. In the old timber barn, the mortise-and-tenon joints are the weak places in the building. They are not nearly as strong as they appear. It takes skill and a great deal of experience to master the art of barn framing under the old methods, where long and cumbersome timbers are to be mortised and tenoned, then pinned at the joints. The truss shown is so simple that four men have erected a large barn of this type without any other help. As the roof arches go up into place one at a time, it will appear that even a carpenter is not necessary to put such a barn together, since there is nothing at all complicated about the whole structure.

The rafters, the studding, and the floor joists are all spaced 2 ft. center to center in this balloon-frame barn. There are no cross braces in the mow space so that this is left entirely open for hay storage.

The floor and footings are of concrete and extend 2 ft. above the grade line, so as to keep all the woodwork away from the soil moisture, which causes rot and decay. The sills and plates are double 2 by 6-in. material, as are also the studs and the rafters, all

being spaced 2 ft. on centers. The roof arches are built up on the ground and are braced at the hips with two 1 by 8-in. boards. When the side walls have been all raised and sided, the roof arches are pulled up with a block and tackle, one man handling one arch at a time. They are spaced directly over the wall studs. The walls are sided horizontally; the roof is covered with sheathing and shingles, or with prepared roofing, and the 2 by 12-in. floor joists are covered with ship-lap flooring. The two girders which support the floor are made from four planks. The material list is for a 14-ft. section of a standard barn. If a longer barn is required, figure on proportionate amounts; and add the materials for the two ends.

```
  112 cu. ft. concrete foundation.
  504 sq. ft. concrete floors.
   56 ft. 2 by  6-in., 16-ft. sills.
   56 ft. 2 by  6-in., 16-ft. plates.
   28 ft. 2 by  6-in., 16-ft. rib plates.
  256 ft. 2 by  6-in., 16-ft. studding.
  256 ft. 2 by  6-in., 16-ft. braces.
  256 ft. 2 by  6-in., 16-ft. rafters.
  192 ft. 2 by  6-in., 12-ft. rafters.
   48 ft. 2 by  6-in.,  6-ft. collar beams.
   43 ft. 2 by  4-in.,  4-ft. lookouts.
  256 ft. 1 by  8-in., 12-ft. hip braces.
  116 ft. 1 by  8-in.,  2-ft. cleats.
   32 ft. 2 by  8-in.,  2-ft. struts.
  384 ft. 2 by 12-in., 12-ft. floor joists, sides.
  224 ft. 2 by 12-in., 14-ft. floor joists, center.
  224 ft. 2 by 12-in., 16-ft. for girders.
  540 ft. drop siding, 6 in. wide.
  650 ft. roof sheathing.
7,000 cedar shingles.
  600 ft. ship-lap flooring.
```

Materials for the two ends of a 36-ft. barn:

```
  290 cu. ft. concrete foundation.
  144 ft. 2 by  6-in., 16-ft. sills.
  240 ft. 2 by 10-in., 16-ft. plates.
1,250 ft. 2 by  6-in., 16-ft. studing.
  160 ft. 2 by  8-in., 16-ft. braces.
2,560 ft. drop-siding lumber.
```

The Shawver system of barn framing gives the barn builder a stiff, plank-framed barn with an unobstructed mow space that will hold an abundance of hay or rough feed. It is a plan that is particularly well-fitted for use in larger structures. The details show a barn that is 36 ft. wide, a width that is now generally accepted as being the best all-around size for two rows of stock. Wider barns may be built, however, and the same general idea of construction may be followed out if desired.

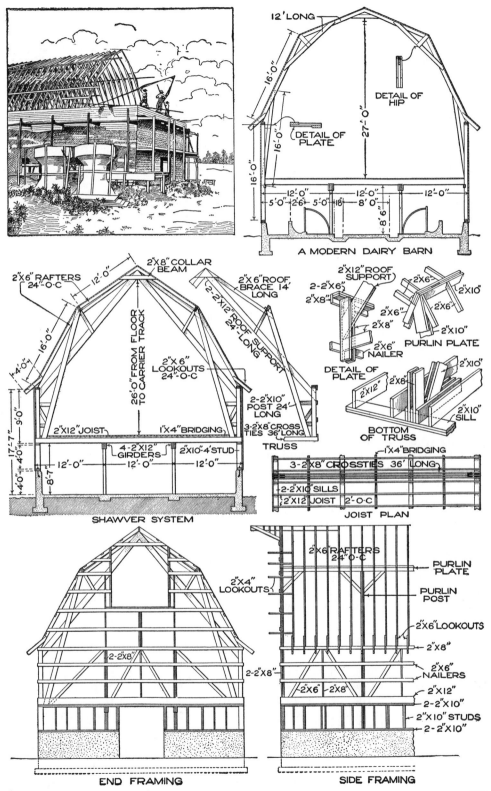

DETAIL OF HIP

12' LONG

16'-0"

16'-0"

27'-0"

DETAIL OF PLATE

16'-0"

8'-6"

12'-0" 12'-0" 12'-0"

5'-0" 2'-6" 5'-0" 18" 8'-0"

A MODERN DAIRY BARN

2"X8" COLLAR BEAM

2"X6" RAFTERS 24"-0-C

12'-0"

16'-0"

4'-0"

26'-0" FROM FLOOR TO CARRIER TRACK

2"X6" LOOKOUTS 24"-0-C

2"X12" JOIST

2"X6" ROOF BRACE 14' LONG

2-2"X12" ROOF SUPPORT 24' LONG

1"X4" BRIDGING

2-2"X10" POST 24' LONG

3-2"X8" CROSS TIES 36' LONG

TRUSS

17'-7"

9'-0"

4'-0"

4'-0"

8'-7"

4-2"X12" GIRDERS

2"X10"-4'STUD

12'-0" 12'-0" 12'-0"

SHAWVER SYSTEM

2"X12" ROOF SUPPORT

2-2"X6"

2"X8"

2"X6" NAILER

DETAIL OF PLATE

2"X12" 2"X8"

2"X6"

2"X8"

2"X6"

2"X10"

2"X10"

PURLIN PLATE

2"X10"

2"X10" SILL

BOTTOM OF TRUSS

1"X4" BRIDGING

3-2"X8" CROSSTIES 36' LONG

2-2"X10" SILLS

2"X12" JOIST 2'-0-C

JOIST PLAN

2"X4" LOOKOUTS

2-2"X8"

2-2"X8"

END FRAMING

2"X6" RAFTERS 24"-0-C

PURLIN PLATE

PURLIN POST

2"X6" LOOKOUTS

2"X8"

2"X6" NAILERS

2"X6" 2"X8"

2"X12"

2-2"X10"

2"X10" STUDS

2-2"X10"

SIDE FRAMING

2633

The concrete work runs up 4 ft. above the grade line. The ground-floor walls, above the concrete work, have 2 by 10-in. studs placed 2 ft. center to center. The double-thick sills are bolted to the concrete every 6 ft., and the plate at the top of the 4-ft. studding is made from two 2 by 10-in. planks, spiked firmly together. The roof trusses are shown in the cross section. These are spaced every 14 ft. in the length of the barn.

The rafters are of 2 by 6-in. material and spaced 2 ft. apart from center to center, after the roof trusses and purlin plates have been put in place. The lower rafters rest on the side-wall plates, and are supported at the hip by the heavy purlin plate, which is carried by the trusses. The floor joists are 2 by 12-in. planks and are spaced every 2 ft. from center to center, running crosswise with the barn. The continuous girders, made of 2 by 12-in. planks, spiked together, are supported by columns in the center, spaced 12 ft. apart across the barn.

If the barn has been braced as shown, and a good quality of material used together with good workmanship, it will stand the pressure of wind and snow.

As a basis for estimate, a 14-ft. section of a 36-ft. barn has been taken. To compute the amount of materials required and to obtain only a general idea of the cost for any other length barn, multiply the amounts listed by the number of times that 14 is contained in the length of barn that is desired. As an example, a 70-ft. barn that is 36 ft. wide would contain five times the material for a 14-ft. section, not counting the ends, which are added to the amount obtained for any length of barn. The builder may add about 50 per cent to the cost of the material for labor, barn equipment, windows, doors, hardware, and paint where up-to-date construction is wanted. The following materials are required for a 14-ft. section:

```
 224 cu. ft. concrete walls.
 504 sq. ft. concrete floor.
  95 ft. 2 by 10-in. sills.
  95 ft. 2 by 10-in. plates.
 150 ft. 2 by 10-in.,  4-ft. studding.
  56 ft. 2 by 12-in., 14-ft. nailers.
  56 ft. 2 by  6-in., 14-ft. nailers.
 112 ft. 2 by  8-in., 14-ft. plates.
 256 ft. 2 by  6-in., 16-ft. rafters.
 192 ft. 2 by  6-in., 12-ft. rafters.
  53 ft. 2 by  8-in., 10-ft. center posts.
  64 ft. 2 by  6-in.,  4-ft. lookouts.
  85 ft. 2 by  8-in.,  6-ft. collar beams.
  92 ft. 2 by 10-in., 14-ft. purlin plates.
  19 ft. 2 by  4-in., 14-ft. purlin plates.
 144 ft. 2 by  6-in., 12-ft. braces.
 400 ft. 2 by 12-in., 12-ft. joists.
 224 ft. 2 by 12-in., 12-ft. girders.
 470 ft. barn-siding lumber.
 650 ft. roof sheathing.
7,000 cedar shingles.
 600 ft. ship-lap flooring.
```

Materials for the two ends:

```
 576 cu. ft. concrete wall.
 120 ft. 2 by 10-in., 16-ft. sills.
 120 ft. 2 by 10-in., 16-ft. plates.
 400 ft. 2 by 10-in.,  4-ft. studding.
 288 ft. 2 by  8-in., 36-ft. crossties.
  96 ft. 2 by  8-in.,  9-ft. posts.
 320 ft. 2 by 10-in., 24-ft. purlin posts.
 224 ft. 2 by 10-in.. 28-ft. roof supports.
  14 ft. 2 by 10-in.,  4-ft. ties.
  48 ft. 2 by  8-in., 16-ft. braces.
  38 ft. 2 by  6-in., 14-ft. roof braces.
 386 ft. 2 by  8-in., 36-ft. nailing girts.
 556 ft. 2 by  6-in., 12-ft. nailing girts.
  75 ft. 2 by  4-in.,  4-ft. lookouts.
2,265 ft. barn-siding lumber.
```

Materials necessary for one Shawver barn truss, 36 ft. wide:

```
 144 ft. 2 by  8-in., 36-ft. crossties.
  48 ft. 2 by  8-in.,  9-ft. posts.
 160 ft. 2 by 10-in., 24-ft. purlin posts.
 112 ft. 2 by 12-in., 28-ft. roof supports.
   7 ft. 2 by 10-in.,  4-ft. ties.
  24 ft. 2 by  8-in., 16-ft. braces.
  29 ft. 2 by  6-in., 14-ft. roof braces.
```

Making Driveway with Tarred Stones

With a solid foundation of stone to begin with, spread about 3 in. of fine crushed stone at the center of the driveway, and rake it off to the outer edges until it is about 1 in. deep; then make the center about 3 in. high with the stone. The depth of this stone will depend on circumstances, but the amount mentioned will give a very durable road. The stone should be rolled down firmly, forming a slight rounding of the bed so that the water cannot form pools. Saturate the bed with water and then roll again. After the water is pretty well dried out, though not entirely so, spread thin tar, or crude asphaltum, over the bed, using a coarse-rose watering can. The stones should be well covered, yet not enough applied to cause the liquid to run off.

Over this, sprinkle some fine-crushed stone, after which allow the roadway to remain unused for a few days. In about a year, another coating of asphaltum should be applied, and no further attention will need to be given it, barring accidents.—Contributed by A. A. Kelly, Frazer, Pa.

Fitting Worn Wheel Tightly on Its Shaft

A certain wheel used on a gasoline engine was brought to my shop for repairs. The wheel originally was fastened to the shaft with a key, but it had become worn so badly that the hole was too large for the shaft. The owner wanted the wheel put on the shaft to stay and run true, and offered a box of cigars as a premium over the cost of the repair if I could do it for him. I first drilled a hole in the shaft end to a depth a little more than the length of the wheel hub, then the shaft end was split with a hacksaw cut, down to the bottom of the hole two ways, as shown. A piece of sheet metal was used to bush

SHAFT SPLIT ON END

the hole in the wheel and take up the wear. After fitting on the wheel as tightly as possible by this means, a pin slightly larger than the drilled hole was driven into it. The wheel was set tightly and in such a manner that it ran true.—Contributed by H. T. Mitchell, Toyah, Tex.

A Bronzing Liquid

A good bronzing liquid is made from gum dammar with benzol, and a small portion of raw oil to give it elasticity. Coat the object with this and dust on the bronze. When the bronze is dry, coat it with thin shellac varnish to protect it from the atmosphere. In this way the bronze will retain its brightness for a long time.

Easy Way to Start an Automobile Engine in Winter

To facilitate starting an automobile motor in cold weather, the device shown in the illustration has been used. It can be made by any automobile owner. It consists of two asbestos gaskets with a coil of wire between them. This takes the place of the regular gasket between the carburetor and intake pipe. The iron wire is connected through a switch to the six-volt ignition battery. This

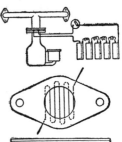

switch is closed just before cranking the motor, and the wire gets hot enough to vaporize the gasoline as it issues from the carburetor. About 9 in. of No. 24 gauge wire will be found quite satisfactory.

Odd-Fluted Taps

Except in the smaller sizes, $\frac{3}{16}$ in. or under, taps for all ordinary work are made with four flutes. Where the hole being tapped does not run through solid metal, or, as is frequently the case, two openings are opposite, an even-fluted tap makes poor work and often breaks for the reason that two opposite flutes drop into the opening at the same time and then engage two sections of metal with so great a strain as to cause a break.

For such work odd-fluted taps are preferable and can be obtained at a slight advance in price. On one particularly difficult

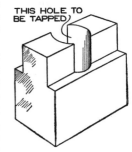

THIS HOLE TO BE TAPPED

piece of work, as shown, several thousand steel pieces were tapped with a seven-fluted tap without breakage.— Contributed by Donald A. Hampson.

Homemade Pressure Gauge

In the construction of all pressure gauges a bent tube is used to operate the pointer, its movements being actu-

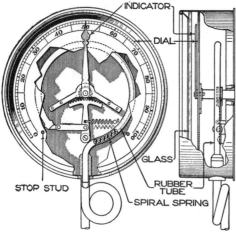

The Bent Tube, Which Is Difficult to Make, is Replaced by a Coil Spring and Rubber Tubing

ated by the tendency of the tube to straighten out when pressure is applied. The gauge illustrated can be easily made, as the tube is constructed of a small coil of brass or copper wire over which a rubber tube is drawn. This makes a tube sufficiently sensitive to record the low pressures used on gas and liquids in the home workshop.

The end of the tube is closed with a cap, and to this cap the connecting link and the gearing are attached. The gear and rack and the method of connecting them are shown clearly, and anyone capable of building the gauge will require very little instruction in addition to the sketch. The small gear is ½ in. in diameter.

Studs are set in the dial to stop the pointer so that the sector and gear will not get out of mesh. The gauge is graduated to show a few pounds over the high limit. The pressure tube must be of a size to give a sectional area of 1 sq. in. The small spiral retaining spring must be of No. 16 gauge spring brass, and the pounds-per-square-inch graduations should be ⅛ in. apart, but as there will be considerable variation in the springs and connections, it is

best to attach a raised vent near the gauge and leave the top open, placing upon it a soft leather pad, and on the pad, a 1-lb. weight. When the pressure raises this weight and escapes, mark the 1-lb. graduation on the dial. Then add 1 lb., making 2 lb. on the open vent, and so on.

It is not necessary to have a number of 1-lb. weights; stones, or anything, will do, just so the weights applied are known.—Contributed by J. B. Murphy, Plainfield, N. J.

Gasoline Filter for Automobile Tanks

When a gasoline filter is fitted to a car it is usually placed somewhere in the pipe line from the tank to the carburetor. A better position is at the base of the tank and projecting inside, where the gauze is constantly washed by the swaying of the gasoline caused by the motion of the car. The finest copper gauze should be used, and it is best shaped by wrapping it on a steel rod, about ⁵⁄₁₆ in. in diameter, while soldering the seam and top. The only difficulty in fitting up this type of filter is in removing the pipe union at the base of the tank, but this trouble is more

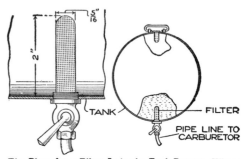

The Place for a Filter Is in the Tank Bottom, Where It will be Kept Clean

than offset by the absence of a stopped jet in the future.—Contributed by Morris G. Miller, New Rochelle, N. Y.

❏A handkerchief, or any piece of cloth, wadded into the canopy of an electric fixture when installing prevents it from catching the dirt which mars the stem when the canopy is pushed up in place.

Catches to Hold Food Deck in a Dinner Pail

Occasionally my dinner pail would upset, and t h e food in the dinner deck push the cover off so that the contents would be spilled. To prevent this, I fastened two clips to the side of the d i n n e r d e c k so that their upper ends would pass over the cover when the d e c k w a s pushed into the pail part.—Contributed by William H. Jones, Ladysmith, B. C.

Cutting Lubricant for Unpickled Steel Castings

For finishing green, unpickled steel castings so as to leave the surface as smooth as possible, use a cutting fluid mixed as follows: To three parts of turpentine add one part lard. Apply this mixture with a brush.

To Set the Jaw of a Monkey Wrench

In using a monkey wrench on nuts or bolts where there are several of one size, it is quite a help to keep the jaw set, since t h e adjusting sleeve will turn and m o v e the jaw one way or t h e other. To remedy this, I d r i l l e d and tapped a hole for a ¼-in. thumbscrew, as shown in the sketch. A slight turn, and the screw tightens on the sleeve and will keep it from turning.—Contributed by Chas. G. England, Washington, Pa.

Disconnector for Electric Horns·on Automobiles

To prevent the small boy from sounding the electric horn, some owners of automobiles loosen one of the terminals when getting out at a stop. This method has the disadvantage that one may forget to replace the connection on returning, which makes an accident possible next time the horn should be sounded. A simple way out of the difficulty is to fit on a small spring switch, as shown in the illustration, under the cushion on the driver's seat.

Remove the cushion and cut a recess, ¼ in. deep, in the center of the front edge of the seat frame. Make the spring from a piece of strong spring

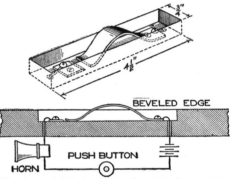

The Concealed Switch in the Circuit is Operated by the Cushion on the Driver's Seat

brass, ⅝ in. wide and curved, so that when it is in place the top of the bend will project ¼ in. above the surface. Fix a small terminal plate just in front of the free end of the spring so that the pressure on top of it will cause the spring to straighten out and rest on the plate. The edge of the plate should be beveled to permit the end of the spring to slide over it freely. Make the connections as shown, passing the wires through holes in the seat. The spring should be strong enough to support the weight of the cushion easily without bending. As soon as the driver takes his seat, the horn is ready for sounding in the ordinary way.—Contributed by Morris G. Miller, New Rochelle, N. Y.

Acetylene Generator for a Bicycle Lamp

Having need of an acetylene generator for a bicycle lamp and not wishing to purchase one, I made a very effective generator at the actual cost of 30 cents and a few odds and ends from my scrap box, and while simple

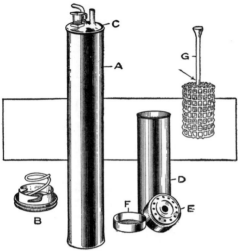

An Acetylene Generator That Applies Water to the Lower Part of the Carbide

in construction it has proved to be more economical in the consumption of carbide than most of the factory-made articles.

As shown in the illustration, the generator A consists of a piece of seamless brass tubing, $1\frac{15}{16}$ in. in diameter and $11\frac{1}{2}$ in. long, with walls about $\frac{1}{32}$ in. in thickness, which cost 30 cents. The bottom cap B was taken from an old bicycle lamp, while the top cap C, which just fits the tube, once kept the dirt out of the works of a dollar watch. The stuffing box and valve stem were parts of the burner of a kerosene heater lamp, while the filler cap and nipple came from a small oil lamp.

The carbide magazine and gas retort D was made from sheet brass, $1\frac{3}{4}$ in. in diameter and $5\frac{1}{2}$ in. long. The top cap E of the retort was taken from an old worn-out wall snap switch, with several $\frac{1}{8}$-in. holes punched in it to permit the free flow of gas, and an old tin pill box, F, did duty as the bottom cap of the retort and as holder for the slaked carbide.

The secret of the economy of this generator lies in the method of feeding the water to the bottom of the carbide instead of letting it drip on the top. The water drips from the needle valve into the funnel tube, shown at G, and passes down the tube to the point indicated by the arrow where several slits, $\frac{1}{4}$ in. long, permit it to reach the bottom layers of the carbide only. Also there is a small hole, about the size of a needle, in the bottom of the tube which lets a small portion of the water drip into the pan below. As the carbide slakes, it sifts through the grate into the space formed by the screen cage, where it is separated from the fresh carbide by an air space. Therefore, when the water is stopped, the slaked particles jolt through the grate and leave the solid unused particles in the magazine dry, while the lamp goes out almost as soon as the water is stopped. The water dropping into the pan from the small hole in the end of the tube, slakes all the particles that may pass through unslaked.

A $\frac{1}{8}$-in. copper tube, 3 in. long, with a small funnel soldered to the upper end forms the feed tube, while the grate and its supporting cage are made of ordinary $\frac{1}{4}$-in. galvanized screen, although the grate has extra wires woven in to reduce the mesh to $\frac{1}{8}$ in. The size of the cage and grate is $2\frac{1}{4}$ in. long by $1\frac{1}{2}$ in. in diameter, which permits it to slip into the shell of the retort easily.

The illustration shows all the parts of the generator except the water chamber and control valve. The water chamber is formed by soldering a disk of brass, ground perfectly round on a grindstone, 6 in. from the bottom of the large tube, the disk having a hole drilled in the center to take the adjusting valve of an old Welsbach burner, which made a splendid needle valve. The disk also has a hole drilled in it to take a $\frac{1}{8}$-in. copper tube, which passes through the water chamber and through the top cap to form the gas supply pipe.

The only difficult part in the construction of this generator is the soldering of the disk in the tube, and this was accomplished in the following manner: First, the needle valve and the gas pipe were soldered in the disk. The inside of the tube and the disk were cleaned with emery and soldering flux was applied; then both were tinned where the solder was to run. Next, the valve stem was soldered to the movable part of the valve and screwed home; and the stuffing box was then soldered to the cap and the valve stem run through the stuffing box. The cap was not fastened permanently, however; only enough to center the valve stem, the stem holding the disk so that the valve would turn true. The gas pipe running through the top cap tended to hold the disk in place while running the solder. By means of the stem the disk was raised and lowered in the tube until it was at the exact point where it was to be permanently fastened. Then a ring of wire solder was placed on, with the bottom of the tube up, and a gasoline torch used on the outside to heat the solder until it flowed into place.. Care must be taken to prevent the disk from getting too hot and loosening the solder out from the valve and gas pipe fastenings. After testing for leaks, the top cap was soldered in place, and the generator was complete.—Contributed by T. T. Sturgeon, Los Angeles, Cal.

Empty Carbide Can Used for a Heating Stove

In Mexico most of the fireplaces produce more smoke than heat, but while the natives do not mind that, we did, and proceeded to make a heating stove from a carbide can, which gave very satisfactory results. We have made quite a number of them as shown in the illustration. A circle was drawn at the place where the stovepipe was to be attached, and the metal cut inside of the circle like cutting the pieces of a pie, and these were bent out so that the joint of pipe could be set over them. The cover was hinged to the

front with bent wire, and a hook made to hold it up. Supports of brick, or

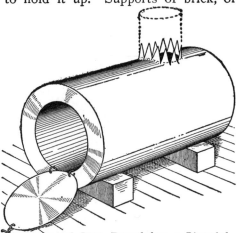

An Improvised Stove, Formed from a Discarded Carbide Can, Used Instead of a Smoking Fireplace

stone, were used to raise the stove from the floor.—Contributed by W. A. Lane, El Paso, Tex.

Centers for Taper Work on a Lathe

To turn a taper between centers on a lathe necessitates the shifting of the tailstock, and to do this with the ordinary lathe centers, as shown at A, is not the best method, as the centers wear on the point and will not run true. A good way is to have a center with a ball point, as shown at B. This center will keep the work true and it can be run at high speed for the softer metals. The method of using the bor-

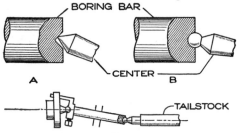

Ball Centers for Use on a Boring Bar in a Lathe to Prevent Wear

ing bar is clearly shown at C.—Contributed by Arthur L. Kerbaugh, Allentown, Pa.

⦅Use sharp cutters for finishing a milling-machine job.

A Translucent Door

A good substitute for a frosted-glass door, or window, may be made as shown in the illustration. Two panes

Tracing Linen Well Lettered and Placed between Two Panes of Glass Makes a Translucent Window

of ordinary window glass are used, and a piece of tracing linen, or oiled paper, the same size, is inserted between them. Any lettering necessary for the door can be placed on the linen or paper. The rear glass may be omitted if desired and the cloth stretched as tightly as possible to a single pane of glass, but the former method makes the more permanent job.—Contributed by Walker O. Nettleton, Washington, D. C.

Flexible-Pipe Conveyor for a Tool-Grinding Machine

This pipe was designed to take the place of the stiff, but slightly adjustable, metal tube used to convey the dust from a tool-grinding machine to the main blowpipe. In making the pipe, a broom handle was used for the arbor, and on this was wrapped soft-iron wire while it turned in a lathe, as in winding a spring. Over this spring was wrapped light canvas and an outside wrapping of strong twine.

At each end, the first two or three turns of wire were fastened with light copper wire, while the twine wrappings were merely tied together. To attach the sections, a piece of light

canvas, large enough to lap over the ends of the tubes, was wrapped around the tubing twice and bound tightly with soft-iron wire. The inside wire lining, the twine wrapping, and the wire of the coupling, all mesh together and form a thoroughly tight joint. Such a tube will give first-class service, but is for inside work only, as it is not made to stand exposure to the weather.

Cutting Brass-Wire Pins to Length

A laborer was set to work in a shop cutting pins from No. 16 gauge brass wire, each to be 5¼ in. long. Having no special tool for this work he made one as shown. A square piece of metal, A, was drilled to fit the plier handle, then drilled and tapped on one side for a setscrew, B. Two holes were tapped for the screws C and the two upper corners rounded off. A piece of sheet metal D was drilled and shaped as shown and then fastened with the screws to A. The stop was set on the lower handle to the required distance from the cutting edge, and a vise held the lower handle. By feeding the wire against the stop, cutting it off, and letting the pieces drop into a box, the

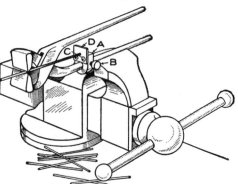

Stop on a Plier Handle for Gauging Pins as They were Cut from the Wire

work was accomplished quickly.—Contributed by Mark Gluckman, Jersey City, N. J.

❡Do not be stingy with varnish, for the more coats applied the better will be the gloss and finish.

Filling Leaks and Blowholes

Where it is necessary to fill a small crack, or leak, in a difficult place, or if soldering cannot be used as a means of closing the opening, an amalgam composed as follows may be used with good results. Melt together 30 parts of zinc and 20 parts of tin, then granulate the mass. A good method is to use filings from the metal combination; however, the granulation can be done by pouring the melted metal through a strong stream of water issuing from the nozzle of a hose. These are well kneaded with mercury until the amalgam, like a dough, is formed. The excess mercury is squeezed out, and the plastic mass forced into the hole and given time to harden. When hard, it can be filed the same as the metal about it. Because of the hardening action, only enough of the amalgam should be mixed for the work at hand.

Repairing a Steam-Gauge Pressure Connection

The nipple by which the steam-gauge pressure pipe connects to the gauge is frequently broken. The mishap occurs commonly as a result of an accidental fall, and sometimes through the too vigorous application of a wrench in drawing up the brazing collar, or nut, of the pipe. After such an accident it is often the practice to order a new tube casting, as the nipple in most standard gauges is a part of the casting. If the lengthwise cross section of the casting were examined, the practical method of repairing such a break would in the majority of cases be readily apparent. There is plenty of stock in the casting for drilling it out deep enough to take a 1/4-in. pipe tap, after which a common 1/4-in. gas-pipe nipple can be screwed in tightly. This will afford, in almost every case, a connection for the gauge which can be easily made.

I was in a contract shop where a great number of gauges were sent in for repair, and the breakage on 60 per cent of them was of the above-mentioned kind. The method described and illustrated was put into practice and resulted in a much cheaper job that was just as satisfactory, as well

Attaching an Ordinary Pipe Nipple in Place of the Steam Connection on a Gauge

as in a quick return of the gauge to the firm, which usually had no other gauge on hand and was therefore eagerly waiting for it.—Contributed by F. W. Bentley, Jr., Missouri Valley, Iowa.

To Detect Water in Paint

The presence of water in white-lead paint, paste, or mixed paint, may be discovered by adding a little eosin dye and rubbing it up on a porcelain slab. The water, if present, will cause the dye to stain the paint. The maximum amount of water in pure white lead should be two per cent, and any amount in excess of this may be regarded as adulteration.

Concealed Support for a Stovepipe

The illustration shows a successful way of keeping a long horizontal length of stovepipe from sagging in an unsightly manner. A piece of old water or gas pipe is inserted as shown and lashed to the stovepipe with loops of copper wire passed through small holes punched in it. The method of assembling is to slip the stovepipe sec-

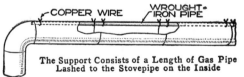

The Support Consists of a Length of Gas Pipe Lashed to the Stovepipe on the Inside

tions over the wrought-iron pipe one at a time and lash each section as it is added. It is advisable to use copper wire, as it will not corrode.

⁅Paper or wood used to hold putty will absorb the oil and cause it to harden quickly.

Pounce-Dusting Pad for Tracing Cloth

Tracing cloth used by draftsmen often has a glossy surface which will not take ink readily. The gloss is re-

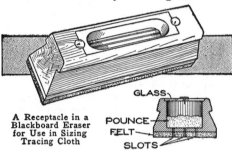

A Receptacle in a Blackboard Eraser for Use in Sizing Tracing Cloth

GLASS
POUNCE
FELT
SLOTS

moved by various means, one of which is to dust the surface with pounce, powdered chalk, or talcum powder, rubbing it over the surface of the cloth with chamois, cloth, or a piece of blotter, then brushing off the excess. One of the handiest ways is to sift a quantity of the pounce on the cloth from a can with a perforated top and then spread it with an ordinary blackboard eraser.

The sketch shows an improvement on this method. A powder magazine is formed in the body of the eraser. Tapping the eraser on the cloth causes a small amount of the powder to sift out, and then it is spread and worked in with the eraser.—Contributed by Donald P. Maxwell, McKeesport, Pa.

Homemade Sandblast

Where compressed air is available, a very convenient sandblast arrangement can be made of pipe and fittings. The main body consists of a 1-in. tee, into which is turned a 1-in. pipe, A. The other two openings of the tee are reduced to ½ in., and ½-in. pipe connections made to them. A long thread is cut on the end of the air con-

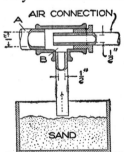

AIR CONNECTION
A
B
SAND

nection so that it can be turned in far enough for the end to pass the sand connection B. The intensity of the blast may be regulated by turning the pipe A in far enough partly to cut off the sand supply.—Contributed by E. K. Marshall, Oak Park, Ill.

Piston-Pin Lubrication

In the case of vertical-cylinder automobile motors where the piston pin is fastened to the piston, the usual construction of a hole in the top of the connecting rod is not always suitable to insure a good supply of oil to the pin. This is because the oil supply is in the form of a fine spray, or mist, churned up from the splash pockets, and the hole in the top of the connecting rod is usually too small to admit enough of the spray for good lubrication.

The illustration shows a remedy for this condition, which can be applied to existing motors of the type mentioned

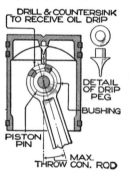

DRILL & COUNTERSINK TO RECEIVE OIL DRIP
DETAIL OF DRIP PEG
BUSHING
PISTON PIN
MAX. THROW CON. ROD

without changing the design or adding too much weight to the piston. The remedy is to place a taper pin in the center of the under side on the piston head. This pin will collect the drops of oil which form from the spray and allow them to drop off the end into a hole in the top of the connecting rod.

The pin, or "drip peg," should be made of steel and well finished. It may be driven, or screwed, into the center of the piston head. Plenty of stock will be found at this point, as the makers have allowed material for the center hole. The top of the connecting rod should be drilled about ⅜ in. and countersunk generously. This will not lower the effective strength of the rod, as its bearing is on the lower side. —Contributed by W. Burr Bennett, Bridgeport, Conn.

Waterproofing Concrete Work

For the purpose of waterproofing concrete there is nothing better than the commercial waterglass, which is a solution of sodium silicate. Dilute the waterglass with four parts of soft water. Apply with a flat brush, thoroughly wetting the surface.

Another method is the use of copper sulphate, also known as blue vitriol. One pound, dissolved in 4 gal. of water and applied the same as the waterglass, will give excellent results. The sulphates of aluminum, zinc, or iron can also be used, but the copper solution is by far the cheapest and most efficient.

Waterglass is the best water-resisting agent, for its combination with the calcium of the cement is a chemical one, forming an insoluble silicate of that element. Incidentally the waterglass may be colored by mineral pigments, thus at the same time forming a waterproof color for concrete.—A. E. Soderlund, New York City.

Wall Paper Window-Display Machine

A dealer in paints and wall paper devised an ingenious display machine to show his stock of wall papers to his patrons. It is also used in the show window during the dull season, and has proven to be a good advertiser out of season.

The machine is driven by a motor, and the elements are three pairs of cylinders which are mounted in a frame and slowly revolved, one pair for ceiling paper, one pair for borders, and one pair for side walls. A canvas belt, about 200 ft. long, connects each pair of cylinders, and as it unwinds from one it winds up on the other, making a large roll. Each pair of cylinders starts to wind at the same time, and when all three are unwound, a reverse gear is slipped in, and the belt runs back on the first roller. The mechanism is provided with an ingenious device to keep the surface speed of the belt always the same. Between each pair of cylinders the belt runs on a tangent, or

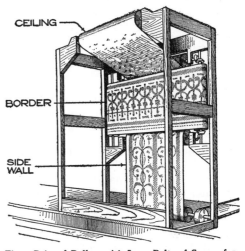

Three Pairs of Rollers with Long Belts of Canvas for Displaying the Combinations of Wall Paper

straightaway, and this part is the part that is visible to the spectators.

On the canvas belt are pasted the wall-paper samples. The machine is so arranged that three harmonizing kinds of paper are visible at a time, thus giving a good idea of how a room would appear with that paper combination. For use in the display room the motor may be disconnected, and each of the three roll systems worked independently by hand. The customer, seated comfortably in a chair, can judge the effect of the different combinations of border, ceiling, and side-wall papers.

⟨The diametral pitch of a gear is the number of teeth to each inch of its pitch diameter.

Advertising Signboard for Farmers' Products

The farmers in one locality use a novel signboard to advertise their farm products. Instead of the usual painted

FRESH EGGS
28¢ PER DOZ
NEW BEETS
RASPBERRIES
SHELL BEANS
FOWL
NEW POTATO

The Signboards are Held in Place between Posts Where They are Quickly Inserted

slab, or blackboard, the passing autoist, or summer visitor, finds a neatly painted sign with all of the good things in the farmers' market for that day, for instance, "New Beets," "Shell Beans," "Fresh Killed Chickens." Upon closer examination the sign will be found to be constructed so different panels with the articles for sale may be quickly inserted. A stock of these painted boards is kept to correspond to the different seasons of the year for the things on sale. The boards are usually painted white with black letters, and present a neat appearance.—Contributed by George H. Davis, Jr., Braintree, Mass.

Transplanting Plants

In changing the location of plants from one place to another they will stand a greater chance for thrifty growing if the earth around the roots remains undisturbed. This can be accomplished by digging a trench around the plant and binding the earth together with a piece of ordinary wire window screen. This screening must reach down as far as the ends of the roots. Cord wrapped around the screen will hold the earth in a compact mass.

The mass can be grasped at the bottom with the fingers, in the earth under the screening, and lifted bodily out, then placed in the new hole, or a spade can be inserted under the screening and the mass lifted. The wire screening need not be removed, as it will rust out in a short time.—Contributed by James A. Hart, Philadelphia, Pa.

Pulling a Well Casing

When a well casing will not start with the jacks, or when it comes up so slowly that it cannot be seen moving, and is pulling hard, stop pulling, run the bailer two or three times, and the casing will come easily. Always leave the bailer down at the bottom of the hole. Should the casing tighten up again, repeat the bailing, and take out two or three more bailers of water. On one occasion when two jacks, each of 40 tons capacity, failed to start 232 ft. of 8-in. casing, we loosened it up by running the bailer three times. Well diggers should try this, and they will never lose another well, or string of casing, by stripping the threads at the joints.—Contributed by J. J. Coughlin, Versailles, Ohio.

A Cradle for a Boat

A pair of sawhorses, with pieces of old garden hose tacked on, to prevent marring the surfaces, make a good cradle for a boat. When not in use for

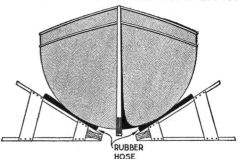

RUBBER HOSE

Pieces of Hose Tacked on the Legs Protect the Boat Surfaces

that purpose the horses can be used in the ordinary manner.—Contributed by J. J. OBrien, Buffalo, N. Y.

MOTORCYCLE TRAILER AND CAMP OUTFIT

By T. T. Sturgeon

INSTEAD of the ordinary sidecar so much used by motorcycle owners I constructed the trailer and camp outfit herein described to take its place. A companion and I made a 600-mile tour with it over some of the worst desert and mountain roads in the western states. The trailer proved its practicability and its advantages over the sidecar. There was no side drag on the motor, and, as the pull was straight backward, the motor was held steady in the sand ruts. Another great advantage over the sidecar is that the trailer can be detached by pulling out a pin when it is desired to make short side trips. Many conveniences may also be incorporated in it that would be impossible with a sidecar permanently attached to a motorcycle.

The complete equipment consists of the following units: trailer car, nested mess kit, tent and sleeping bags, and a complete photographic developing outfit for field work. The total weight of the outfit, with the necessary foodstuffs and motor-repair parts, is slightly under 250 lb. This weight may seem excessive, but it did not prove so, even on bad roads, and upon one occasion 100 miles of good road was covered in five hours.

The first part of the equipment to be taken up in detail is the trailer chassis, which is shown in Fig. 1 ready for the installation of the body. The illustration shows the axle straight. A 3 or 4-in. dip made in it will lower the center of gravity. The bend in the axle being outside the springs, the tread will be about 6 in. wider, but otherwise the dimensions given are satisfactory.

The measurements for the chassis are as follows: The axle is of steel, 33 in. long and $\frac{7}{8}$ in. in diameter, turned down at the ends to fit the cones of the ordinary sidecar wheels, and threaded on each end to receive a $\frac{1}{2}$-in. castellated nut, which is locked with a cotter. The springs were obtained from the junk pile of a local wagon maker. They consist of the lower halves of ordinary buggy springs, measuring 33 in. long and $1\frac{1}{4}$ in. wide. As the springs were too stiff, only the three larger leaves were used, these being secured to the axle with strap bolts or axle clips.

One of the rear-corner joints is shown in Fig. 2. The sidepieces are $38\frac{1}{2}$ in., and the ends 19 in. long, and of $1\frac{1}{2}$ by $1\frac{1}{2}$-in. angle iron. One face of the end pieces is cut 22 in. long, to permit a $1\frac{1}{2}$-in. lap for riveting to the side members, as shown at A. The method of mounting the springs is shown at B. A piece of $\frac{1}{8}$-in. sheet steel, 3 by $4\frac{1}{2}$ in., forms the rear bracket, which should be of such quality that it will stand hardening. A slot,

1½ in. long by 5⁄16 in. wide, is cut through the sides to receive a hardened-steel bolt passing through the spring end in such a manner that it will ride in the slots of the bracket. The front-spring bracket is similar but without a slot, having a hole for the bolts, and does not need to be hardened.

The tongue, drawhead, and automatic brake are shown in Fig. 3. The tongue consists of two pieces of 1 by ⅛-in. angle iron, 52 in. long, and the drawhead is made of a 6-in. length of ¾-in. pipe, with a pipe cap. The lengths of angle iron are bent slightly, at C, to permit bolting them parallel with the drawhead, and to make a spread of about 10 in. where they connect with the front member of the frame. The drawhead is attached to the tongue pieces with machine screws locked with lock washers. The ends of the screws that project inside of the pipe should be dressed off smoothly, to permit the free action of the drawbar.

The drawbar is made of a machine-steel eyebolt, 6 in. long and ½ in. in diameter. The bolt slides through a hole in the cap, against which a spring is placed. It exerts pressure on two nuts on the end of the drawbar, working easily inside of the drawhead. The spring can be adjusted by the nuts on the bar. This arrangement forms a swivel-and-spring drawhead, which is very important, as the safety of the trailer depends greatly upon it. The nuts on the end of the drawbar should be securely locked, to prevent them from coming off and thus releasing the drawbar. A little cup grease should be packed in the spring for lubrication, as the drawbar is constantly working back and forth when on the road.

The automatic brake may appear unnecessary, but it is a great convenience when some of the draft rigging breaks. Also, in an emergency the trailer may be cut off while in motion to prevent a "spill," and the brake will prevent it from running over a bank or into another vehicle. When making camp, it saves searching for something with which to chock the wheels. If

the car is taken down a steep place by hand the brake is needed. It is self-locking and equalizing when set. It took considerable experimenting to find the exact shape and dimensions of the levers.

The working details are shown in Fig. 4. Two brake beams and shoes are required, which are made from metal, ½ in. wide and ¼ in. thick. The beams are bent as shown at D, which is the center of the angle and the point where the tangents of the two legs cross each other, the exact locations of the holes being found from this point. The shoes E are made of steel, 1 in. wide and 1⁄16 in. thick, riveted to the beams at F. The two beams are pivoted to the frame at G, Fig. 3, 4½ in. from the front end piece, and ½ in. from the edge of the side member, inside measurements, the pivot bolts being 3⁄16-in. stove bolts with lock washers.

The bends, to make the peculiar shape of what may be called the trigger, must be made accurately, to insure the proper adjustment and operation of the mechanism, hence the working details must be observed. The lever is attached, at H, Fig. 5, to the right brake beam, the short piece J being coupled to the trigger, at K, and to the left beam; stove bolts with lock-nuts being used throughout.

The automatic release, Fig. 6, consists of an 8-in. auxiliary wheel supported in a U-shaped bracket, made of ¾-in. channel iron, 6 in. long on each leg. A 1-in. slot, wide enough to permit the shaft of the small wheel to slide freely in it, is cut in each leg. The bracket is fastened to the cap on the drawhead with a machine screw. The sides of the channel are filed at an angle to fit the cap snugly, when the bracket, drawbar, and braces are joined. They should be joined so that the longer sides of the triangle formed are equal.

The braces are made of 5⁄16-in. iron rod, having eyes formed in their lower ends to fit the wheel shaft. They are flattened on the opposite ends for bolting to the tongue sections, their length

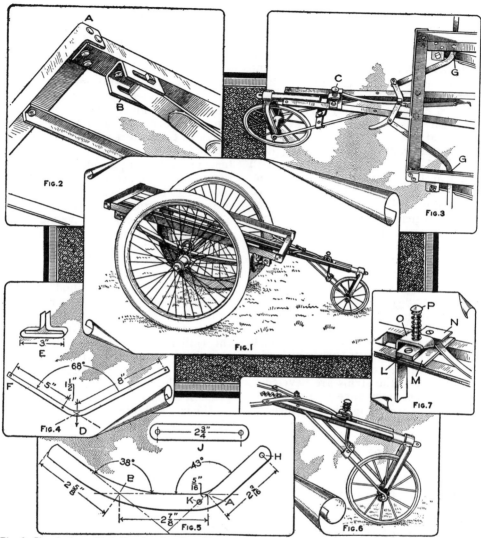

Fig. 1, Chassis Assembled, Showing Auxiliary Wheel and Rigging; Fig. 2, Rear Corner of the Chassis Frame, Showing Corner Joint A, and Spring Fastening B; Fig. 3, The Auxiliary Wheel Frame and the Braking Mechanism; Fig. 4, Brake Beam and Shoe; Fig. 5, Trigger and Trigger Strap; Fig. 6, Auxiliary Wheel, Showing Trigger Device, Braces, and Slotted U-Bar; Fig. 7, The Trigger Device

being such that the center of the shaft will be about 13 in. from the point at which they bolt to the tongue. If the parts are set properly the auxiliary wheel will work freely in the slots, the natural spring in the brace rods tending to hold the wheel at the bottom.

The release-catch feature is simple. At a point 8½ in. from the front member of the frame, two holes are drilled and tapped for machine screws. Two plates, L and M, Fig. 7, one 2¾ in. long, 1½ in. wide, and 1/16 in. thick, and

the other 2¾ in. long, ¾ in. wide, and ¼ in. thick, are attached to the tongue by the screws, as shown. A small piece of metal, N, is placed on top of the thicker plate, to prevent the trigger from rising out of place when the catch O is pushed up. A carriage bolt, P, is screwed into the plates at their center, with a locknut to hold it on the under side. The catch O is drilled to permit free action on this bolt. A light spring is placed between the catch O and the head of the bolt. The release is fastened to the braces by means of a strap and stove bolts, as shown in Fig. 6.

The action of the brake is as follows: When the trailer is released from the motor the tongue drops; the auxiliary wheel, coming in contact with the road, rises in its slots, pushing the catch up to clear the trigger, and a coiled spring at the middle draws the brake beams into action. This spring does not hold the brakes in contact with the wheels, but merely starts the action. The braking power is derived from the back pressure on the rod braces, which is communicated to the lever arrangement on the brake beams. The greater the weight pressing down on the auxiliary wheel the greater the braking power.

The design of the body and the arrangement of the covers to form tables are shown in Fig. 8. The dimensions of the box are such that it will fit snugly in the chassis frame. It is made of ½-in. lumber with corner and edge strips to reinforce the joints. The inside edges of the strips are beveled to give a neat appearance to the panels. The box is water-tight, 13 in. deep at the center and 11½ at the ends, the floor resting on the side members of the frame and on the tongue at the center.

A tank, 17 in. long, 10 in. wide, and 4 in. high, of 3-gal. capacity, for a gasoline supply, is set in the rear of the body. It is held in place with cleats, and is made of galvanized iron, with reinforcing plates on the ends.

The front cover is so arranged that it can be attached to the rear of the body for use as a mess table, and for photographic purposes. Folding standards, at the end of the tongue, at the rear of the chassis and under the table, together with the brake make the whole stand firmly. When the table is used for photographic purposes the rear cover, which is hinged to the body, is braced in a vertical position, as in Fig. 9. A collapsible wire frame is attached to the cover by means of screw eyes, on the under side, and a light-proof bag, large enough to inclose the table and the operator, forms a dark room. As it is used only at night, it is satisfactory for this kind of work.

As the motorcycle was electrically equipped for lighting, a small lamp, not shown in the illustration, was bracketed to the rear of the body. The feed wires were conducted to the end of the tongue, where slip connections were provided to connect with a terminal on the motor draft rigging. A long extension cord was provided, permitting the motor to be set at a distance from the car when in camp. The lamp proved to be convenient, being used as a tail light for night traveling, as a dark-room light, and as a table lamp, when the red lens was removed.

The method of coupling the trailer to the motorcycle is shown in Fig. 10. As slightly differing methods will be necessary with varying types of motorcycles, it is offered as a suggestion only. The motorcycle which was used to tow the trailer was provided with sidecar lugs immediately forward of the rear axle, and with small luggage-carrier lugs on the rear forks. A U-shaped piece of strap iron, 1¼ in. long and ¼ in. thick, was bolted to the sidecar lugs at such an angle that the drawhead of ⁵⁄₁₆ by 1-in. steel, bolted at the center, would hold the trailer horizontal. The upward thrust of the trailer was prevented by the U-piece resting against the nuts on the rear axle of the motor, the downward thrust being held with ½-in. stay rods running from the lugs, on the rear forks, to the outer curve of the U-piece.

A large cotter, slightly spread, forms the coupling pin, and a cord is attached to it so that the man on the rear seat may release the trailer in the event of a skid or fall. All nuts and bolts must be locked either with split washers or cotters. The load should be packed with the heaviest articles in the center in order to balance the car. Several screw eyes should be placed in the sides of the body near the floor, and a lash rope run through them, with which to lash the load solidly in the car. This prevents shifting and protects the contents in the event of a "tip-over."

Fig. 8, The Trailer Supported to Make Table Accommodating Two Persons for Meals or Recreation   Fig. 9, Arranged for Photographic Purposes Showing Dark-Room Curtain   Fig. 10, Manner of Attaching the Trailer to Motorcycle for Road Transportation

The Mess Outfit

The mess outfit is well adapted for camping, as it provides nearly everything necessary for two persons, and is contained in a small package. While it is designed particularly for motorcycle use, it should prove a serviceable addition to the equipment of the automobile tourist and could easily be made to serve for four or more persons, without enlarging the space occupied by it. Space for extra cups and plates may be obtained by utilizing the space used for food, in the kit for two persons.

An elaborate set of tinners' tools is not necessary in making the outfit; vise, snips, mallet, pliers, hammer, and a soldering iron being the articles required. Short lengths of angle iron, of different sizes, clamped in a vise form the mandrel upon which the bends are made.

The complete outfit nested inside the combination stove ready for transportation is shown in Fig. 11. It occupies a space 7¼ by 7¼ by 12 in., and weighs slightly less than 11 lb. without foodstuffs. It contains the following utensils: coffeepot, two cups, one bowl, stewpan, frying pan, two plates, sugar can, two sets of knives and forks, an extra spoon, and a 2-gal. bucket. There is room also for 3 lb. of bacon, ½ lb. of butter, cans of pepper and salt, ¼ lb. of tea, and a small dishcloth.

Three sheets of heavy tinplated sheet metal, a piece of light galvanized iron, 12 by 36 in., and a piece of black sheet iron, 15 by 50 in., of medium

thickness, will provide all the necessary pieces with the exception of the gasoline tank for the stove. If it is desired to use the type of stove shown, a small amount of galvanized iron, of medium thickness, will also be required.

The patterns for cutting and forming the different utensils are shown in Fig. 12. The main pattern Q is for one of the sides. The sheet metal is folded on the dotted lines and the joint placed in the center of one side. On each edge

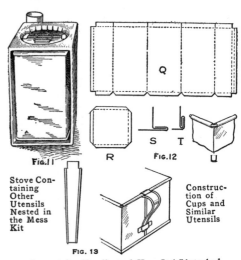

Fig. 11, Stove Containing Other Utensils Nested in the Mess Kit

Fig. 12

Fig. 13, Construction of Cups and Similar Utensils

Layout for Handle and How It is Attached

⅛ and ¼ in. are provided to form the clinch seam, and ⅛ in. on the bottom edge for the joint. At the top ³⁄₁₆ in. is provided to form a roll around the reinforcing ring.

The bottom pattern is shown at R, the dimensions of which is best determined after the sides have been formed. It is ⅛ in. larger than the bottom half

Mess Outfit Partly Nested

of the clinch. The first operation of attaching the bottom plate is shown at S. The lap of the bottom is folded over the side lap, and clinched as shown at T. The top roll around the ring, which consists of ordinary galvanized telephone wire, is formed as shown at U. The side seams are clinched in the same manner. A small piece of steel, similar to a rivet set, with a notch the size of the seams cut in its face, aids in making the clinch properly.

The detachable handle of the cups and the coffeepot are constructed and attached as shown in Fig. 13. The tongue at the top is formed into a hook and hooked under the wire ring, a bit of the metal of the side having been cut out to permit its insertion. A small strap soldered to the side of the utensil, permits the handle to slip down under it when squeezed slightly. The handles are reinforced along the edges with a small wire and a roll.

All the utensils are made in the same manner, with the exception of the stewpan, which has the ends clinched in, the sides and the bottom being made of one piece. The handles of the stewpan are not detachable, but form clasps to hold the lid tight, when the equipment for it and other contents are nested inside. The construction of the bucket is similar, except

that larger seams are made. Since a clinch seam is not water-tight, all joints in the bucket must be soldered.

The frying pan is made of the black sheet iron. It is constructed without seams, as shown in Fig. 14, the corners being folded and riveted. A strap is riveted on one end, to receive the detachable handle, which is a short piece of ⅛ by ¾-in. strap iron, with a hook bent upward on the end.

The construction of the plates is shown in Fig. 15. They have a ½-in. double, flat brim around the edge.

Beginning with the smallest utensil, shown in the rear row in Fig. 16, the inside measurements are as follows: first cup, 3½ in. square by 4 in.; second cup, 3¾ in. square; coffeepot, 4 in. square by 8 in.; bowl, 4¼ in. square; sugar can, 1 by 3½ by 6 in.; plate, including rim, ⅞ by 5½ by 9¾ in.; stewpan, 5½ by 6 by 9¾ in.; frying pan, 1½ by 6¼ by 10 in.; bucket, 6½ in. square by 11 in. The covers of the coffeepot and the stewpan are made to fit. The method of forming the edges of the covers and of attaching the handles is shown in Fig. 17.

The assembling of the mess kit is shown in Figs. 16 and 18. When the articles are nested inside the coffeepot, enough room is left on top for the half pound of butter and the bacon. The lid of the stewpan is shown removed in Fig. 18, and space can be seen at the top for cans to hold salt, pepper, tea, and similar supplies.

The stove was designed so that wood or gasoline could be used for fuel. Double the space is needed when gasoline is used, in order to provide a storage tank for the gasoline.

The stove is constructed of heavy sheet iron. The measurements inside are 7¼ in. square by 12 in. A 3-in. hole is cut in one end, and a 6-in. hole in the other. An old brazing torch was used to make the burner for the gasoline stove.

The gasoline supply was set in a galvanized-iron tank, 4 in. by 7 in. square, in much the same manner as it was in the original torch. The generating pan was removed from the feed stem and placed on the valve stem, permitting generation of gas in the usual way. The pump was placed in a corner. In order to spread the flame over a larger area, a burner cap, taken from a gasoline stove, was attached to the top of the fire head. A stay bolt was run through the center of the tank to reinforce it to withstand the air pressure. Care must be taken not to have too great a pressure in the tank.

When the stove is used with wood as a fuel, it is placed in a horizontal position, with the open side over a small depression in the ground. A heavy wire screen is hooked over the inside edges, where they are turned in, forming a grate. This gives a draft for the fire.

The Photographic Outfit

The photographic equipment need not be detailed completely, as the only point of special interest is the method of washing and drying plates. After taking them from the hypo tank, they were placed in the wash tank. The bucket hanging at the rear lid of the body of the car was filled with water, and a rubber siphon drew the water down to the wash tank, from which it ran to the ground. After the plates had been washed, they were placed in an alcohol tank. The alcohol displaced the water in the emulsion, causing the plates to dry in a few moments, when placed before an electric fan driven by current from the motorcycle storage battery.

The Tent and Sleeping Bag

For the making of the small tent, and two sleeping bags, 21 yd. of canvas are necessary, 8-oz. double-twist khaki drill being the most suitable. One or more blankets for each bag are needed, depending on the temperature in which the bags are to be used.

The dimensions of the tent are approximately 6½ ft. long, 5 ft. high, and 5 ft. wide. This is sufficient to cover a motorcycle and two persons. Two bamboo poles support the tent at the front and rear, a rope ridge support being used.

The method of cutting and joining the canvas, which is 36 in. wide, is shown in Fig. 19. Thirteen yards are necessary for the tent. From this four

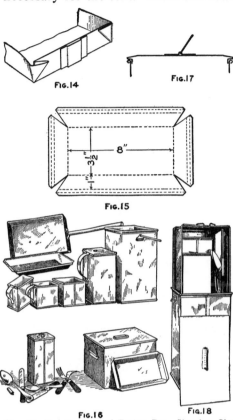

Fig. 14, Construction of Frying Pan, Showing Slot for Handle; Fig. 15, Layout for Cutting Metal for Plates; Fig. 16, Mess Outfit Ready for Nesting; Fig. 17, Cover Construction and Fastening of Handles; Fig. 18, Mess Outfit Nested

lengths, 6 ft. 7½ in. long, are cut, thus allowing ¾ in. on each end for the corner seams, stitched together with laps, as shown. One seam is at the ridge and the other in the center of the sides. A ½-in. hem is placed along the bottom edges.

The remainder is now divided and each section equally divided to form the four large gores, A, as shown in Fig. 19. Two of the gores are stitched together their full length, forming the back of the tent, and the other two are stitched about one foot down from the ridge, leaving an opening for an entrance. The front and back are next stitched to the side walls along their slanting edges. They will be a few inches too long. The part left over is cut off, and the small gores B are made from these scraps. A hem simi-

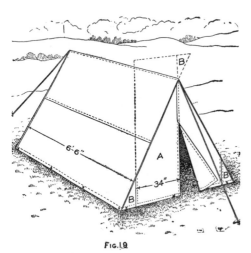

FIG. 19

Tent, Showing Method of Cutting Canvas Economically to Make the Ends

lar to the one upon the sides is next placed on the bottom edge of the end. Eyelets with ⅜-in. holes are fitted along the bottom edges to receive the large spikes used for tent pegs. The ridge rope is then run through the apex of the ends and fastened.

The sleeping bags are each made of 4 yd. of canvas, fashioned like a long envelope. The upper side is 5½ ft.

long and the bottom 6½ ft., accommodating a person of medium height. The blankets used inside of the bags should be stitched together with the seam uppermost, and in the middle. The top of the blankets should be left unstitched for about 18 in., as the bag may thus be more readily entered, and the blankets brought closely around the neck of the user. A cord should be run through the bottom seam of the inner bag and through eyelets in the corners of the outer bag, so that the bag may be anchored to a peg, making it easier for one to get out of it.

In connection with the sleeping equipment, a poncho is desirable and can be made from a 48 by 72-in. piece of black oilcloth. A hem should be run around the edges of the oilcloth, and five garment snaps should be sewed on one long edge, in order that the poncho may be thrown around the shoulders and fastened in front.

A poncho of this type protects the upper part of the body when walking or riding in the rain, and may be spread over the sleeping bags to protect them when used in the open. Two ponchos may be snapped together to form an auxiliary roof for the tent. A poncho is the handiest article in camp on a wet day, with the possible exception of a water-tight match safe, and, of course, every camper should have one of these.

Dresser as a Drafting Table

A dresser, or bureau, may be made to do service as a drawing table and will be found convenient by students and others who make drawings occasionally. The sketch shows how the board is rested on the edge of the open drawer, and held under the dresser top.

For use in a standing position the dresser will be found convenient, whereas a bureau gives better service for the seated position.

The board should be placed at the left-hand edge of the dresser, so that the same edge of the board extends about 1 in. beyond the side. If the

drawer is not firm, small wedges may be inserted between it and the slides

The Board Rests upon the Edge of the Drawer and is Held by the Top

on which it rests.—Contributed by Raymond B. Rogers, Newberg, Ore.

Substitute for a Slide-Rule Glass

In using the slide rule I have found that one of the chief difficulties is the constant breaking of the glass runner. The glasses being quite expensive, the cost of renewing them every time one drops the rule is no small item. A very good and practically unbreakable substitute for these glasses can be made from an old celluloid, or xylonite, triangle which might otherwise be thrown away. The material can be cut to the required shape with a sharp knife. The hair line can then be scratched on with a needle and colored with India ink. I have found this indicator to be fully as good as glass in work requiring the greatest accuracy.—Contributed by George Caynor Hyde, Hoboken, N. J.

Repairing a Broken Brake-Lever Handle

The handle on the brake lever of an automobile broke at the point indicated in the illustration, and knowing

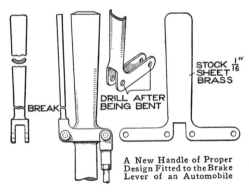

A New Handle of Proper Design Fitted to the Brake Lever of an Automobile

that the break was due to faulty design, I decided to make up a new, entirely different handle.

A piece of sheet brass, $\frac{1}{16}$ in. thick, was procured and cut to the proper size and shape, the dimensions being taken from the two portions of the broken handle. The four holes shown were not drilled until the piece was bent into shape. After fitting the new handle, it was carefully buffed and polished.—Contributed by Adolph Kline, New York City.

To Typewrite on Druggists' Labels

A druggist, desiring a neat appearance of labels, found it difficult to typewrite on small sizes, as they could not

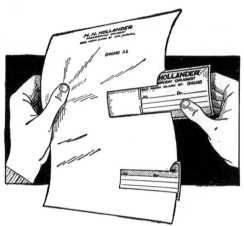

Labels are Inserted into Places Made for Them on a Full-Sized Typewriter Sheet

be kept in the proper place on the typewriter roll. This difficulty was easily overcome by making the holding slip shown in the illustration. An insert was formed for each size of label by pasting a piece of paper on a full-sized typewriter paper, leaving an opening for the insertion of the labels. The opening in front is of such a size as to present the lines on the labels to be filled in.—Contributed by H. N. Hollander, Chicago.

Forming Tool for Pipe Clamps

The sketch shows a pipe clamp shaped from light steel, and a handy tool used to form it. To use the tool, which is made in the form of a pair of tongs, it is opened and the straight piece of steel to be formed is inserted. The upper part of the

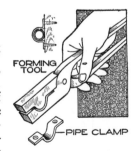

forming tool is then struck a blow with a hammer, and the clamp is formed.

Holder for a Telephone

In order to clear a small desk of a telephone and still have the latter at

hand a wall bracket notched to receive the instrument was made and fastened to the wall above the desk. The notch must be made deep enough so that the telephone will not slip out of it easily.—Contributed by Theodore J. Becker, Kansas City, Mo.

Covering Space on an Automobile Crank Handle

The space between the revolving sleeve and the pinhead on the starting crank of my automobile allowed the

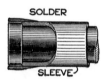

flesh of the hand to squeeze in and get pinched, or cut, when starting the engine. This space I covered as follows: A piece of brass tubing, ½ in. long and of a size to snugly fit the sleeve on the crank, was placed directly over the space and soldered to the sleeve. The soldered end was then filed down tapering and made smooth. —Contributed by Adolph Kline, New York City.

Lock for Sliding Doors

The sketch shows a lock for a sliding door. It consists of three pieces, a slotted bolt, A; the plate with the

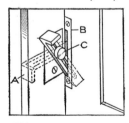

little block on which it rests, and the plate B. The bolt is loosely fastened in place by means of the pin C, and in such a position as to slide snugly into the socket in the

wood, as indicated by the dotted lines. A feature of this lock is that it tends to prevent the door from rattling in the wind. As the door rattles, the wedge point of the bolt works its way downward until the door is held firm. —Contributed by Malcolm E. Moran, Rosario, Wash.

Removing a Corkscrew Attachment from a Penknife

Having a very good penknife with a corkscrew attachment, which was very much in the way, I opened up the

corkscrew and cut the shank off close to the handle on the line AB, then filed the edges of the portion remaining in the handle to the shape of the sides holding it.

As I had previously spoiled a perfectly good knife by removing the corkscrew entirely, and then found I had greatly weakened the spring, I decided this time I would leave a portion of the corkscrew in the handle, which proved a success.—Contributed by James M. Kane, Doylestown, Pa.

To Prevent Safety Pin from Coming Loose

Most safety pins bend in the center

when there is any strain on them, which causes the pin part to slip out of its sheath. If the pin is curved as illustrated, it cannot bend so that the pin part will slip out.—Contributed by J. Cooper Mott, Great Neck Station, Long Island.

Removing Poppet Valves

The amateur motorist often finds it quite a proposition to get the valves out of an engine without removing the springs. Each valve has a groove in its upper end, and a stick can be quickly cut so that it can be driven into this groove tightly enough to be used as a handle to pull the valve out. This method has been used with great success in removing the outlet valves of a horizontal force pump for priming, without injuring the rubber facings. A small hole, about ¼ in. deep, was drilled in the top of each valve to receive the stick.—Contributed by P. E. Riggar, Ottawa, Can.

To Prevent a Flag from Winding around the Pole

A simple and easy way to prevent a flag from becoming entangled, or winding around the pole as the wind changes, is shown in the sketch. A hardwood disk, from 4 to 6 in. in diameter, and from 1¼ to 2 in. thick, depending on the size and height of the pole, is provided with two holes near its outer edge, about 2 in. apart, with a groove cut to connect them on the upper side. A pulley may be used if a means is provided to prevent the rope from running off when it becomes slack. An iron rod is placed in the top of the pole and a washer over the rod, or if the pole end is made smooth enough the washer may be omitted. The disk is then put in place, after greasing the holes as well as the bottom surface of the groove with tallow or paraffin. The ball is placed in position and the rope run through the greased holes and groove of the disk. When the wind changes the flag acts

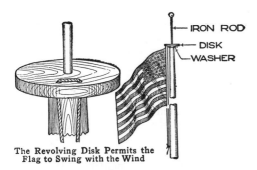

The Revolving Disk Permits the Flag to Swing with the Wind

as a weather vane, the disk revolves, and the flag is always on the side of the pole opposite to the wind.—Contributed by W. E. Day, Pittsfield, Mass.

Weather Vane with Inside Indicator

It is quite convenient to know the direction of the wind, especially in stormy weather, and as the old-fashioned vane is unsightly and altogether

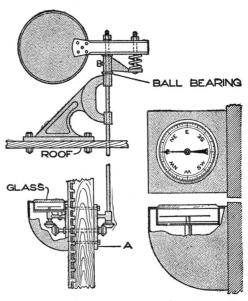

A Neat Weather Vane with a Mechanically Driven Indicator in the House

undesirable, the one shown was designed to make a neat and real ornament for any building. The design makes it easy to build, and as it has so few parts, they are not likely to get out of order.

The vane is set upon the roof by means of a bracket and is securely clamped to the vertical rod. This rod has miter gears at the lower end, where it is connected to a horizontal shaft passing through the wall, and then with another set of gears to the vertical indicator shaft. The indicator and its dial are shown in the projection.

The plate A serves as bearing for the horizontal shaft and for the lower end of the vertical shaft. The indicator should be inclosed in some neat form of a box. The coil spring in the upper part is merely a cushion and the bolt serves to hold the vane bearing horizontal.—Contributed by J. B. Murphy, Plainfield, N. J.

Twisting Locomotive Link Hangers

After repairing links and their parts, and in assembling them on a locomotive, almost always the jaws of the

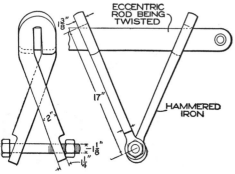

Powerful Twisting Device for Fitting Link Hangers and Eccentric Rods on Locomotives

eccentric rod will be out of line with the link, and the hanger will need a little twisting to make the parts fit properly. The sketch shows plainly a device for twisting the link hangers, and how it is used. The ends are put on the hanger from 12 to 18 in. apart, and the bolt, which is 12 in. long, is used to draw the lever arms in making the twist.—Contributed by Joseph K. Long, Renovo, Pa.

A Swinging-Chair Hammock

The illustration shows a hammock that can be used either in an upright position or at any reclining angle by simply adjusting the ropes. The space required is so small that it may be

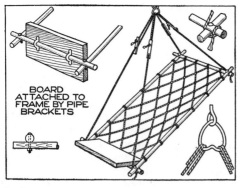

Reclining-Chair Hammock That can be Used Upright or at an Angle by Adjusting the Ropes

used on short porches. It gives greater comfort than the ordinary hammock, which takes up room that is not always available.

The cost of the hammock is very small. The frame can be made of four discarded broom handles. These are joined together in a rectangle with small bolts at the corners. The net is made of awning rope, requiring about 1 lb. of the material. If the fish-net knot cannot be tied the ordinary knot will answer the purpose.

The net soon adjusts itself to the form of the body, making the most comfortable swinging, or reclining, chair that can be had, and far superior for reading to the ordinary hammock, as the body is entirely relaxed without making it necessary for the occupant to strain the eyes in looking upward at the paper or book.—Contributed by T. F. Krey, Detroit, Michigan.

Banking Material for Pouring Babbitt

When pouring babbitt into bearings, or lead into cable fastenings, it is necessary to bank up the openings in order to confine the molten metal where it is desired. The most common material for the bank is wet clay, which can be molded into the required shape to fit the openings. A better method is to mix asbestos wool with heavy engine oil. This preparation not only serves the purpose better, but is practically indestructible. It is always ready for use, while the clay must be wetted and worked to the proper degree of plasticity each time it is used.

Waxing a Varnished Floor

A varnished floor may be waxed to save it from scratches, and the wax finish, when defaced, may be easily renovated by rubbing on more wax, or cleaned off with turpentine. Wax finish on a floor has its disadvantages, but it is easily applied and is easily renovated, besides being fit to walk upon as soon as it is applied.

A Concrete-Block Milk House

By W. E. FRUDDEN

THE use of concrete in the construction of small farm buildings means the substitution of an everlasting, non-decaying type for those constantly in need of painting and repairs. Concrete construction is fire-resisting and has many other points in its dation, that extends down below the frost line and is flared out at the base, as shown. Mix the concrete with 1 part cement, 3 parts sand, and 5 parts well-graded gravel, and pour into the trenches carefully so that dirt will not fall into the mixture.

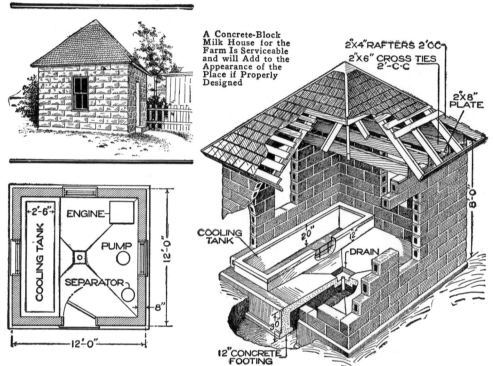

A Concrete-Block Milk House for the Farm Is Serviceable and will Add to the Appearance of the Place if Properly Designed

favor, and has become a very popular building material among farm owners. The concrete-block milk house is most ideal. It is permanent and sanitary, and will last indefinitely. Such a structure is shown in the illustration. The one built is 12 ft. square and made entirely out of concrete, except the roof, which is of frame covered with cedar shingles. The materials for the building are as follows:

    7 bbl. of cement.
    3 yd. of sand.
    5 yd. of screened gravel, or stone.
    4 pieces for plates, 12 ft. long, by 2 by 8 in.
    12 pieces for rafters, 10 ft. long, by 2 by 4 in.
    7 pieces for crossties, 12 ft. long, by 2 by 6 in.
    3 window frames.
    1 door frame.
    3 windows, 4 ft. 10 in. by 12 in.
    1 door, 2 ft. 8 in. by 7 ft.
    240 ft. of sheathing for the roof.
    2,000 cedar shingles.
    275 concrete blocks for the walls.

The building rests on a 12-in. foun-

The rules for the laying of concrete blocks, which are used in the walls, are very simple. Neat and rapid work can be done without much training. The equipment necessary is inexpensive and can be built on any farm. The things needed are a mortar-mixing box, about 3 by 5 ft.; a mortar board, about 30 in. square, made of 1-in. lumber; a trowel, a hand level, a straightedge, and a plumb board. Soak the blocks before laying them, or they will take up the moisture in the mortar and thereby weaken it. Lay the block walls up true and plumb, and in a perfect line, and test frequently to see if they are level. Good cement mortar is made in proportions of 1 part cement and 2 parts sand, mixed with enough water to make it of the required consistency. Cement mortar starts to harden very quickly, and it is best to mix up small batches at a time, or enough to be used in less than one hour's time.

A 2 by 8-in. plate is bolted to the top course of blocks, and the roof rafters are spiked to it in a substantial manner. The rafters are 2 by 4-in. material, spaced 2 ft. from center to center, and covered with sheathing and cedar shingles, laid 4½ in. to the weather, and fastened with galvanized shingle nails.

The milk-cooling tank is made of concrete, 2½ ft. in width. Where the standard 14-in. cans are used, this width will be just right for two rows of cans. The tank used was built to extend a short distance below the floor, which allows the farm hand to lift the cans with ease by obtaining a maximum purchase at the point where the cans are hardest to raise, or just when they are leaving the water. The floor of the cooling tank is just 8 in. below the grade of the milk-house floor. The tank is 20 in. deep inside. The standard-size milk cans, when resting on the bottom of the tank, will then be surrounded by water up to their necks. The tank is made of concrete in one operation. The floor of the tank is 6 in. and the walls 4 in. thick. The concrete is reinforced with ¼-in. rods, spaced 7 in. the long way, and 12 in. the short way. The rods are bent up into the walls of the tank and are tied securely at all intersections.

Concrete for the cooling tank is mixed to a quaky consistency, using 1 part cement, 2 parts sand, and 3 parts of screened gravel, or stone. The top edge of the tank, over which the cans must be lifted, should be protected with a 4-in. channel iron, which is anchored to the concrete wall every two feet.

Handy Form for a Screwdriver

Screwdriver points of different widths and thicknesses are a neces-

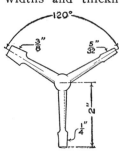

sity on many classes of work. The sketch shows how a three-pointed driver can be easily hammered out of a small piece of steel. The two points not in use furnish an excellent leverage for the work the point in use is being applied to. For a very handy little homemade tool of this nature it is hard to beat.

To Locate a Stud in a Partition

When it is desired to hang a heavy picture on the wall, or fasten a new shelf to it, the studs must be located in order to obtain something solid for holding the nails, or screws. The ordinary method is, of course, to sound the wall by tapping it with a hammer until the stud positions are found. If the ears are not sharp enough for this, small wire brads may be driven in at various places until the studs are located. Not many brads will be required by even the most inexperienced person, and if they are driven in all the way they will never be seen in the wall.

Spring to Hold Down Latch Bar

Annoyance by the springing open of doors having bar latches may be

avoided if the device shown in the illustration is attached to the latch. A piece of spring steel, or a strong wire, is bent to exert pressure on the latch bar. The upper end of the spring or wire is fastened to the barn door with staples. The small curve where the spring and the bar connect is important in that it prevents the spring from slipping off of the bar.

Welding Crank Cases

In accidents, automobile crank cases are often broken or cracked, and the natural desire is to have them fixed if possible. Usually the fixing takes the form of an oxyacetylene weld. Unless new factory parts are very high in price, or the break is only a minor one, or the welder is a real expert, it is a good plan to consider the cost of the welded job. Often the cylinder face has to be replaned, the main bearings rebored, the cam-shaft bearings bored, and special-size odd parts fitted. Considering all this, and the salvage from the old one, a new case is often much cheaper.

Shade Holder for a Chandelier

The shade holder shown in the sketch obviates the necessity of disfiguring the ceiling with hooks and can be applied to either light fixture. If desired a second holder may be placed on the other side.

The holder can be raised and lowered by lifting the end nearest the shade and sliding the upper loop A along the vertical pipe of the gas fixture. The weight of the shade causes the lower arm of the holder to bind against the

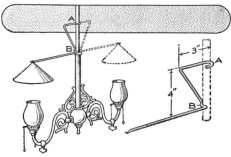

A Shade Holder Made of Heavy Wire to be Attached to the Vertical Pipe of a Gas Fixture

vertical pipe at B and prevents the device from slipping downward.—Contributed by J. A. Fitzpatrick, Altoona, Pennsylvania.

¶A cubic foot of water weighs 62.5 pounds.

An Instantaneous Water Heater

A portable water heater of my own construction and which will heat 25 gal.—enough for a bath—at a cost of

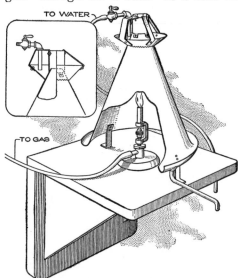

The Water, Running over the Outside Surface of the Funnel, is Heated Quickly

about one cent, is shown in the illustration.

The funnel, which is 11 in. in diameter at the widest point and 12 in. high, is made of sheet metal, riveted at the seam. The chimney at the top is 2 in. in diameter and fits over the top of the funnel, being riveted to it by straps.

Braces support the water reservoir and the water spout from the supply pipe. The view at the left shows the details of the construction at the top.

Instead of the Bunsen burner shown, the fixture from an ordinary mantle gas light may be used, by removing the mantle and adjusting the small collar through which the air supply is received. A steady blue flame will give more heat than a yellow flame.

The heater may be transported to any part of the house where a gas supply is available. If necessary, a water bucket may be set high enough so that water may be supplied through the tube in this manner. Care must be taken that the rubber or other tubes used fit tightly over the nipples, and for purposes of safety, a piece of asbestos or sheet metal should be placed under the heater.

The supply of water should be carefully adjusted in order that only as much as can be heated properly is permitted to flow over the funnel, and the reservoir is not overflowed.—Contributed by James E. Noble, Toronto, Can.

Nail Guard for Open Barrels

In stores and factories where material must be scooped by hand from barrels a nail guard saves a great deal

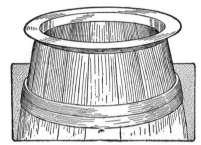

Guard for a Barrel Top to Prevent Injury on the Projecting Nail Points

of time. When the barrels are opened there are so many nails around the upper edge and they are so troublesome to remove that the workman usually allows them to remain. The scooping is then done with such care to avoid injury that an unnecessary amount of time is consumed. A simple guard made of sheet metal, as shown in the sketch, permits the barrel to be emptied quickly.

Preparing New Surfaces of Galvanized Iron for Painting

New galvanized iron needs to be treated before painting, otherwise the paint will peel. There are a few ways of doing this, but the simplest, and one of the best, is to apply a coating of iron acetate, which is vinegar that has surrounded iron for a time. A coat of this will do the trick. Another method is to give the surface a coat of equal parts of spar varnish and turpentine. The government specifies sponging the surface with strong vinegar, which is also a sure method.

Starting Piston Rings in a Cylinder

In overhauling a four-cylinder motor recently, I had considerable trouble in getting the piston rings back in place. The cylinders, being cast in pairs, were quite heavy and hard to handle, and all the twisting and wriggling possible would not let them enter, and the rings, which were of the leak-proof kind, refused to close in by hand. I hit on the idea of taking a piece of pasteboard, about 2 in. wide and long enough to reach around the piston, and tying it tightly in place with a stout cord. By lifting the cylinders over the pistons and letting them enter, the weight was sufficient to push the pasteboard down, at the same time keeping the rings closed so that they would enter. Considerable time was lost before this idea was tried out, but with its aid the job was completed in 10 minutes.—Contributed by A. Dane, Pottstown, Pa.

Protection Hood for Pressure-Ram Indicator Gauges

Pressure gauges on hydraulic rams of almost any make are frequently broken, even though the workmen are careful in handling the material brought into place for the action of the ram. Accidents are not uncommon as a result of the pieces, swung by the cranes into the ram blocks, coming into

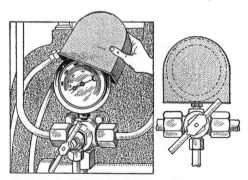

Covering to Protect the Gauge on a Pressure Ram

contact with the glass dial cover of the gauge.

The illustration shows a safety hood of the type adaptable for almost any kind of gauge located in connection with a pressure of a hydraulic press. The hood is removed only when the gauge is in actual use for controlling the action of the ram, and is replaced when the pressure is removed. In this manner not only are workmen protected against injury from flying splintered glass, but the gauge itself is safeguarded.—Contributed by F. W. Bentley, Missouri Valley, Iowa.

Air-Cylinder Packing to Prevent Leaks

Hemp, or flax, packing is most generally used in air cylinders in preference to iron rings. The iron rings will rust and cause them to cut the cylinder, which will soon make them leak. The sketch shows the proper way in which to fit hemp packing. Holes are drilled at the base of the packing so that half of their diameters will be in the pack-

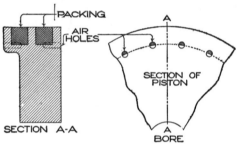

SECTION A-A

BORE

The Drilled Holes Permit the Air to Pass under the Rings and Push Them Out

ing groove. The holes allow the air to get under the packing, which forces them against the cylinder walls. Rings packed in this way will wear longer, make a tight fit, and give no trouble.

Oiling Inaccessible Bearings

Lubrication of bearings which are ordinarily inaccessible may be accomplished by application of the principle that liquids tend to seek their own level.

The illustration shows a shaft bearing housed in a cast-iron frame into which an oilcan, no matter how long the spout, cannot reach. A hole was drilled in the bottom of the bearing and one of the same size was drilled

in the frame. A tube was fitted into the openings and the outer end of it cut off slightly above the level of the oil in the bearing. This level must be

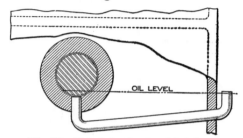

The Oil will Seek Its Level and Lubricate the Bearing

determined in order that a proper quantity of oil may be supplied. By filling the outer portion of the tube to the top, the oil will find its level at the desired point, lubricating the bearing.—Contributed by Frank H. Mayoh, Pawtucket, R. I.

Replacing a Broken Rung in a Ladder

When a rung breaks in a ladder, do not nail a board across the front edges of the uprights, but make the repair as shown in the illustration. A new rung is made having a length to fit snugly between the side rails or uprights. Two blocks are bored to fit the ends of the rung and they are fastened to the side

Two Blocks are Fitted on the Inside Surfaces of the Uprights to Take the Rung

rails with screws. This does not make an unsightly repair and the ladder will be as good as new.

Homemade Flexible-Shaft Hanger

An improvised flexible-shaft hanger is shown in the illustration. The bearing is made from a piece of wrought - iron pipe with a babbitt lining. Several small holes are drilled in the pipe previous to the babbitting to serve as anchors for the l i n i n g. The flexibility is secured by supporting the bearing between the ends of two round-point setscrews. The sockets in the pipe for receiving the setscrew ends are merely shallow holes made with a large drill. The frame is formed from flat bar steel.

A Temporary Automobile Light

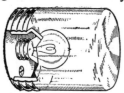

During my vacation I broke the globe on one of my automobile side lights. A cold-cream jar and cover, however, was all that was necessary until I reached the city again. A tobacco jar will answer the same purpose.—Contributed by J. F. Southwell, Lynn, Mass.

Toothed Pawl for Removing Lost Motion

Sometimes when a ratchet wheel is actuated by a pawl it will stop because of the irregularity of its teeth. If the space between any two teeth happens to be longer than the working stroke of the p a w l, the reciprocating movement of the latter will not be sufficient to enable the pawl to pass over the tooth point

where it will engage the next tooth. By filing several small teeth in the working face of the pawl this difficulty is overcome, as there is always one pawl tooth in position to engage a ratchet tooth. Care must be taken in proportioning the pawl teeth in order to insure one full tooth movement on the ratchet for each reciprocation of the pawl.

An Improvised Candle Holder

Not having any connection for gas or electric light in a small, dark room, the ingenious owner made a serviceable candle holder of a discarded gas jet cock. The candle was inserted into the threaded socket to which the gas pipe was connected. A heavy wire was sharpened and formed into a spike by which the holder was stuck firmly to the wall.

Foundry-Flask Pins

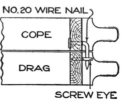

Receiving a rush order for 40 small castings, I was obliged to construct a few flasks, the castings being too large for the snap flasks on hand. How the flask pins were made in a hurry is shown in the illustration. A common 20-penny wire nail was driven in the end piece of the flask and bent at right angles to fit in a large screw eye. This made a simple pin that answered the purpose well.—Contributed by M. Johnson, Kenosha, Wisconsin.

⁋In jointing boards for a glue joint, white crayon rubbed on the edge of one of the boards will make impressions on the other, thus fixing the high points.

Locating and Repairing Small Leaks in Automobile Radiators

A slight leak in a radiator is very often hard to locate and in some cases almost impossible. Such a leak may be found quite readily by removing the radiator and, after plugging all the openings except one, running the end of a tire pump through a cork of suitable size and placing this cork in the remaining opening. Put the radiator in a tub or tank of water and pump air into it, and bubbles will issue from the points of leakage. These points should all be carefully marked before the radiator is removed from the water. The surface of the metal around the hole should be thoroughly cleaned and then soldered. It is always best to test the radiator after making the repairs, as very often the opening is not completely closed.

In some cases small leaks may be closed by using ordinary bran mixed with water and placed in the radiator instead of clear water, but such a practice is not recommended, as it tends to produce a poor circulation, and the engine will heat.

Small leaks may be sealed as a result of cleaning out the circulating system with a strong alkali, such as soda. The soda coming into contact with some of the metals forms an insoluble filling and may close the opening entirely.

A convenient means of making a temporary repair in a leaky honeycomb radiator is to take two small washers with sheet-rubber surfaces and place them on opposite ends of the opening through the radiator in which the leak occurs, and draw them together with a piece of small wire, or short spiral spring.

Large-Area Sprinkler

Pipe fittings of standard sizes were used in making the sprinkler shown in the illustration. The area watered varies from 100 to 120 ft. in diameter, according to the water pressure. The device may be made easily by buying the fittings and joining them, as shown, with white lead rubbed into the joints. A farmer at Quilcene, Wash., used several of them with great success during a dry spell.—Contributed by F. B. Willoughby, Katalla, Alaska.

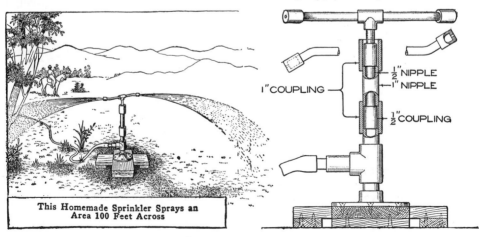

This Homemade Sprinkler Sprays an Area 100 Feet Across

½" NIPPLE
1" NIPPLE
1" COUPLING
½" COUPLING

Track for Painting Tanks or Silos

Tanks and silos on the farm, or elsewhere, must be painted from time to time and with changes in the seasons their bands should be adjusted. This work is troublesome because a ladder must be moved frequently in order to do the work. The device shown in the sketch obviates this and is of simple construction. If it is made properly with a safety iron, as shown, there should be no danger.

The workman is suspended in a sling seat and raises and lowers himself by means of blocks and tackle. The rigging is suspended from a double-roller hanger which rides on a track made of band iron. The hanger and the rigging may be readily put into place and as readily removed when the work is completed. Its compact form makes it convenient for storing, when not in use.
—Contributed by I. L. Sears, Waverly, Illinois.

An Improvement on Grinding Machines

An improvement for grinding machines in general can be applied as follows: On all machines having a variable speed through a belt and cone pulley, the marking can be cut on the cone. Where a variable-speed motor is used, the same result may be obtained by marking the switch or, properly speaking, the controller, instead of the faces of the steps on the cone pulley. This idea will surely eliminate many accidents and prevent considerable loss by broken wheels.

The idea is quite simple and consists in stamping, or etching, on the face first the speed of the grinding spindle when the belt is on that particular step of the cone, in revolutions per minute; the largest size wheel it is safe to use at this speed, a safe average being taken for cup wheels, dish wheels, straight-face wheels, etc.; and to this may be added, if desired, the surface speed of the maximum-size wheel in feet per minute.

All the information needed may be readily obtained from the catalog of any manufacturer of abrasive wheels. Many well-known firms will sanction this idea as being of practical value.

Thinner Oils Used on Automobiles in Winter

As cold weather tends to thicken oils, it is quite necessary to remove this oil from the gear sets on an automobile, and lubricate them with a thinner oil. In doing so, drain the heavy oil and flush out the box with kerosene, to remove any gummy deposit.

Holder for Cellar Doors

Four pipe fittings and five pieces of pipe can be fashioned into an excellent device for securely holding two cellar

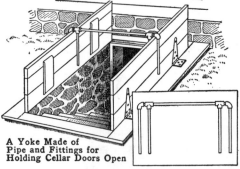

A Yoke Made of Pipe and Fittings for Holding Cellar Doors Open

doors open. The holder is slipped over the doors after they are raised into a vertical position.

Adding Luster to Brown Iron Paint

Brown iron-oxide paint has been noted to lose its luster soon, and while this may be partly due to the possible addition of turpentine, yet the flat drying is rather a peculiarity of the paint, and it is helped by using boiled oil with it instead of the raw oil and omitting all turpentine or benzine driers.

Platform for Mixing Concrete

Concrete has become one of the best materials for building construction on the farm, as elsewhere, and knowledge as to its proper mixing is of importance. One of the requisites is a mixing platform, and that shown in the illustration may be made readily. Farmers, or others who prepare concrete from time to time, will be repaid for the making of such a platform.

The materials necessary are three pieces, 12 ft. long and 4 in. square, for the runners; 14 planks, 7 ft. long, 10 in. wide, and 2 in. thick, and two pieces of 2 by 4-in. material, 12 ft. long. It is built on skids so that it may be hauled from place to place. The planks should be surfaced on the upper sides so as to be suited for the shovel-

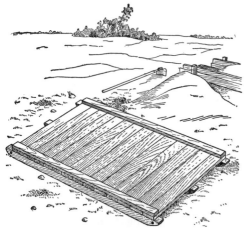

The Concrete-Mixing Platform may be Hauled into Place Readily

ing of concrete. Holes are bored in the rounded ends of the skids so that clevises may be attached to them.

Preventing Ditch Washouts

Spillways placed in irrigation and mining ditches on hilly ground prevent washouts during periods of high water.

Spillways in Irrigation and Mining Ditches on Hilly Ground Prevent Washouts

The spillways may be made of wood and should be placed as shown in the sketch, about one-fourth of a mile apart. The bottom of the trough should be grooved into the sides to make a substantial construction.—Contributed by H. W. Offins, Grants Pass, Oregon.

Keeping the Buttonhook Handy

Suspending the children's shoe buttonhook on a piece of fishline above a footstool ended the daily search for the hook when the youngsters were in haste to dress for school. Each one goes to the buttonhook, knowing that it will be in place, instead of carrying it away and causing another a search. The stool was also found convenient in that it spared furniture from the marks of shoe nails.—Contributed by J. F. Long, Springfield, Mo.

A Novel Cigar Holder

A unique cigar holder can be fashioned from the claw of a lobster. It not only answers the purpose well, but its color is much more pleasing than many a meerschaum. — Contributed by James M. Kane, Doylestown, Pa.

Carburetor Air-Valve Shaft Covering

The bushing that guides the shaft on the auxiliary air valve of my carburetor was of the open type, and 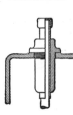 the dust and grit would collect between the shaft and the bushing, causing the valve to stick badly. I decided that the bushing must be closed in some manner, which resulted in the repair illustrated herewith. The hole in the bushing was redrilled to a larger size, and a piece of thin steel tubing was pressed into it, as shown. A thread was provided at the upper end of the tubing for the purpose of attaching a small cap. This cap was turned from brass-bar stock. —Contributed by Adolph Kline.

Oiling a Drill

Oil may be constantly applied to a drill point as shown in the sketch. Wrap a small piece of cotton waste  around the drill at the top, and saturate it with oil. If the drill becomes heated the oil will flow more freely and keep the point well lubricated. — Contributed by Harry Quinter, Steelton, Pa.

❐Emery powder may be kept handily in an old salt shaker.

Glare Dimmer for Automobile Drivers

A 6-in. disk of transparent, green celluloid, pasted to the windshield a trifle below the normal line of vision, will prevent the momentary semi-blindness which the glare of an approaching headlight inflicts on the automobile driver. By stooping slightly over the steering wheel one can look through the disk into the glare without eye strain.

A Homemade Lawn Rake

A round piece of wood, about 18 in. long, constitutes the head for the rake teeth, and is marked for ¼-in. holes, 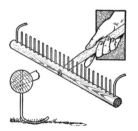 about ½ in. apart, whereupon the holes are drilled and the teeth inserted. The latter are made of ¼-in. iron, about 4 in. long, with the projecting ends made round. The teeth must be the same length and project from the head the same distance. The end holes are used for the runners. These are also made of ¼-in. round iron, somewhat longer than the regular teeth, and bent as shown. The runners extend about ¼ in. farther than the teeth, thus preventing them from injuring the roots of the grass. A rake of this kind is easy to use and will make a good, clean job.—Contributed by Charles Homewood, Waterloo, Iowa.

A Remedy for Heated Bearings

Prepare an oilcan by filling it with kerosene and flake graphite, about 1 part graphite to 7 parts of oil, and have it ready for any bearings that are likely to become heated. Force the mixture into the heated bearing until it flows out between the bearing surface and the shaft, then follow with a small quantity of thin machine oil.

CARE of the BAND SAW

by Charles A. King

MAXIMUM output and a high grade of work on a band saw are possible only with the combination of a skillful workman and a well-designed machine, having a blade without kinks, brazed, set, and filed properly.

The machine should be set level and firmly, so that its vibration is reduced to a minimum; the wheels should be balanced and their rubber rims must be in good order. The edges and side of the blade should run at right angles to the table, when in its normal position, and the machine should be fitted with an efficient, adjustable saw guide. A makeshift will not permit the saw to attain its maximum efficiency, and shortens the life of the blade.

A band saw should not be permitted to stand overnight at the tension necessary for satisfactory operation, as the night temperature of a shop may cause the blade to break. This danger has been minimized in the best types of modern machines by an arrangement of springs which regulates the tension so that a serviceable saw is not in danger of breaking. It is best, however, not to keep the saw at high tension longer than necessary, and the upper wheel should be dropped a little whenever the saw is not in use, for a saw may be slightly defective and yet give no evidence to the naked eye.

In starting a band saw, test the blade with the fingers to insure that it has the proper tension, and give the upper wheel a turn or two by hand before shifting the belt. The friction of the blade on the lower, or power, wheel causes it to turn the upper wheel. The motion communicated from the upper to the lower wheel will permit the belt to be shifted more evenly, and will minimize the starting strain. It will also insure that obstructions are not in the way of the wheels.

An important condition in the efficiency of a band saw is the speed at which it is operated. If the countershaft travels at the speed recommended by the manufacturer, it will be satisfactory, but if this information is not available, the blade should be operated at a rate of 10,000 ft. a minute.

Judgment must be applied in adapting a saw to the work in hand, and frequently small blades are ruined by attempting extremely heavy cuts with them. Do not force a wide saw to cut around a curve of small radius; this should be attempted only with a narrower one. Take time to change, or sharpen, saws, rather than use one that is improperly set or sharpened. Use the largest blade which the nature of the work will permit. The larger saw resists the tension better, and there is less danger of breaking it, or of pulling it from the wheels, when necessary to back out of a cut.

A band saw will run for some time after the belt has been shifted to the loose pulley. To stop it quickly, apply moderate pressure to the lower edge of the top wheel with a piece of wood. A thick piece of wood must not be pressed against the blade to stop the machine. The diminishing power does

FIG. 1
Grasp the Blocks and Apply the Proper Pressure to Remove Kinks or Twists

not permit the teeth to cut properly nor to clear themselves, causing undue strain on the blade.

Straightening a kinked, bent, or twisted saw blade so that it will cut smoothly, is difficult. The defect may be remedied to a considerable extent, and sometimes apparently removed. A minute crack in the saw may result from a small bend, and in time may cause a break. After a blade has been broken while running and has suffered incidental bends and twists, it is more likely to break. To reduce a kink or twist in a saw, make a cut in one edge of each of two small pieces of wood, and holding them as indicated in Fig. 1, apply a twisting pressure as required.

Handle the blade very carefully when removing it from the machine. Do not hang it up at full length, but fold it into a circle of three turns, in which form it can be handled easily and safely. Every one who has occasion to handle a band saw should understand the method of folding the blade, illustrated in the sketches herewith, as by following it a blade may be arranged in compact form without harm to bystanders, the operator, or the saw. The method is shown in Figs. 2 to 6 and is as follows:

The saw blade should be held vertically with the teeth toward the ope-

rator, as shown in Fig. 2, and grasped by each side, at the middle of its height. Permit the bottom loop to rest lightly upon the floor. The hands should be in the position indicated; the thumbs at A and B, upon the outside of the blade, being the essential feature of this part of the process. Hold the saw firmly to prevent it from turning in the hands. Turn the thumbs in and down, as at A and B, Fig. 3. This will give the loop C a tendency to drop. Permit it to touch the floor about 2 ft. away and in front of the lower loop D. Cross the loops A and B, passing the left through the right, or A through B, changing hands as they pass, and the loops will be in the positions indicated at A and B, Fig. 4.

Move the left hand from B and grasp the front crossing of the loop at E, Fig. 4, as indicated at E, Fig. 5, and with a swinging motion of the left hand, draw the outer loop C, Fig. 4, upward and to position CC, Fig. 5. Reach through the loops A and B, as at F, Fig. 5, with the right hand and grasp the loop C, at the same time grasping the back crossing of the loops at G, Figs. 4 and 5. Holding the crossed loops G and the loop C in that position, open the fingers of the left hand, and permit the two loops forming the crossing E, to drop lightly forward into the third loop D, which has not been moved from its original position.

Do not drop the blade to the floor in the final stage of the process, in a spectacular manner, for this is likely to turn the edges of some of the teeth. The saw is now in the form of three circles, probably of different sizes, Fig. 6. Make them uniform by adjustment. Hang the saw where it will not be endangered. It should be unfolded correctly when used again, as blades are more often injured in unfolding than in actual use, or in folding them.

Some workmen pick up the loop with which the hands first come in contact and shake the blade until it straightens itself, so that it can be placed upon the machine. Sometimes this method results satisfactorily;

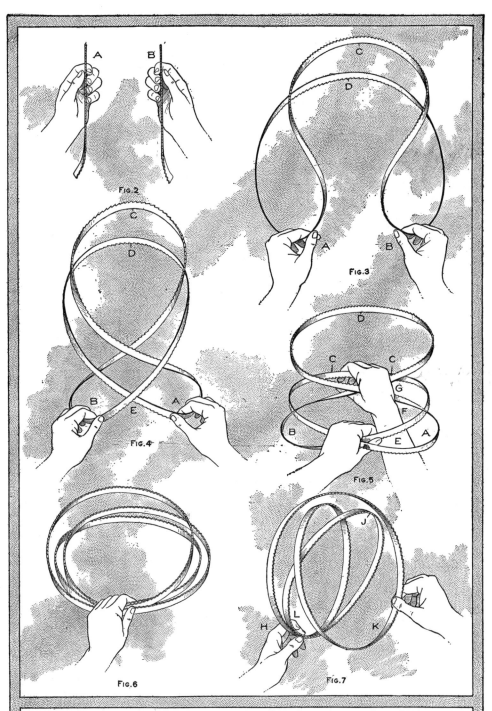

How to Fold and Unfold a Band Saw without Injury to Bystanders, Operator, or Saw: Grasp the Blade at the Middle of the Sides, Fig. 2, Thumbs on the Outside, Teeth toward Operator, Lower Loop Touching Floor Lightly; Turn the Thumbs In and Down, Fig. 3, Permitting Loop C to Touch Floor in Front of Loop D. Pass Loop A through Loop B, as in Fig. 4, Changing Hands. Draw Loop C Forward with Left Hand, Applying Pressure at E, Fig. 5, and Grasp Crossing G and Loop C in Right Hand, F. Release Hold of Left Hand at E, Fig. 5, Permitting the Three Loops to Spring Together, as in Fig. 6. Grasp Blade with Left Hand, as in Fig. 6, and Make Circles Uniform. To Unfold, Grasp Loop K in Right Hand, Fig. 7, and by Controlling Pressure at L Gradually Permit Blade to Spring Open more often it causes a kink in the saw. In order to avoid this danger, hold two of the three loops at H, Fig. 7, with the left hand, the teeth of the saw being toward the right. Using both hands, separate the folds carefully until they are in the position indicated. Make sure that loop J is not interlocked with either of the others. Drop loop K to the floor from the right hand, which will give loop J an upward impulse. Assist this by an upward swing with the left hand at H, and loop J may then be caught by the right hand. Release the crossing of the loops in the left hand at H, retaining the under loop L. Raise the hands shoulder high, and the blade will straighten itself without undue strain. The teeth will be toward the operator, in proper position for placing the blade upon the machine.

⟨A solution which will provide an excellent dimmer for headlights for automobiles may be made by dissolving Epsom salts in water. The solution applied to the inside of the glass will produce a fairly permanent frosted effect.

A Segment-Cutting Jig

Segments for circular patterns and similar work are sometimes made in a slipshod manner and consequently are

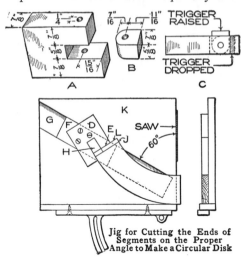

Jig for Cutting the Ends of Segments on the Proper Angle to Make a Circular Disk

expensive. They are often cut ⅛ to ¼ in. longer than the actual length of the segment, and the surplus is cut off on a trimmer or by planing, as each piece is fitted in building up the pattern.

The jig shown in the sketch has been found efficient and is for use on a circular saw. By its use the segments may be assembled as they are cut at the saw. Time is thus saved, and this method is further valuable in that the sawed ends have a superior gluing surface.

The parts A and B, assembled as at C, constitute the regulator D. The face of the regulator must always be at an angle of 60° to the line of the saw cut. To keep it in this position for any radius, the regulator is fastened to a block, F, which slides in a groove, G, of the fence board K, 1 in. wide and ¼ in. deep.

In adjusting the jig, make a template the exact length of the segment to be cut. Drop the trigger H, and shove it up against the template, as at J, allowing the opposite end of the template to clear the saw as it is pushed alongside of the latter. Screw the regulator to the fence K, and the jig is ready for the cut.

After having sawed the required number of segments, leaving them ¼ in. longer at each end than the true length, raise the trigger H and place a segment, as at L. Saw off the opposite end, then reverse the segment, drop the trigger, placing the freshly sawed end against it, and saw off the other end.—Contributed by D. D. Gurnee, Hempstead, N. Y.

Emergency Methods for Starting Automobile Engine

Occasionally the starter on an automobile fails to operate, and the driver is compelled to resort to the crank, if he is fortunate enough to have one. An emergency method for starting the engine may be used instead.

Throw the transmission gear into high speed. The car may be pushed along, causing the engine shaft to revolve, and unless there is something wrong, it should start after it is turned over a few times. It may also be pulled along by another automobile. This method is of service in starting an engine that has been taken down for repairs and must be worked into shape. Another method that may be resorted to, when neither help nor another car is available, is as follows: Put the gear into high speed, jack up one of the rear wheels, and turn the engine over by turning the raised wheel. In any of these methods it is best to have some one at the wheel to control the car. This is essential in the latter method.

Graduated Index Finger for Tool Grinding

Grinding cutting tools, such as reamers, milling cutters, boring cutters, countersinks, counterbores, and kindred tools, is usually a matter of guesswork in so far as the clearance is concerned, yet the clearance is as important as the quality of the tool steel used in the cutter. The sketch illustrates an easy method of substituting certainty for guesswork, and any angle may be produced perfectly.

The emery wheel used is cup-shaped and small. The cutter shown is carried on an arbor in the spinning head, or sometimes a special head is supplied with the tool grinder by the manufacturer. The spinning head is set square on the table, as is also the bracket, both being fastened with bolts. The index finger is held in the outer end of the bracket and is adjustable vertically.

The machine shown is set for a square cut; that is, no clearance. If the flat spring, shown in solid shade, is lowered until the figure 10 is flush with the top of the bracket boss, when the bracket is adjusted laterally on the table, the wheel will grind a clearance of 10°, and so on. While it is not necessary that the center line of the grinding spindle be central with the cutter,

it is better to have it so if possible. The table is raised and lowered as required by means of the screw provided for that purpose.

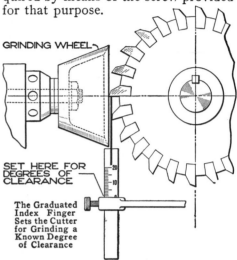

GRINDING WHEEL

SET HERE FOR DEGREES OF CLEARANCE

The Graduated Index Finger Sets the Cutter for Grinding a Known Degree of Clearance

The index finger is easily graduated. If a 12-in. cutter is placed in the machine, the distance from the center is 6 in. If the tooth is lowered .5 in. from the horizontal, the face of the tooth will have an inclination of 1 in. to the foot, and so on. A table of "tapers and angles" will give the number of degrees and center line of this taper, or inclination, thus making the graduation easy and certain. Graduate in whole degrees only.

In the sketch the clearance shown is exaggerated to make it clear. Actual clearances cannot be given, as they vary with material, also for machines and general conditions, such as lubrication, degree of finish required, etc.—Contributed by J. B. Murphy, Plainfield, N. J.

To Surface-Harden Cast Iron

Small castings, such as gears, cams, etc., that are subjected to wear, can be made quite hard on the surface and toughened considerably by heating them to a dull red, then quenching them in a saturated solution of cyanide of potash while it is as near the boiling point as possible. An iron pot, filled with the solution and kept near the fire, will make it handy for the workman.

Small Lifting Magnet

Persons working about an automobile will find the lifting magnet shown in the illustration of great service in recovering bolts, nuts, or other small

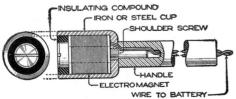

INSULATING COMPOUND
IRON OR STEEL CUP
SHOULDER SCREW
HANDLE
ELECTRO MAGNET
WIRE TO BATTERY

The Magnet Aids in Recovering Small Machine Parts Otherwise Inaccessible

parts, from oil pans or other partly inaccessible places into which they have fallen.

Its lifting power is derived from an electromagnet which may be obtained from an old electric bell. The magnet is held in an iron, or steel, cup by means of a shoulder screw. Its power is derived from dry cells, which should be connected with the cords at the end of the handle.

An insulating compound should be used to seal the space between the head of the shoulder screw and the cup.

To Prevent Draft through Openings in Automobile Floor

The discomfort due to cold drafts coming through the openings in the floor of an automobile, around the various levers and pedals, may be greatly

reduced by attaching a piece of rubber, or very heavy canvas, with a slit in it, on the under side of the floor, as shown in the sketch. This covering is especially serviceable on cars which have short mud pans, or none at all, as the chassis is very open under the floor of the front compartment, and the cold air may readily enter through the openings in the floor.

¶A hand reamer should never be used for power reaming.

Bleaching Linseed Oil

If it is desired to bleach linseed oil for some special purpose, mix it with some five per cent of peroxide of hydrogen in a tin, or glass, vessel and shake it from time to time. It will require only a few days to bleach the oil, which then may be poured off, the peroxide having been reduced to oxide of hydrogen, water. There are several ways of bleaching linseed oil which require about a month in making the change, but this is the simplest and quickest method.—Contributed by A. A. Kelly, Frazer, Pa.

Emergency Repair on Stripped Stuffing-Box Nuts

Stripped stuffing-box nuts on small steam, water, or air pumps are quite a common occurrence, and sometimes

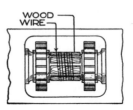

WOOD
WIRE

they cause considerable delay, as the application of a new stuffing box requires the removal of the pump heads, and the taking out of the piston, to get a new box over it.

Working near a construction job when a stuffing-box nut stripped from the box on a small water pump that was draining the water accumulating in a pit in which a number of men were working, I made the repairs as follows: Complete repairs to the pump would have delayed the work, with much damage to the pit and loss of time. The sketch shows the temporary repair. Small wood strips were cut and wired to the piston, the strips being of a length exactly the distance between the two nuts when both were securely drawn up against their respective packing glands. This made a very satisfactory repair that worked just as well as if the box and nut had been held together with perfect threads.

This kind of a repair can be used in almost every case where two packing nuts are within reasonable distance from each other, on any kind of a pump, and will, in many instances, prevent a serious delay on important work until complete repairs can be made.—Contributed by F. W. Bentley, Missouri Valley, Iowa.

Waterproofing a Serving Tray

Serving trays are frequently spoiled by liquid coming into contact with the embroidery, picture, or other work which may be placed beneath the glass to beautify the tray. In order to prevent this, a water-tight joint between the edge of the glass and the edge of the tray, extending over the glass, should be made.

To do this, bicycle tape, about ⅞ in. wide, should be inserted into the joint. Remove the bottom from the tray, and then the glass. Clean the inner edge of the tray frame of glue and rough spots. Press the tape into the square corner around the edge of the frame. The four corners may be turned by cutting the tape on the upper edge and stretching it into the proper form. If the tape is cut in two at the corners there is more likelihood of a leak. The open spaces in the corners should be filled with small pieces, but care must be taken not to form lumps. Replace the glass and see that it rests evenly on the tape all the way around, and reassemble the tray.

A Bearing Scraper

When old journal bearings need re-babbitting they are usually placed in a former and babbitted. Often it is necessary to true up the bearing with a scraper. This method is not satisfactory, as it does not give a true bearing surface and leaves some high spots.

A better arrangement for truing up babbitt in bearings is shown in the illustration. The four cutters are made of steel and threaded with eight V-threads to the inch. When it is desired to true up a journal bearing it is placed upon the appropriate cutter and rubbed back and forth until a true bearing surface is obtained.

The shavings from this operation drop into the wooden box below, which may be cleaned readily from time to

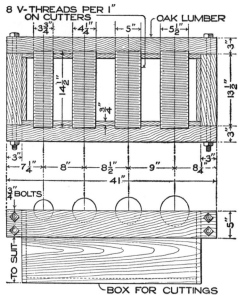

A Journal-Bearing Scraper That will Insure True Bearing Surfaces

time. Whenever desirable the cutters may be revolved in order that all parts of the threaded portion may be used.—Contributed by J. R. Minter, Washington, Ind.

An Over-Arm Steady Rest

The over-arm steady rest shown was designed to hold long shafts of small diameter while machining them, without using a cumbersome steady rest. A steel block was bored out to fit the tailstock spindle, and also had a hole drilled in it to receive the over-arm bar, both holes being fitted with setscrews. The end of the bar was drilled

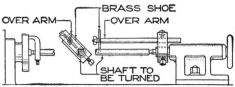

A Handy Over-Arm Steady Rest for Lathe Work on Long Shafts of Small Diameter

and tapped, and a stud screwed in. A slotted brass shoe, a washer, and a wing nut completed the outfit.

Kink for Counting or Grasping Paper Sheets

Sheets of paper, handbills, or similar matter, may be counted easily or ar-

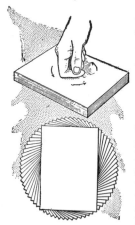

ranged in a convenient pile from which to take single sheets by a simple process shown in the sketch.

Place the pile of sheets on a table, and arrange them evenly. Place the second joint of the forefinger on the center of the pile, and with a moderate pressure turn the hand in the direction of the arrows. The finger may be raised in order to secure a new contact. The result will be surprising, and interesting to observe. A pile of sheets, as shown in the lower figure, will result.—Contributed by George H. Holden, Hill-Crest Lodge, Chesterfield, England.

Match Safe Attached to Gas Fixture

Finding matches in the dark in order to light a gas fixture is often a trying experience. Suspending a

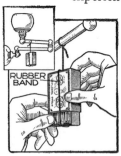

match safe from the fixture, as shown in the illustration, solves the difficulty. The match box is suspended on a string and a rubber band is placed around it. While the matches are being withdrawn the box is held open, and as soon as it is released the band closes it. This makes it safe to strike the match on the box without danger of igniting other matches.—Contributed by J. Davis, Poughkeepsie, N. Y.

Repairing Broken Rubber on Wash Wringer

While washing one day some time ago, I had the misfortune to damage the upper roller on my wringer, and wishing to finish quickly, I repaired it in the following manner: I wrapped a piece of stout bandage, about 4 in. wide and 18 in. long, tightly around the injured roller. This was intended to be used only temporarily, but it served so long that I found it unnecessary to procure a new roller.—Contributed by Mrs. Anna M. B. Romig, Allentown, Pennsylvania.

Oiler for a Connecting-Rod End

The upper portion of a connecting rod on an automobile engine is lubricated by the oil splashed in the crank

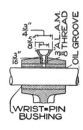

case, but in quite a few cases this method does not work satisfactorily. In making repairs on an engine where the bushings were burned out, caused by inefficient oiling, an attachment was tried out with success. This consisted in making a small oiler, similar to a regular oil cup, and screwing it into a hole drilled and tapped into the upper part of the bearing. An oil groove was cut in the new bronze bearing to connect with the hole of the oil cup. It was easy to maintain a constant supply of oil to the bearing with this device.

Repainting Exterior Woodwork

Exterior woodwork painted the first time fails to show as good and lasting a result as when it has been painted again after two years' wear. Repainting over a good white-lead surface that has become dry and floury will yield a good wearing finish. The chalking of white-lead paint is no disadvantage, for in this condition it will take the new paint better than a hard surface, and will not scale.

Emergency Electric Switch

When a temporary electric switch is needed in the home, or shop, where a stock of electrical supplies is not available, a satisfactory switch may be made of a lamp socket and key. In order to transform a socket into a switch, screw a fuse plug into the place intended for the lamp. The circuit may be opened or closed by turning the key as if turning on or turning off a light. Fuse plugs for the purpose are usually to be found in a home, as they should be on hand to replace fuses blown out.—Contributed by F. W. Buerstatte, Pullman, Wash.

Carrying a Stepladder

A handle, fixed on the side of a stepladder so that the ends balanced, overcame the difficulty ordinarily experienced in carrying it. It is worth while to spend sufficient time in fastening the handle to insure that it will be

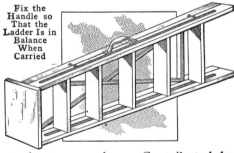

Fix the Handle so That the Ladder Is in Balance When Carried

at the proper place.—Contributed by W. C. Loy, Rochester, Ind.

Making Reliners Out of Old Tires

Reliners, with which to support portions of automobile or other tires worn considerably, may be readily made out of old tire casings. The tool necessary for the trimming of the casing into a reliner, with a featheredge all around, as shown in the sketch, may be made from a table knife.

Nick the surface of the knife blade with a cold chisel on a diagonal as at AB. Grind the edge along this line smooth, after breaking the blade by striking it a sharp blow as the point

end of the blade is held fast in a vise or clamp. The jaws of the vise or

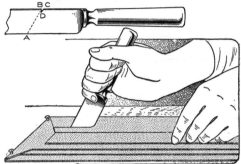

Insert the Point of Knife into Top Layer and Cut along Line

clamp should be even with the line AB. Now grind a V-shaped nick into the back edge of the blade as shown at C. Grind the edge BD as sharp as possible and smooth off the other adjoining edges.

The material for the reliners is obtained as follows: Cut out the better portions of an old casing, in such a way that the cut edges would be in direct line with the spoke nearest them, if the tire were on a wheel. Then cut off the tire beads by which it was held in the rim. Rip off the more badly worn outer layers from the casing.

Lay the section of the casing flat on a bench, the inner side down. With a pencil, or a piece of crayon, mark off the "steps" in the several layers of the casing by the cutting of which the featheredge is to be produced, gradually thinning out. Insert the point B of the knife into the top layer and trim along the chalk line, cutting the smaller of the oblongs shown. Repeat this process, tearing away the outer portions of each layer, around the oblong for that layer.

The reliners may be made of various lengths and breadths to meet the requirements of tires of various sizes and worn portions of similar range.—Contributed by H. W. Bohrman, Los Angeles, Cal.

⊂Dirty materials will not make first-class concrete, either in strength or appearance.

Conductor-Pipe Holders

Three designs are shown of holders for conductor pipes on houses. Two of the three illustrated are made of wire,

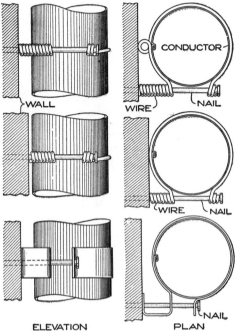

ELEVATION PLAN
Methods of Holding Conductor Pipe by Using Only One Nail with Wire or Sheet Metal

coiled about a nail and around the pipe, and the third consists of a strip of sheet metal, all three being fastened with a nail driven into the siding. These holders have considerable advantage over the ordinary hook and will hold the pipe firmly in place.

Surfacing Tracing Cloth to Take Fine Ink Lines

Many methods are in use for preparing the surface of tracing cloth to receive the ink, but I have found the following way to work best where very fine lines are to be drawn. The dull, or unglazed, surface of the cloth is used, and after stretching the cloth on the board, it is sized as follows. Moisten the cloth well with gasoline and go over the entire surface, rubbing lightly to remove all dirt and surface grease. While the cloth is still wet with the gasoline, sprinkle well with talcum powder of the grade used in automobile tires, and then rub vigorously. This fine abrasive roughens the surface so that fine, close-drawn lines take well. Wipe clean, and the tracing cloth is ready for use.—Contributed by M. Burr Bennett, Bridgeport, Conn.

Light-Saving Kink

Electric-light bills are sometimes increased needlessly through permitting light to burn unnoticed in the pantry, coal room, or other small rooms. I cut round holes in the upper panels of the doors of these rooms and placed glass in them. This caused the otherwise forgotten lights to attract attention, and there was small likelihood of these lights burning needlessly. — Contributed by John Hoeck, Alameda, Cal.

Aprons for Hot-Air Registers

It is a common experience that dust is blown into the rooms of a house from the registers through which the hot air from the furnace passes. This was overcome by placing a piece of cheesecloth over the register. The air has sufficient force to blow the cloth away from the register slightly, thus permitting the warm air to enter, while most of the dust is caught in the cloth.

The strips by which the cloth is held can be made of wood and finished to match the woodwork of the room. The bolts are fastened in the piece of wood nearest the wall and holes are bored in the front piece at corresponding points. The piece in which the bolts are secured is then fastened to the wall with screws, care being taken that they strike the studding. By releasing the wing nuts fresh cloth may be inserted. —Contributed by J. A. Fitzpatrick, Altoona, Pa.

Sanding Track for an Automobile

Occasionally in winter when the streets are covered with ice an automobile gets stuck in a rut, or for some other reason the wheels turn around without moving the car. This sometimes happens even if the car is equipped with chains. This difficulty can be easily overcome by carrying a box, or bag, of sand under the seat and sprinkling it on the surface under the wheels, as in sanding the track on a railroad.

Preventing an Alkaline Solution from Backing into Boiler

A hot alkaline solution used in an establishment had a way of attacking

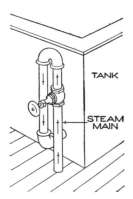

the seat of the steam valve and forcing its way back into the boiler, causing the water in the boiler to foam. A steam fitter rigged up the device shown in the illustration so as to prevent the solution from coming in direct contact with the seat of the steam valve.

To Prevent Fire While Pouring Gasoline through Chamois Skin

Fires occurring without apparent cause while gasoline was being poured into automobile tanks through chamois skin were found to have been caused by electric sparks from ungrounded funnels. The pouring of gasoline through chamois skin develops static electricity, which accumulates in the funnel, if it is set into a wooden seat or similar place while in use.

When a considerable accumulation has taken place a sharp contact of the funnel and the metal edge of the tank may cause a spark, resulting in an explosion. In order to prevent the accumulation of electricity the funnel should be grounded by fastening a light chain to it, as shown in the sketch. The chain should be long

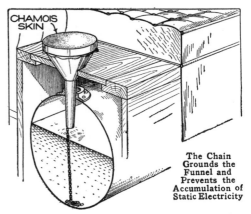

The Chain Grounds the Funnel and Prevents the Accumulation of Static Electricity

enough to remain in contact with the bottom of the tank.—Contributed by E. A. L., Ames, Ia.

Supporting Bricks on a Roof for Chimney Construction

Bricks and material for the reconstruction of a chimney may be safely and conveniently placed on a roof by using the frame shown in the sketch. It is simple in construction and requires less lumber than a platform.

The Frame Hooks over the Ridge and Holds the Bricks and Material

The latter, if rested on the roof gutter, may cause damage, and if the gutter is not in good condition an accident may result.

To Stop Noise of Rattling Automobile Hoods

The constant vibration of an automobile causes such parts as the hood
to become loose, noisy, and rattling. This noise can be stopped in the following
manner: The noise usually occurs at the point where the hood rests against the

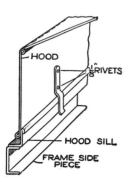

hood sill, which is bolted to the vehicle frame. A small strip of
steel, $\frac{1}{16}$ in. thick and about $\frac{3}{8}$ in. wide, is bent into the shape shown so that,
when the hood is down and in the right position, the strip rests snugly on the
hood sill. Two strips on each side of the hood will be sufficient.

Starting a Siphon by Air Pressure

A siphon that is absolutely safe to use in handling acids or other corrosive
or harmful liquids, because it is started

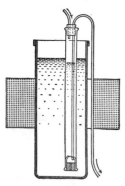

by blowing, can be made as follows: A suitable length of glass
tubing of fairly large diameter— say, $\frac{1}{2}$ to $\frac{3}{4}$ in.
for ordinary laboratory use—is provided with tight-fitting rubber stoppers at
both ends, one having two perforations and the other a very small
one. In the two-holed stopper are inserted one short, slightly bent piece of
glass tubing extending just below the stopper, and a U-shaped tube, both
about $\frac{1}{8}$ in. in diameter. The inner arm of the U-tube reaches near the end of
the wide tube, and the outside arm below it, as shown. When this device
is inserted in the vessel containing the liquid to be siphoned, the liquid seeks
its level inside and outside of the large tube, and by blowing through the short
small tube an air pressure is created in the wide tube which forces the liquid
out through the U-tube, because all of it cannot pass back into the liquid container through the small perforation in
the bottom stopper of the siphon. When once started, the device, of
course, works automatically like an ordinary siphon.

Lengthening a Gas Burner

While assisting a gas fitter to build up some sections of brass tubing with
burners, we found one piece a trifle too short. No other
piece being at hand, I cut a section from
a gas burner, the part below the line
AB in the sketch, and filed the upper
portion of it so as to

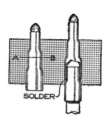

fit into the lower section of another burner. This section was screwed on
the tube and the burner slipped over it and soldered, as there were no
threads on the cut-off section. The tube being covered with an imitation
candle, the repair could not be seen.— Contributed by James M. Kane,
Doylestown, Pa.

A Cash Register Used as an Adding Machine

A person having a number of long columns to add but no adding machine,
used his cash register as a substitute. By pushing the keys and opening and
shutting the drawer in the usual way each horizontal line of figures was registered, and the totaling mechanism
showed the sum correctly. As it was impossible to register $100 on the machine at one operation, the large
amounts were split and made in two counts. Aside from being rather
noisy, the substitute adding machine was a decided success.

SHOP NOTES FOR 1917

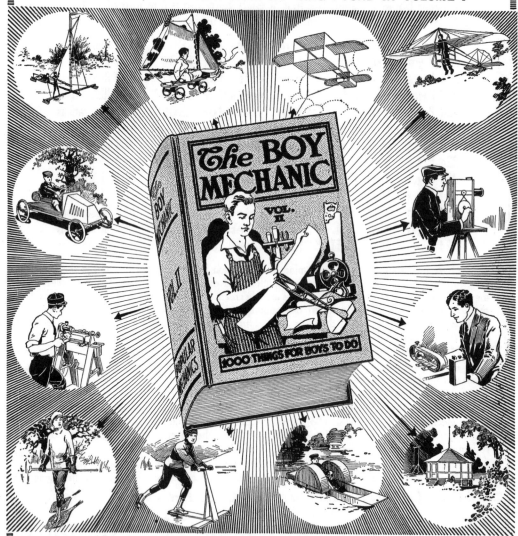